Scale and Conformal Symmetry in Hadron Physics

Scale and Conformal Symmetry in Hadron Physics

Edited by

R. GATTO

**Institute of Physics,
University of Rome,
Rome, Italy**

A WILEY-INTERSCIENCE PUBLICATION

JOHN WILEY & SONS, New York · London · Sydney · Toronto

Library of Congress Cataloging in Publication Data
Main entry under title:

Scale and conformal symmetry in hadron physics.

"A Wiley-Interscience publication."
Papers presented at a 1972 meeting organized in Frascati by the Advanced School of Physics at the National Laboratories of CNEN.
1. Hadrons—Congresses. 2. Symmetry (Physics)—Congresses. 3. Quantum field theory—Congresses.
I. Gatto, Raoul, ed. II. Frascati. Laboratori nazionali. Advanced School of Physics.

QC721.S287   539.7'216   73-4324
ISBN 0-471-29292-3

Printed in the United States of America

10 9 8 7 6 5 4 3 2 1

Contributors

W. A. BARDEEN, Physics Department, Stanford University, Stanford, California

L. BONORA, Institute of Physics, University of Padua, Padua, Italy

S. CICCARIELLO, Institute of Physics, University of Padua, Padua, Italy

E. DEL GIUDICE, Institute of Physics, University of Naples, Naples, Italy

P. DI VECCHIA, Cern, Geneva, Switzerland

S. FERRARA, Frascati National Laboratories of CNEN, Frascati (Rome), Italy

H. FRITZSCH, Max Planck Institute for Physics, Munich, West Germany

S. FUBINI, Physics Department, Massachusetts Institute of Technology, Cambridge, Massachusetts

R. GATTO, Institute of Physics, University of Rome, Rome, Italy

M. GELL-MANN, Physics Department, California Institute of Technology, Pasadena, California

A. F. GRILLO, Frascati National Laboratories of CNEN, Frascati (Rome), Italy

H. A. KASTRUP, Institute of Theoretical Physics, Institute of Technology, Aachen, West Germany

H. KLEINERT, Institute of Theoretical Physics, Free University, Berlin, West Germany

H. LEUTWYLER, Institute of Theoretical Physics, University of Bern, Bern, Switzerland

G. MACK, Institute of Theoretical Physics, University of Bern, Bern, Switzerland

R. MUSTO, Institute of Physics, University of Naples, Naples, Italy

P. Otterson, Institute of Theoretical Physics, University of Bern, Bern, Switzerland

G. Parisi, Frascati National Laboratories of CNEN, Frascati (Rome), Italy

G. Preparata, Institute of Physics, University of Rome, Rome, Italy

G. Sartori, Institute of Physics, University of Padua, Padua, Italy

B. Schroer, Institute of Theoretical Physics, Free University, Berlin, West Germany

M. Tonin, Institute of Physics, University of Padua, Padua, Italy

J. Wess, Institute of Theoretical Physics, University of Karlsruhe, Karlsruhe, West Germany

Preface

In May 1972 an informal meeting on the topic "Outlook for Broken Conformal Symmetry in Elementary Particle Physics" was organized in Frascati by the Advanced School of Physics at the National Laboratories of CNEN. The present volume contains most of the general reviews that were presented at the meeting, organized in a consistent fashion and in some parts expanded by the authors. It is hoped that the book will provide an ample and advanced account of the wide subject of scale and conformal symmetry. The broader topic, rather than strictly conformal symmetry, was chosen because of the inextricable connections between the two subjects, conformal symmetry usually being introduced as a natural extension of scale symmetry.

The interest in such symmetries arises naturally from the need for a better understanding of the crucial problem of short-distance behavior in quantum field theory. Theoretically the connection seems to be rigorously derivable, at least for certain renormalizable field theories, by study of the so-called Gell-Mann/Low limit. In its turn the requirement of conformal symmetry can act as a powerful and consistent constraint on the solutions of the Green function integral equations. Vacuum expectation values and operator product expansions are severely limited by conformal symmetry, and, interestingly, they exhibit mathematical structures reminiscent of the duality formalism. In particular, two- and three-point functions are uniquely determined, apart from the values of the coupling constants and scale dimensions.

The by-now famous SLAC experiments on inelastic electron scattering aroused wide interest in scale symmetry and its possible extensions. The notion of "exact scaling" when inserted into a conformal framework appears, however, to be quite far-reaching and demanding. The problem is that of canonical dimensions and of theories possessing additional conservation laws. Anomalies in Ward identities are independently known to appear in certain problems, raising theoretical questions of great interest.

The contributions in this volume touch upon most of the theoretical problems on which the interest of theoreticians is presently concentrated. Prospects for future work appear highly exciting; fascinating confluences of various approaches and viewpoints, some of them at first sight quite divergent, hint, perhaps, of some powerful synthesis. Although the contributions cover a rather vast spectrum, they are always focused on the general problematics of short-distance behavior in elementary particle theory.

The inductive aspects of the problem are treated with great rigor by Leutwyler and Otterson in an exhaustive review of the theoretical problems of deep inelastic scattering. The central role of the energy-momentum tensor is emphasized in the contribution by Wess, who presents a possible dynamical scheme, built in analogy to vector meson dominance for the currents. A central problem to the whole approach is faced by Schroer, who examines in particular the conformal invariance of the Gell-Mann/Low limit. The work by Ferrara, Gatto, Grillo, and Parisi summarizes the results of a concentrated effort to study the general consequences of conformal symmetry, mainly in a kinematical sense, by avoiding as much as possible additional dynamical assumptions. Very recent and powerful developments in conformal covariant quantum field theory are described by Mack. Conformal symmetry in Wilson's expansion is also discussed by Bonora, Ciccariello, Sartori, and Tonin.

The contribution by Bardeen, Fritzsch, and Gell-Mann is a remarkable and successful effort toward a final unification of the main concepts that have emerged in these last years in the description of elementary particles. Of such concepts Murray Gell-Mann has very often been the originator. The appealing prospect of possible contact with duality is dealt with by Del Giudice, Di Vecchia, Fubini, and Musto. Preparata's contribution reviews the concepts of light-cone dominance and the newly raised problem of crossing in the physics of the light cone. In Kleinert's work the problem of scaling is approached from the viewpoint of the infinite-component field formalism. The last contribution is from Kastrup, one of the pioneers of conformal symmetry, and addresses the problems of astrophysics, for which conformal symmetry suggests attractive speculations.

At the meeting in Frascati a most elegant introduction was given by Professor Drell, who reviewed his work with T. D. Lee on scaling and bound-state nucleons, and also some work by K. Johnson on quark description. The text of this paper was not submitted for the present volume since full accounts of these researches have in the meantime appeared in print (S. D. Drell and T. D. Lee, *Phys. Rev. D* **5**, 1738, 1972; K. Johnson, *Phys. Rev. D* **6**, 1101, 1972).

Particular thanks are due to the numerous physicists who gave their enthusiastic and generous help to the Frascati meeting: to Professor C. Villi, President of the Italian National Institute of Physics; to Professor I. F. Quercia, Director of the Laboratories; to Dr. M. Greco and Dr. M. Ghigo-Ricci for their invaluable help in the organization; to Mr. S. Stipcich for his continuous assistance; to Professors W. Bardeen, G. Costa, J. Prentki, I. F. Quercia, L. Radicati, B. Renner, K. Symanzik, and B. Touschek, who acted as chairmen; and to the speakers and participants. While this book was being printed we learned of the death of our unforgettable friend Bruno Renner. Most of the physicists who have contributed to this volume knew him personally and were among his closest friends. I am sure all contributors will want to join me in dedicating this work to his memory.

I would like to commend the publishers for accepting a volume on a still-developing subject which I hope will provide us with a better understanding of fundamental interactions.

R. GATTO

Rome, Italy
February 1973

Contents

CHAPTER 1

Theoretical Problems
in Deep Inelastic Scattering

H. LEUTWYLER AND P. OTTERSON

The first part (Sections 1–8) of this work is concerned with a number of *questions* concerning the analysis of inelastic electron scattering. (The discussion can easily be extended to weak processes and to nonforward matrix elements, but we stick to the prototype $e + p \rightarrow e + $ anything because this process is best known experimentally.) The questions we want to discuss are the following:

1. Do the cross sections σ_L, σ_T determine the matrix element $\langle p | [j_\mu(x), j_\nu(0)] | p \rangle$ uniquely?

2. In particular, does the validity of the scaling laws imply canonical leading light-cone singularities?

1

3. Conversely, suppose that the leading light-cone singularities of the electromagnetic current are canonical. Does this imply scaling?

4. Is it possible to determine the equal-time commutator of the electromagnetic current from the data on σ_L, σ_T? In particular, is it possible to measure the Schwinger term?

5. Conversely, suppose that the Schwinger term vanishes. What restriction does this impose on the cross sections?

6. Do the cross sections σ_L, σ_T determine the (virtual) forward Compton amplitude?

7. Is it possible to determine the electromagnetic mass shift from measurements of σ_L, σ_T?

In this first part we draw heavily from work done in collaboration with Georgelin and Stern.[1, 2] The interested reader will find a very interesting discussion of related problems in the Hercegnovi lectures by Stichel.[3] The main emphasis of our analysis is on the fact that the present experimental data do not exclude the presence of fixed poles at $\alpha = 0$. We attempt to analyze this problem in a rather systematic fashion and apologize for not quoting papers that have dealt with related questions in various contexts, particularly in connection with the mass difference problem.

In the *second part* (Sections 9–11) we briefly sketch some *speculative ideas* concerning the subject that was treated on a conservative basis in the first part. We point out that knowledge of the *high-energy behavior of virtual longitudinal photons* is extremely inadequate, and formulate a model in which this high-energy behavior deviates from conventional Regge phenomenology. Finally, we discuss some recent work on one-particle saturation of the *finite-energy sum rules* satisfied by the virtual Compton amplitude.

1. DO THE CROSS SECTIONS σ_L, σ_T DETERMINE THE CURRENT COMMUTATOR UNIQUELY?

Of course, the relation between the cross sections of the process $e + p \to e +$ anything and the matrix elements of the electromagnetic current commutator involves a respectable amount of theory. This theory is based on the assumption that the leading contribution arises from one-photon exchange; the leading contribution is then radiatively corrected to take the nonleading contributions roughly into account. We do not have anything to add concerning the validity of this procedure; in the following we will assume that the radiatively corrected cross sections σ_L, σ_T are indeed data related to the structure functions

$$W_{\mu\nu} = \frac{1}{4\pi} \int dx \, e^{iqx} \langle p | [\, j_\mu(x), j_\nu(0)\,] | p \rangle$$

$$= (q_\mu q_\nu - g_{\mu\nu} q^2) V_1 + [(p_\mu q_\nu + p_\nu q_\mu)\nu - p_\mu p_\nu q^2 - g_{\mu\nu} \nu^2] V_2 \qquad (1)$$

through the equations (we put the proton mass equal to 1)

$$V_1 = \frac{N(\sigma_L \nu^2 + \sigma_T q^2)}{-q^2}$$

$$V_2 = N(\sigma_L + \sigma_T) \qquad (2)$$

$$N = \frac{1}{8\pi^2 \alpha} \frac{2\nu + q^2}{\nu^2 - q^2}$$

In this notation the more frequently used functions W_1, W_2 are given by

$$W_1 = q^2 V_1 + \nu^2 V_2$$

$$W_2 = -q^2 V_2 \qquad (3)$$

In terms of V_1, V_2 the Bjorken scaling laws read

$$V_1(q^2, \nu) \quad \rightarrow \quad \frac{1}{2\nu\xi} F_L(\xi) \left.\right\} \qquad \xi = \frac{-q^2}{2\nu} \qquad \begin{array}{l}(4)\\[1.5em](5)\end{array}$$

$$V_2(q^2, \nu) \quad \rightarrow \quad \frac{1}{2\nu^2\xi} F_2(\xi)$$

where

$$F_L(\xi) = -F_1(\xi) + \frac{1}{2\xi} F_2(\xi) \qquad (6)$$

The first problem that we want to discuss is the following. Since the momentum of a virtual photon emitted by an on-shell electron is spacelike, the data on the process $e + p \rightarrow e + \text{anything}$ cover only negative values of q^2. The functions V_1 and V_2 are therefore measurable only for $q^2 \leqslant 0$. This makes it impossible to directly invert the Fourier transform in Eq. 1 and thereby to determine the matrix element of the current commutator between protons in coordinate space from the data on σ_L, σ_T. In particular, it is not possible to determine the behavior of the commutator on the light cone, $x^2 = 0$, without further information.

The claim that this is, nevertheless, almost possible, at least in principle, is based on the theoretical prejudice according to which the current commutator is causal, that is, $[j_\mu(x),j_\nu(0)]=0$ for $x^2<0$. In fact, a theorem by Bogoliubov and Vladimirov[5] states that a tempered distribution $W(q^2, \nu)$, which vanishes for $q^2<0$, can have a causal Fourier transform only if it is a polynomial in ν:

$$W(q^2,\nu) = \epsilon(\nu) \sum_{n=0}^{N} \nu^n \rho_n(q^2)$$

Applied to our present problem, this theorem implies that the cross sections σ_L and σ_T determine the functions V_1 and V_2 not only for spacelike momentum transfer but also for all values of q^2, up to polynomials in ν. Let V_1, V_2 denote one particular causal continuation of the data from the spacelike to the timelike region. Any other causal extension must then be of the form

$$V_i^*(q^2,\nu) = V_i(q^2,\nu) + \epsilon(\nu) \sum_{n=0}^{N} \nu^{2n} \rho_i^{(n)}(q^2) \tag{7}$$

where $\rho(q^2)=0$ for $q^2\leqslant 0$. (Only even powers occur because of the symmetry properties under crossing.)

There is a certain analogy between this result and the well-known fact that the values of the electromagnetic form factors at spacelike momentum transfer determine their behavior in the timelike region. Note, however, that the functions V_1, V_2 are not analytic in q^2 and ν.

As is the case for the form factors, the following, *stronger statement* holds: It suffices to know the functions V_1, V_2 in an arbitrarily small strip $a<q^2<b\leqslant 0$; causality determines the rest up to the freedom mentioned above. (A proof of this statement is given in the Appendix.[23]) The functions V_1, V_2 are therefore not entirely arbitrary even in the spacelike region. Causality demands certain restrictions on the behavior of these functions for $q^2\leqslant 0$. We have not been able, however, to convert these restrictions into a form that can be used to test causality with the available data.

Concerning the actual computation of the functions V_1, V_2 in the timelike region, it should be clear that one has to expect the continuation to be rather unstable, small changes in the spacelike region leading to large changes in the timelike domain.

In order to resolve the remaining ambiguity exhibited in Eq. 7 further information concerning the current commutator is required. In the following we will for definiteness consider only the prototype of this ambiguity and put $N=0$:

$$V_i^*(q^2,\nu) = V_i(q^2,\nu) + \epsilon(\nu)\rho_i(q^2) \tag{8}$$

We will relate the quantities ρ_1 and ρ_2, which are not determined by σ_L, σ_T, to subtractions in fixed q^2 dispersion relations. If unsubtracted dispersion relations are assumed to hold, then V_1 and V_2 are uniquely determined by their spacelike values. In this case the data on $e + p \rightarrow e +$ anything determine the current commutator uniquely. Unfortunately, however, the currently accepted Regge phenomenology predicts subtractions in the dispersion relation involving V_1. Therefore, there is at present no basis for ignoring ρ_1. We will come back to this point later.

2. DOES THE VALIDITY OF THE SCALING LAWS IMPLY CANONICAL LEADING LIGHT-CONE SINGULARITIES?

Let us now examine the second question. Suppose that the commonly accepted interpretation of the data is correct, that is, suppose that the structure functions satisfy Bjorken scaling in the spacelike region, for example,

$$V_1(q^2, \nu) \rightarrow \frac{1}{2\xi\nu} F_L(\xi), \qquad \xi = \frac{-q^2}{2\nu}, \qquad \nu \rightarrow \infty \qquad (9)$$

(The data indicate that F_L is small and possibly vanishes.) Does it follow from this scaling law that the leading singularity of $\tilde{V}_1(x)$ on the light cone is of the canonical type

$$\tilde{V}_1(x) = \frac{1}{2\pi i} \epsilon(x^0) \delta(x^2) g(px) + \text{less singular terms (l.s.t.)} \qquad (10)$$

where g is the Fourier transform of F_L?

The answer to this question is no. It suffices to give a counterexample. Consider the absorptive part of the function

$$T_1 = (s - q^2)^{-2} [(-q^2 - 2\nu) \ln(-q^2 - 2\nu) + (-q^2 + 2\nu) \ln(-q^2 + 2\nu)]$$

$$V_1 = (s - q^2)^{-2} \epsilon(\nu) [(q^2 + 2\nu) \theta(q^2 + 2\nu)$$

$$+ (q^2 - 2\nu) \theta(q^2 - 2\nu)], \qquad q^2 \leqslant 0 \qquad (11)$$

This quantity possesses a causal Fourier transform and, *for spacelike q^2*, satisfies the scaling law (Eq. 9) with

$$\frac{1}{\xi} F_L(\xi) = \xi^{-2} (1 - |\xi|) \theta(1 - |\xi|) \qquad (12)$$

Its leading light-cone singularity is not canonical. Therefore scaling in the region $q^2 \leqslant 0$ does not guarantee that the leading light-cone singularity of the current commutator is canonical, even apart from the ambiguity mentioned earlier. If, however, scaling holds properly *for all* q^2, then the leading light-cone singularity is canonical; this statement will be made more precise in the next section.

3. DOES A CANONICAL LEADING LIGHT-CONE SINGULARITY IMPLY SCALING?

We now turn to the inverse problem and ask, What are the momentum space properties of an amplitude whose leading light-cone singularity is canonical? Let us begin with the remark that, if the commutator of two operators has a canonical light-cone singularity, say $(z = x - y)$

$$[A(x), B(y)] = (2\pi)^{-1} \epsilon(z) \delta(z^2) C(x,y) + \text{l.s.t.} \tag{13}$$

then the leading light-cone singularity of the operator product is also canonical and, moreover, is determined by the same bilocal field $C(x,y)$:

$$A(x)B(y) = (4\pi^2 i)^{-1}(z^2 - i\epsilon z^0)^{-1} C(x,y) + \text{l.s.t.} \tag{14}$$

The same is true of the T-product:

$$T[A(x)B(y)] = (4\pi^2 i)^{-1}(z^2 - i\epsilon)^{-1} C(x,y) + \text{l.s.t.} \tag{15}$$

It is therefore immaterial whether we assume a specific singularity for the commutator or for the operator product. We prefer to work with the commutator only because this object is causal and therefore satisfies a set of sum rules which we will discuss shortly.

Consider some matrix element of the commutator

$$\tilde{V}(x) = \langle f|[A(x), B(0)]|i\rangle \tag{16}$$

For a canonical leading light-cone singularity of the type in Eq. 13 this quantity may be written as

$$\tilde{V}(x) = (2\pi i)^{-1} \epsilon(x^0) \delta(x^2) g(x) + \tilde{R}(x) \tag{17}$$

where $g(x)$ is a matrix element of the bilocal field $C(x,y)$:

$$g(x) = i\langle f|C(x,0)|i\rangle \tag{18}$$

We claim[1, 2] that the behavior of the Fourier transform

$$V(q) = \frac{1}{2\pi} \int dx \, e^{iqx} \tilde{V}(x) \qquad (19)$$

in the Bjorken limit is determined by the leading light-cone singularity, that is, by $g(x)$, whereas the remainder $\tilde{R}(x)$ is irrelevant. To prove this assertion two specifications are necessary.

1. Bjorken scaling is to be understood in the following sense. Consider momenta of the form $q = k + En$, where n is a lightlike vector, $n^2 = 0$, and take the limit $E \to \pm \infty$, with k, n fixed. We will say that the amplitude $V(q)$ satisfies Bjorken scaling if

$$V(k + En) \to \frac{1}{E} F(k, n), \qquad E \to \pm \infty \qquad (20)$$

We emphasize that this scaling law is a limit relation between distributions. Explicitly, scaling law (20) requires

$$\lim_{E \to \pm \infty} E \int d^4k \, \varphi(k) V(k + En) = \int d^4k \, \varphi(k) F(k, n)$$

for any smooth test function $\varphi(k)$. Note that the limit is to be taken *after* smearing. If one does not understand scaling in this specific sense, but, for example, requires only that Eq. 20 hold for fixed k, it is not difficult to give counterexamples to the asserted relation between light-cone singularities and scaling; in fact, counterexamples that are by no means pathological may be found in the literature.[3]

2. The remainder $\tilde{R}(x)$, which describes the interior of the light cone, must be sufficiently smooth. Obviously, a necessary and sufficient condition for $\tilde{R}(x)$ not to contribute in the Bjorken limit is the requirement that the smeared Fourier transform $R(q)$ of $\tilde{R}(x)$

$$r(E) = \int d^4k \, \varphi(k) R(k + En) \qquad (21)$$

vanish faster than E^{-1} as $E \to \pm \infty$. The function $r(E)$ is the Fourier transform of the quantity $\tilde{r}(\tau)$ obtained by sampling $R(x)$ on the lightlike surface $nx = \tau$:

$$\tilde{r}(\tau) = \int d^4x \, \delta(nx - \tau) \tilde{\varphi}(x) \tilde{R}(x) \qquad (22)$$

The asymptotic behavior of the Fourier transform $r(E)$ concerns the local properties of $\tilde{r}(\tau)$. One of the advantages of the formulation of the Bjorken limit adopted here is the fact that the problem is thereby reduced to functions of a single variable, for which the relation between local properties and asymptotic behavior of the Fourier transform is well studied. Some relevant statements concerning this connection may be found in the Appendix.

We summarize this discussion as follows.

Theorem.[1, 2]   The amplitude $V(q)$ satisfies the scaling law (Eq. 20) if and only if the leading light-cone singularity is of the canonical form (Eq. 17) with a smooth remainder $\tilde{R}(x)$ in the sense of specification 2. Furthermore, the scaling function F depends on the vector k only through the projection kn, and we have

$$F(kn,n) = \frac{i}{2} \int_{-\infty}^{\infty} d\lambda \, e^{i\lambda kn} g(\lambda n) \tag{23}$$

If the function $V(q)$ depends only on the two invariants q^2 and ν, $V = V(q^2, \nu)$, the scaling law takes the form

$$\lim_{\nu \to \pm \infty} \nu V(-2\xi\nu - \eta, \nu) = F(\xi) \tag{24}$$

where ξ and η are two parameters subject to the restriction $\eta \geqslant \xi^2$. Again, the limit is to be taken after smearing with a suitable test function in ξ, η. The scaling law may fail pointwise, for example, at $\xi = 0$, without upsetting the leading light-cone singularity. (Indeed, the data indicate that the scaling functions may be singular at $\xi = 0$.) The points $q^2 = -2\xi\nu - \eta$ lie on a straight line in the (q^2, ν) plane. The scaling law asserts that the limits $\nu \to \pm \infty$ along this straight line are given by the same limiting value, which, moreover, depends only on the slope of this line and not on its position (as long as $\eta \geqslant \xi^2$, i.e., as long as the line does not cut the parabola $q^2 = \nu^2$). The theorem states that, if the scaling law (Eq. 24) holds for spacelike as well as timelike momenta, the leading light-cone singularity is canonical. (The counterexample given in Section 2 does not scale for $q^2 > 0$.)

An analogous discussion applies to the *smoother singularity*:

$$\tilde{V}(x) = (-4\pi i)^{-1} \epsilon(x^0) \theta(x^2) h(x) + \text{l.s.t.} \tag{25}$$

In this case the scaling law reads

$$V(k + En) \to \frac{1}{E^2} F(kn, n) \tag{26}$$

The data seem to indicate that in the spacelike region the functions V_1 and V_2 behave according to Eq. 4, where F_L possibly vanishes. *If these* scaling laws indeed reflect canonical leading light-cone singularities of the type

$$V_1(x) = (2\pi i)^{-1}\epsilon(x^0)\,\delta(x^2)\,g(\,px) + \text{l.s.t.}$$

$$V_2(x) = (-4\pi i)^{-1}\epsilon(x^0)\theta(x^2)h(\,px) + \text{l.s.t.}$$

(27)

then it immediately follows that the functions V_1, V_2 must also scale with the same scaling functions in the timelike region. In particular, since the limits $\nu \to +\infty$ and $\nu \to -\infty$ must then be the same, the functions V_1 and V_2 must tend to zero faster than ν^{-1} or ν^{-2}, respectively, in the physical region of the process $e^+ + e^- \to p + \text{anything}$. It should be noted that this process is described not by the current commutator itself, but rather by a semidisconnected piece contained in it, that is,

$$V_i = V_i^{\text{ann}} + \bar{V}_i$$

Of course, it is possible that, say, V_2^{ann} scales with a finite scaling function F_2^{ann} (this was in fact shown to be the case in specific models[6]), but then the remainder $\bar{V}_2$ must also scale and compensate V_2^{ann} in the Bjorken limit.

Let us briefly discuss the implications of the *ambiguity* in the causal continuation mentioned in Section 1. We consider only the prototype of this ambiguity:

$$\delta V(q^2, \nu) = \epsilon(\nu)\rho(q^2)$$

In coordinate space, this quantity is represented by

$$\delta \tilde{V}(x) = -i \int_0^\infty ds\,\rho(s)\,\Delta(x, s)$$

and, on the light cone, it possesses a canonical singularity of the type

$$\delta \tilde{V}(x) = (2\pi i)^{-1}\epsilon(x^0)\,\delta(x^2)g + \text{l.s.t.}$$

provided the integral

$$g = \int_0^\infty ds\,\rho(s)$$

converges. If this integral vanishes, and if the first moment

$$h = \tfrac{1}{2}\int_0^\infty ds\,s\,\rho(s)$$

converges, then the leading singularity is of the smoother canonical type

$$\delta \tilde{V}(x) = (-4\pi i)^{-1} \epsilon(x^0)\theta(x^2)h + \text{l.s.t.}$$

The ambiguity in the causal continuation of V_1 and V_2 remains, therefore, even if canonical singularities are imposed on the light cone. The change

$$V_i^*(q^2,\nu) = V_i(q^2,\nu) + \epsilon(\nu)\rho_i(q^2)$$

affects the scaling functions defined by Eq. 4 as follows:

$$\frac{1}{\xi}F_L^*(\xi) = \frac{1}{\xi}F_L(\xi) + g\delta(\xi)$$

$$\frac{1}{\xi}F_2^*(\xi) = \frac{1}{\xi}F_2(\xi) + h\delta'(\xi)$$

(28)

where

$$g = \int_0^\infty ds\, \rho_1(s), \qquad 0 = \int_0^\infty ds\, \rho_2(s), \qquad h = \int_0^\infty ds\, s\, \rho_2(s) \qquad (29)$$

4.   EQUAL-TIME SUM RULES

The information on the behavior of the commutator on the light cone suffices to determine the equal-time commutator, provided the remainder $R(x)$ is sufficiently smooth. In particular, if the leading light-cone singularity of $V_1(x)$ is given by Eq. 27, one concludes[1, 7] that, at $x^0 = 0$:

$$\langle p|[j_0(x), j_i(0)]|p\rangle = ig(0)\, \partial_i \delta^3(\vec{x}) \qquad (30)$$

$$g(0) = \int_{-1}^1 d\xi\, \frac{1}{\xi}F_L(\xi) \qquad (31)$$

This "Schwinger term sum rule" is strictly valid. The quantity $g(0)$ is necessarily finite if the scaling law (Eq. 4) holds. This is at first sight surprising, because the scaling function $\xi^{-1}F_L(\xi)$ may be a singular object and, for example, behave like ξ^{-2} at $\xi = 0$. (Such behavior is expected to arise if the Pomeranchon couples to the longitudinal scaling function.) The right-hand side of Eq. 31 is nevertheless perfectly well defined since the scaling law specifies the quantity $\xi^{-1}F_L$ not as a function, but as a distribution, for which integrals of the type in Eq. 31 are without any problem.

As an example, take the causal amplitude

$$V_1(q^2,\nu) = \frac{1}{2\nu} \left| \frac{2\nu}{s-q^2} \right|^{\alpha+1} \theta\{|2\nu| - |s-q^2|\} \tag{32}$$

which is analytic in α with the exception of poles at $\alpha = 0, 2,\dots$. An amplitude of this type might represent the contribution of the Pomeranchon ($\alpha = 1$) or of the A_2 ($\alpha \cong \frac{1}{2}$). The scaling function associated with this amplitude is given by

$$\frac{1}{\xi} F_L(\xi) = |\xi|^{-\alpha-1}\theta(1-|\xi|) \tag{33}$$

The quantity

$$\int_{-1}^{1} d\xi \, \frac{1}{\xi} F_L(\xi) = -\frac{2}{\alpha} \tag{34}$$

is well defined for $\alpha \neq 0$, and one verifies that it indeed coincides with the Schwinger term as defined by the equal-time limit of $\langle p|[j_0(x),j_i(0)]|p\rangle$. Analogous remarks apply to the equal-time sum rule for V_2:

$$\delta(x^0)(\partial_0)^3 V_2(x) = 2i\,\delta^4(x)h(0) \tag{35}$$

$$h(0) = -\int_{-1}^{1} d\xi \, F_2(\xi) \tag{36}$$

We are now in a position to answer questions 4 and 5. We first note that the ambiguity in the causal continuation of the function V_1 affects both the Schwinger term and the scaling function in such a way as to preserve the sum rule (Eq. 31). The Schwinger term is therefore not a directly measurable quantity. Additional information is needed to fix the ambiguity in $\xi^{-1}F_L(\xi)$ at $\xi=0$. Finally, as exemplified by the amplitude (Eq. 32), the sum rule need not produce a positive Schwinger term despite the fact that $\xi^{-1}F_L$ is positive for $\xi \neq 0$. This difficulty occurs because the positivity conditions holds only in the region $q^2 \leqslant 4m_\pi^2$. (The functions V_1, V_2 describe only the connected part of the current commutator, whereas positivity holds for the full commutator.) This implies, in particular, that a vanishing Schwinger term, $g(0)=0$, does not require a vanishing longitudinal scaling function F_L.

5. CAUSALITY SUM RULES AND DISPERSION RELATIONS

Let us again consider a causal function $V(x)$ with a canonical leading light-cone singularity as given by Eq. 17. The corresponding scaling law

(Eq. 21) does not exhaust this information about $V(x)$. Scaling essentially derives from the fact that the function $V(x)$ contains a specific jump on the light cone. Scaling is not affected if one adds a smooth function to $V(x)$, even if this function does not vanish outside the light cone. The requirement that $V(x)$ not only possess a specific singularity on the cone but also vanish outside implies that its Fourier transform $V(q)$ satisfies a sum rule first given by Leutwyler and Stern:[1, 8]

$$\lim_{N \to \infty} \int_{-N}^{N} dE \, V(k+En) = P \int_{-\infty}^{\infty} \frac{dx}{kn-x} F(x,n) \qquad (37)$$

Furthermore, the retarded amplitude $\tilde{V}^{\text{ret}}(x) = \theta(x^0)\tilde{V}(x)$ satisfies the dispersion relation

$$V^{\text{ret}}(k+En) = \frac{1}{2\pi i} \int_{-\infty}^{\infty} \frac{dE'}{E'-E-i\epsilon} V(k+E'n) \qquad (38)$$

and the scaling law

$$V^{\text{ret}}(k+En) \to \frac{1}{E} F^{\text{ret}}(kn,n) \qquad (39)$$

with

$$F^{\text{ret}}(x,n) = \frac{1}{2\pi i} \int_{-\infty}^{\infty} \frac{dx'}{x'-x-i\epsilon} F(x',n) \qquad (40)$$

The nice feature of these relations is that the subtractions are controlled by the light cone: The dispersion relation (Eq. 38) and the sum rule (Eq. 37) necessarily converge because of the scaling law satisfied by $V(k+En)$. (Note also that these relations are not affected by the ambiguity in the causal extension.) It is again essential, however, that these relations be taken as what they are: relations between distributions. In more explicit notation, the dispersion relation (Eq. 38), for example, states that

$$\int d^4k \, \varphi(k) V^{\text{ret}}(k+En) = \frac{1}{2\pi i} \int \frac{dE'}{E'-E-i\epsilon} \int d^4k \, \varphi(k) V(k+E'n)$$

The smearing operation has to be carried out before the dispersion integration is done.

In the case of the amplitude V_1, which depends only on the invariants q^2, ν, the sum rule (Eq. 37) takes the form

$$\int_{-\infty}^{\infty} d\nu \, V_1(-2\xi\nu - \eta, \nu) = \tfrac{1}{2} P \int_{-1}^{1} \frac{d\xi'}{\xi'-\xi} \frac{F_L(\xi')}{\xi'} \qquad (41)$$

Applied to V_2, the sum rule reads

$$\int_{-\infty}^{\infty} dv\, V_2(-2\xi v - \eta, v) = 0 \tag{42}$$

whereas an application to the quantity V_2 leads to

$$\int_{-\infty}^{\infty} dv v\, V_2(-2\xi v - \eta, v) = \tfrac{1}{2} P \int_{-1}^{1} \frac{d\xi'}{\xi' - \xi} \frac{F_2(\xi')}{\xi'} \tag{43}$$

Finally, we note the expression for the retarded amplitudes:

$$V_i^{\text{ret}}(-2\xi v - \eta, v) = \frac{1}{2\pi i} \int_{-\infty}^{\infty} \frac{dv'}{v' - v - i\epsilon} V_i(-2\xi v' - \eta, v') \tag{44}$$

6.   FIXED MASS DISPERSION RELATIONS

The distribution character of the sum rules and dispersion relations listed in Section 5 reveals itself most clearly when their fixed mass limits are considered. Let us start with the dispersion relation for V_1^{ret}:

$$V_1^{\text{ret}}(-2\xi v - \eta, v) = \frac{1}{2\pi i} \int \frac{dv'}{v' - v - i\epsilon} V_1(-2\xi v' - \eta, v') \tag{45}$$

If we simply put $\xi = 0$ into this relation, we obtain the familiar fixed q^2 dispersion relation ($q^2 = -\eta \leqslant 0$). This relation need not converge, however, since the light cone does not exclude Regge contributions $V_1 \sim v^\alpha$ (α is the $t = 0$ intercept of the trajectory), which explode as $v \to \infty$, q^2 fixed. Thus relation (45) in general fails to be correct at $\xi = 0$. To arrive at a correct fixed mass dispersion relation we have to know the behavior of V_1 in a small wedge defined by $|q^2 + \eta| \leqslant 2\epsilon|v|$. If it were true that inside this wedge $V_1 \to 0$ for $v \to \pm \infty$, then the transition to the limit would be without problems.

Let us first get rid of the Regge contributions with $\alpha > 0$ by assuming that these contributions to V_1 may be taken into account by an explicit representation V_R, which satisfies scaling and causality. If this is the case, then V_R and the corresponding retarded amplitude V_R^{ret} also obey the dispersion relation (Eq. 45), and the same is therefore true of the difference $V_1 - V_R$. The problem then reduces to the question, Are there any other contributions that do not vanish in the wedge as $v \to \pm \infty$?

We *assume* that the only other contribution with this property is a term of the form $\epsilon(\nu)\rho_1(q^2)$, which contains the ambiguity in the continuation of V_1 from the spacelike region to the timelike domain. (We assume $\rho_1=0$ for $q^2 \leqslant 0$.) We are thus postulating that V_1 may be written as

$$V_1 = V_R + \epsilon(\nu)\rho_1(q^2) + V_1' \tag{46}$$

where V_1' tends to zero as $\nu \to \pm\infty$ in the entire wedge, $|q^2+\eta| \leqslant 2\epsilon|\nu|$. The retarded amplitudes associated with the three terms in Eq. 46 satisfy the dispersion relation of Eq. 45 individually. Furthermore, the transition to the limit $\xi=0$ is correct in the dispersion relation for V_1'. The fixed q^2 dispersion relation therefore reads as follows:

$$V_1^{\text{ret}}(q^2,\nu) = V_R^{\text{ret}}(q^2,\nu) + \frac{1}{2\pi i}\int_0^\infty \frac{ds\,\rho_1(s)}{s-q^2-i\epsilon q^0}$$

$$+ \frac{1}{2\pi i}\int_{-\infty}^\infty \frac{d\nu'}{\nu'-\nu-i\epsilon}[V_1(q^2,\nu') - V_R(q^2,\nu')] \tag{47}$$

We thus have the result that the ambiguity in the causal extension of V_1 shows up as a subtraction term in the fixed mass dispersion relation for $V_1^{\text{ret}} - V_R^{\text{ret}}$. In Regge language, this term may be referred to as a fixed pole at $\alpha=0$. The relevance of contributions corresponding to such a fixed pole in fixed mass dispersion relations has been stressed by Cornwall, Corrigan, and Norton.[9] We emphasize that the dispersion relation of Eq. 47 is valid only if the decomposition (Eq. 46) holds. It is of course possible that the absorptive part V_1 contains a contribution of the type $V_1 \to \epsilon(\nu)\beta(q^2)$ at $\nu \to \pm\infty$ even in the spacelike region. In this case the amplitude V_1^{ret} contains a term $V_1^{\text{ret}} \sim \beta(q^2)\ln|\nu|$ at $\nu \to \pm\infty$. We do not discuss this possibility further but emphasize that, if such a term is present, it has to be included in V_R, V_R^{ret} to keep the dispersion relation of Eq. 47 intact.

The same analysis applies to the amplitude V_2. Since this amplitude does not receive Regge contributions that blow up as $\nu \to \infty$ ($V_2 \sim \nu^{\alpha-2}$), there is no need to subtract them, and we get

$$V_2^{\text{ret}}(q^2,\nu) = \frac{1}{2\pi i}\int_0^\infty \frac{ds\,\rho_2(s)}{s-q^2-i\epsilon q^0} + \frac{1}{2\pi i}\int_{-\infty}^\infty \frac{d\nu'\,V_2(q^2,\nu')}{\nu'-\nu-i\epsilon} \tag{48}$$

The amplitude $V_2^{\text{ret}}(0,\nu)$ contributes to the forward cross section for *Compton scattering*. If at $q^2=0$ the subtraction term involving ρ_2 were different from zero, the cross section $d\sigma/dt$ would rise in proportion to ν^2. This is ruled out experimentally, however, and we thus conclude that $\int ds\ s^{-1}\rho_2 = 0$. It is reasonable to assume that the high-energy behavior is the same for virtual photons, and hence $\rho_2(s) = 0$. (In Regge language the contribution from ρ_2 amounts to a fixed pole at $\alpha = 2$.) The amplitude V_2^{ret} then satisfies an unsubtracted dispersion relation at fixed q^2, and the data on V_2 for $q^2 = 0$ suffice to uniquely determine V_2 for all q^2. In particular, there is no ambiguity in the scaling function $(1/\xi)F_2$ at $\xi = 0$.

The answer to question 6 is therefore the following. The virtual forward Compton amplitude V_2^{ret} is uniquely determined by the data on σ_L, σ_T. This is not the case, however, for the amplitude V_1^{ret}, which is sensitive to the ambiguity $\rho_1(q^2)$ in the causal extension of V_1. Of course, the forward Compton amplitude for *real* photons involves only V_2^{ret} and is therefore uniquely determined by the photoproduction cross section $\sigma_\gamma(\nu)$ $= \sigma_T(0, \nu)$.

7. THE CORNWALL-CORRIGAN-NORTON SUM RULE

We now turn to the three causality sum rules (Eqs. 41, 42, and 43) satisfied by V_1 and V_2 and investigate the limit $\xi \to 0$ in these relations. We first note that the sum rules 41 and 42 are trivial in this limit, since V_1 and V_2 are odd functions of ν; we therefore focus on Eq. 43. To obtain the limit $\xi \to 0$ in this relation we again have to know the asymptotic behavior of $V_2(q^2, \nu)$ in a small wedge $|q^2 + \eta| \leqslant 2\epsilon|\nu|$. Since Regge poles contribute to V_2 in proportion to $\nu^{\alpha - 2}$, we again need to take into account all Regge contributions with $\alpha > 0$. Let us denote by V_R an explicit, causal representation of these contributions which obeys the scaling law

$$V_R(q^2, \nu) \to \frac{1}{2\nu^2\xi} F_R(\xi) \qquad (49)$$

Since both V_2 and V_R satisfy the causality sum rule (43), we consider the difference $\bar{V}_2 = V_2 - V_R$ and denote by $\bar{F}_2 = F_2 - F_R$ the corresponding scaling function. In this notation the causality sum rule 43 reads

$$\int_{-\infty}^{\infty} d\nu\nu\,\bar{V}_2(-2\xi\nu - \eta, \nu) = \tfrac{1}{2}P \int_{-\infty}^{\infty} \frac{d\xi'}{\xi' - \xi} \frac{\bar{F}_2(\xi')}{\xi'} \qquad (50)$$

(The Regge representation need not have the correct support properties in momentum space; the support of the scaling function F_R may correspondingly extend over the entire real axis and not be confined to the interval

$-1 \leqslant \xi \leqslant 1$.) The Cornwall-Corrigan-Norton (CCN) sum rule[9] is obtained from this relation by going to the limit $\xi = 0$ and assuming that the integral may be interchanged with the limit:

$$\int_{-\infty}^{\infty} d\nu\nu\, \overline{V}_2(q^2,\nu) = \int_0^{\infty} \frac{d\xi}{\xi^2} \overline{F}_2(\xi) \tag{51}$$

In order to justify the limit operation it is necessary to make sure that V_2 tends to zero as $\nu \to \pm \infty$ in the small wedge defined above. In this way the presence of an $\alpha = 0$ fixed pole in the absorptive part is essentially excluded. As an example[9] of an amplitude which *does* contain such a fixed pole let us consider the function

$$V_B^{\text{ret}}(q^2,\nu) = \frac{1}{2\pi i} G(q^2)[(-q^2-2\nu)^{-1}+(-q^2+2\nu)^{-1}] \tag{52}$$

where

$$G(q^2) = \int_0^{\infty} \frac{ds\, g(s)}{s-q^2} \tag{53}$$

The only singularities of this amplitude in the spacelike region are simple poles at $q^2 = \pm 2\nu$, that is, the Born terms. In fact, with an appropriate choice of the spectral function $g(s)$ the residue $G(q^2)$ could be fitted to reproduce the physical Born terms as described by the electromagnetic proton form factors. Let us, in particular, take into account that the elastic contribution tends to zero rapidly as $q^2 \to -\infty$:

$$\int_0^{\infty} ds\, g(s) = 0 \tag{54}$$

In this case the absorptive part V_B scales faster than ν^{-2}, that is, the corresponding scaling function F_B vanishes. It is not difficult to verify that the amplitude V_B is causal and indeed satisfies the sum rule 50 for $\xi \neq 0$:

$$\int_{-\infty}^{\infty} d\nu\nu\, V_B(-2\xi\nu - \eta, \nu) = 0 \tag{55}$$

If we put $\xi = 0$ and evaluate the fixed mass sum rule, we get, however,

$$\int_{-\infty}^{\infty} d\nu\nu\, V_B(q^2,\nu) = -\tfrac{1}{2}q^2 G(q^2) \tag{56}$$

In other words, the limit $\xi \to 0$ cannot be interchanged with the integral. The reason for this failure of the CCN sum rule is of course the fact that at $\xi = 0$ the integral over ν no longer cuts the singularities of V_B at $q^2 = s$ in the timelike region. The energy dependence of these singularities corresponds to a fixed pole at $\alpha = 0$.

More generally, let us assume that after subtraction of the Regge contributions with $\alpha > 0$ the absorptive part may be written as

$$\bar{V}_2(q^2, \nu) = \frac{\epsilon(\nu)}{\nu^2} \sigma_2(q^2) + V_2(q^2, \nu)' \tag{57}$$

where σ_2 vanishes for $q^2 \leqslant 0$, whereas $\nu^2 V_2'$ tends to zero as $\nu \to \pm \infty$ in the wedge $|q^2 + \eta| \leqslant 2\epsilon |\nu|$. In this case the fixed mass causality sum rule reads:

$$\int_{-\infty}^{\infty} d\nu\nu\, \bar{V}_2(q^2, \nu) = \int_0^{\infty} \frac{d\xi}{\xi^2} \bar{F}_2(\xi) - \int_0^{\infty} \frac{ds\sigma_2(s)}{s - q^2} \tag{58}$$

The essential point here is that, if the absorptive part contains a fixed pole at $\alpha = 0$, the right-hand side of the CCN sum rule is not independent of q^2. The contribution from the fixed pole at $\alpha = 0$ shows up only at small q^2. In fact, for large q^2, the sum rule 58 is trivial: V_2 approaches its scaling limit and the left-hand side becomes identical with the first term on the right-hand side, whereas the second term disappears.

Dominguez, Ferro Fontan, and Suaya[10] and Damashek and Gilman[10] have evaluated the left-hand side of Eq. 58 at $q^2 = 0$ by using the data on total photoproduction cross sections, $\sigma_\gamma(\nu) = \sigma_T(0, \nu)$:

$$\nu V_2(0, \nu) = (4\pi^2 \alpha)^{-1} \sigma_\gamma(\nu) \tag{59}$$

Using a Regge parametrization of the type $(\alpha = 1, \tfrac{1}{2})$

$$\nu V_R(q^2, \nu) = \beta_1(q^2) + \beta_2(q^2)|2\nu|^{-1/2} \tag{60}$$

and adjusting $\beta_1(0)$ and $\beta_2(0)$ in such a way as to obtain a good fit to the high-energy behavior of $\sigma_\gamma(\nu)$, they evaluate the left-hand side of Eq. 58 with the result

$$\int_{-\infty}^{\infty} d\nu\nu\, \bar{V}_2(0, \nu) \cong 1 \tag{61}$$

(This result states that the Regge amplitude essentially cancels the *inelastic* contribution to V_2. What remains is the contribution from the Born terms.)

Estimates of the quantity $\int d\xi \xi^{-2} \bar{F}_2$ have been carried out by Rajaraman and Rajasekharan,[11] by Elitzur,[12] by Brandt, Breidenbach, and Vinciarelli,[13] and by Close and Gunion.[14] Unfortunately, there are not enough accurate data at small q^2 to reliably determine the Regge residues $\beta_1(q^2), \beta_2(q^2)$ in representation 60 for V_2. In the following we quote only the fits of Brandt et al. and of Close and Gunion to give an idea of the difficulties involved.

Brandt et al. find that the fit

$$\beta_1(q^2) = C_1(\mu^2 - q^2)^{-1}$$

$$\beta_2(q^2) = C_2(\mu^2 - q^2)^{-1/2}$$

(62)

with $C_1 = 0.285$, $C_2 = 0.275$, and $\mu^2 = 0.248$ reproduces the data well in the region $\nu > 8(|q^2| + \mu^2)$. This representation leads to

$$F_R(\xi) = C_1 + C_2|\xi|^{1/2}$$

(63)

and

$$\int_0^\infty d\xi \xi^{-2} \bar{F}_2(\xi) = -2.01$$

Close and Gunion, on the other hand, point out that possibly the Pomeron and $A_2 - f$ contributions dominate in a much smaller domain, while a very large contribution from a trajectory with $\alpha = -\frac{1}{2}$ is responsible for a sizable fraction of the data in the region $\nu > 8(|q^2| + \mu^2)$. Such a contribution may affect the parameters C_1 and C_2 significantly. In fact, the scarcity of the data makes it possible to attribute as much as 50% of the "Pomeron" of Brandt et al. to the trajectories with $\alpha = \frac{1}{2}, -\frac{1}{2}$ and to obtain a fit with $C_1 = 0.12$, $C_2 = 0.462$. If this interpretation is correct, the first term on the right-hand side of Eq. 58 changes sign and a value consistent with the left-hand side may be obtained:

$$\int_0^\infty d\xi \xi^{-2} \bar{F}_2(\xi) = 1$$

(This was actually imposed as a constraint in the fit of Close and Gunion.)

Clearly a more detailed experimental study of the interplay between scaling behavior and Regge behavior is needed to decide the issue. It should be noted, however, that, if one does not look at the presently available data with the prejudice that the fixed pole at $\alpha = 0$ should be independent of q^2 (and hence not be present in the absorptive part, $\sigma_2 = 0$), the data indicate that the sign of $\int d\xi \xi^{-2} \bar{F}_2$ is negative.

Brandt, Ng, Preparata, and Vinciarelli[15] have pointed out that a fixed pole at $\alpha = 0$ in the absorptive part would show up, for example, in the photoproduction of ρ. Clearly, a direct verification of this prediction would be a more reliable test of the presence of such a fixed pole in V_2.

We emphasize that, although a fixed pole in the absorptive part of the amplitude $\gamma + p \to \gamma + p$ should show up in the process $\gamma + p \to \rho + p$, the latter does not entail a fixed pole in the hadronic amplitude $\rho + p \to \rho + p$. Hadronic amplitudes are severely constrained by unitarity, and fixed poles in elastic amplitudes in general require a subtle shielding mechanism in order not to contradict the probability interpretation. This Pandora's box is not opened by fixed poles of the type discussed here.

8. ELECTROMAGNETIC MASS SHIFT

Let us now turn to the last question listed in the introduction: Is it possible to determine the electromagnetic mass shift from measurements of σ_L, σ_T? The answer is no, unless the ambiguity ρ_1 in the amplitude V_1 can be pinned down. The ambiguity $V_1 \sim \epsilon(\nu)\rho_1(q^2)$ affects the mass shift as follows:

$$\delta m_{\rho_1} \sim \int d^4q \int_0^\infty ds \frac{\rho_1(s)}{s - q^2 - i\epsilon} \tag{64}$$

This contribution is convergent, provided $\int ds \rho_1 = \int ds s \rho_1 = 0$. Explicitly, one finds

$$\delta m_{\rho_1} \sim \int_0^\infty ds s \ln s \rho_1(s) \tag{65}$$

It is therefore impossible to express the mass shift in terms of the cross sections σ_L, σ_T without explicitly assuming that V_1 does not contain a contribution at $\alpha = 0$.

9. SPECULATION: SMOOTH HIGH-ENERGY BEHAVIOR

The following speculation may indicate a way out of the difficulties associated with V_1. The generally accepted Regge pole phenomenology asserts that Regge poles contribute to V_1 with the power ν^α. There is, however, no experimental support for this assertion. It appears that in the deep inelastic region longitudinally polarized photons couple very weakly;

F_L is small if not zero. We now conjecture that the same weak coupling phenomenon also occurs in the Regge region; Regge poles may only couple to V_1 with the power $v^{\alpha-2}$.

Some theoretical support for this conjecture may be drawn from an analysis of the amplitude $\langle p|[j_\mu(x), j_\nu(0)]|p\rangle$ in terms of irreducible representations of the t-channel Lorentz group.[16] In the t-channel one subjects the proton momentum p to a Lorentz transformation, keeping the photon momentum q fixed. The generators of these Lorentz transformations are

$$L_{\mu\nu} = i\left(p_\mu \frac{\partial}{\partial p^\nu} - p_\nu \frac{\partial}{\partial p^\mu}\right) \tag{66}$$

We consider the amplitude $W_{\mu\nu}$ defined by Eq. 1 and look for contributions that transform irreducibly under the action of $L_{\mu\nu}$, that is, contributions with a specific eigenvalue of the Casimir operator:

$$\tfrac{1}{2} L_{\rho\sigma} L^{\rho\sigma} W_{\mu\nu} = \alpha(\alpha+2) W_{\mu\nu} \tag{67}$$

It is straightforward to translate this condition into eigenvalue equations for the invariant amplitudes $V_i(q^2, v)$. We find

$$(v^2 - q^2) V_1'' + 3v V_1' - 4v V_2' - 4V_2 = \alpha(\alpha+2) V_1$$
$$(v^2 - q^2) V_2'' + 7v V_2' + 8V_2 = \alpha(\alpha+2) V_2 \tag{68}$$

where the prime indicates a partial derivative with respect to v.

Our main point here is that Eqs. 68 have *minimal solutions* in which $V_1(v, q^2)$ falls off as $v^{\alpha-2}$ (up to logs occurring at exceptional values of α), as well as the expected solutions in which V_1 behaves as v^α. This can be verified by solving Eq. 68; as simple illustrations we mention the cases $q^2 = 0$, in which the solutions are easily written down, and the case $q^2 \neq 0$, $\alpha \neq$ integer. In the latter case the general solution is given by

$$V_2 = \sum_{i=1}^{2} C_i \frac{\partial^2}{\partial v^2} R_i(v, q^2) \tag{69}$$

and

$$V_1 = \sum_{i=1}^{2} C_i (q^2)^{-1}\left[\alpha^2 - \left(v \frac{\partial}{\partial v}\right)^2\right] R_i + \sum_{i=1}^{2} D_i R_i \tag{70}$$

where the R_i $(i = 1, 2)$ are linearly independent solutions of

$$(v^2 - q^2) R_i'' + 3v R_i' - \alpha(\alpha+2) R_i = 0 \tag{71}$$

(Note that V_1 cannot vanish unless V_2 also vanishes.) The solutions of Eq. 71 behave asymptotically as (we take $\alpha > -1$)

$$R_i \to r_i(q^2)\nu^{\alpha}\left[1 + \tfrac{1}{4}(1-\alpha)\frac{q^2}{\nu^2} + \cdots\right] \tag{72}$$

The minimal solution corresponds to setting $D_1 = D_2 = 0$ and behaves like

$$V_1 \to (1-\alpha)\beta(q^2)\nu^{\alpha-2}$$
$$V_2 \to \alpha\beta(q^2)\nu^{\alpha-2} \tag{73}$$

whereas solutions with $D_1, D_2 \neq 0$ of course behave like $V_1 \sim \nu^{\alpha}$. The asymptotic behavior of the cross sections corresponding to minimal coupling is

$$\sigma_L \to e^2\pi(-q^2)\beta(q^2)\nu^{\alpha-3}$$
$$\sigma_T \to e^2\pi\alpha\beta(q^2)\nu^{\alpha-1} \tag{74}$$

This behavior leads to the simple prediction that, if the Regge trajectories with $\alpha > 0$ indeed couple minimally to V_1, the longitudinal cross section should vanish in the Regge limit, more precisely ($\nu \to \infty$, q^2 fixed):

$$\frac{\sigma_L}{\sigma_T} = \frac{(-q^2)}{\nu^2} + O(\nu^{-5/2}) \tag{75}$$

It should be possible to test this prediction in the near future. If Eq. 73 indeed expresses the correct high-energy behavior of V_1, its leading power in the Regge limit would be $\nu^{-3/2}$. In this case one would expect the ambiguity ρ_1 discussed earlier to disappear, both V_1 and V_2 then being uniquely determined by σ_L, σ_T.

A remark concerning the *light-cone algebra* of the quark-model type is perhaps in order here. It has been proposed by a number of authors[17] that the leading light-cone singularity of the electromagnetic and weak currents may in fact be smoother than the singularity corresponding to Bjorken's original proposal. If the leading light-cone singularities can be abstracted from the quark model, as advocated in particular by Fritzsch and Gell-Mann, then V_1 behaves according to

$$\tilde{V}_1(x) = (-4\pi i)^{-1}\epsilon(x^0)\theta(x^2)h_1(px) + \text{less singular terms} \tag{76}$$

$$V_1(q^2,\nu) \to \frac{1}{2\nu^2\xi}G_1(\xi)$$

rather than according to Eqs. 9 and 10. In this case, the behavior of the cross sections σ_L, σ_T in the Bjorken limit is given by

$$\sigma_L \rightarrow e^2 \pi \nu^{-2} (1-\xi)^{-1} [G_1(\xi) + F_2(\xi)]$$

$$\sigma_T \rightarrow e^2 \pi (-q^2)^{-1} (1-\xi)^{-1} F_2(\xi)$$

$$(77)$$

and we get

$$\frac{\sigma_L}{\sigma_T} \rightarrow \frac{(-q^2)}{\nu^2} \left[1 + \frac{G_1(\xi)}{F_2(\xi)} \right] \qquad (78)$$

We emphasize that the quark-model light-cone algebra not only predicts $\sigma_L / \sigma_T \rightarrow 0$, but also predicts that this ratio scales according to Eq. 78. An experimental test of Eq. 78 is therefore a very sensitive test of the quark-model light-cone algebra.

The *standard* Regge phenomenology $V_1 \sim \nu^\alpha$ then suggests that $G_1(\xi)$ should be very singular at $\xi \rightarrow 0$ in order to match the Regge and Bjorken regions:

$$G_1(\xi) \sim \xi^{-2} \qquad (79)$$

If, however, V_1 couples *minimally* to Regge poles with $\alpha > 0$, we find

$$G_1(\xi) \sim \xi^{1/2} \qquad (80)$$

and then expect that the quantity $1 + G_1/F_2$ relating σ_L to σ_T should not change by an order of magnitude if we pass from the Regge region to the deep inelastic domain; Eq. 75 should then give a rough estimate of σ_L / σ_T even in the deep inelastic region.

We remark, finally, that if V_1 is as well behaved as conjectured here the electromagnetic mass shift may indeed be expressed in terms of σ_L, σ_T through the Cottingham formula.[18] The actual value of the resulting mass shifts is, however, still entirely open since an evaluation of δm requires very precise measurements of σ_L. In fact, the contributions of V_1 to δm are of the same weight as those of V_2. What we have been suggesting here is merely that V_1 and V_2 are of the same order of magnitude in the Regge region. The light-cone philosophy based on the free quark model suggests that V_1 and V_2 also behave similarly in the Bjorken limit. Even if V_1 satisfies both these wishes, we do not have enough information about this quantity to evaluate the mass difference, which may still be any number, including $-\infty$ and $+\infty$, a rather delicate cancellation between V_1 and V_2 being necessary to obtain a finite mass difference [the integral $\int d\xi (2G_1^{n-p} + F_2^{n-p})$ must vanish[1, 7]].

10. EVALUATION OF CAUSALITY SUM RULES

In the final part of this chapter we return to the causality sum rules discussed in Section 5. We focus on the sum rules satisfied by V_2:

$$\int d\nu\, V_2(-2\xi\nu - \eta, \nu) = 0$$

$$\int d\nu\nu\, V_2(-2\xi\nu - \eta, \nu) = \tfrac{1}{2} P \int \frac{d\xi'}{\xi' - \xi} \frac{F_2(\xi')}{\xi'} \tag{81}$$

It has been pointed out in Ref. 8 that these sum rules are identically satisfied if we replace V_2 by the scale-invariant quantity

$$V_2^{sc}(q^2, \nu) = \frac{1}{\nu(-q^2)} F_2\left(\frac{-q^2}{2\nu}\right) \tag{82}$$

This is so because the quantity V_2^{sc} possesses a causal Fourier transform and of course satisfies the same scaling law as V_2. This observation implies that the sum rules (Eq. 81) may alternatively be written as ($q^2 = -2\xi\nu - \eta$):

$$\int d\nu \{ V_2 - V_2^{sc} \} = 0$$

$$\int d\nu\nu \{ V_2 - V_2^{sc} \} = 0 \tag{83}$$

In other words, the causality sum rules are constraints on the *deviations* from scaling which occur at small q^2 and small missing mass.

More generally, the sum rules may be written in the form ($q^2 = -2\xi\nu - \eta$)

$$\int d\nu \{ V_2 - V_2^{int} \} = 0$$

$$\int d\nu\nu \{ V_2 - V_2^{int} \} = 0 \tag{84}$$

where V_2^{int} is any function of q^2 and ν with two properties: (*a*) it is *causal*, that is, its Fourier transform vanishes outside the light cone, and (*b*) it *scales*, that is, in the Bjorken limit, V_2^{int} agrees with V_2. Any causal interpolation V_2^{int} of the scaling law is suitable. One such interpolating function was given above: $V_2^{int} = V_2^{sc}$. A slightly modified interpolating function which remedies the failure of the scaling law at $q^2 = 0$ has been proposed in ref 8:

$$V_2^{int}(q^2, \nu) = \frac{1}{\nu(a - q^2)} F_2\left(\frac{a - q^2}{2\nu}\right)$$

A number of other interpolating functions which satisfy the two conditions listed can be found in ref. 4.

In sum rules 84 the deep inelastic region, say $W > 2$ GeV, $q^2 < -1$ GeV^2, does not contribute, since in that region $V_2^{int} \cong V_2$. In general, the quantity $V_2^{int} - V_2$ contributes significantly only in the nucleon resonance region $W < 2$ GeV and in the vector meson region $-1 < q^2 < m^2$, where m is a mass of the order of 1–2 GeV. (Note that the scaling law holds also for $q^2 > 0$.) The freedom in the choice of V_2^{int} may be exploited in such a way that the interpolating function agrees with V_2 in a domain which is larger than the deep inelastic region and extends, for example, to $q^2 = 0$.

Unfortunately, it is not possible to study the contributions from the vector meson region to the sum rule, since there are no data on V_2 for $q^2 > 0$. We therefore focus on an evaluation of the contributions from the nucleon resonance region. Leutwyler and Stern[8] evaluated Eq. 84 for the particular choice $\xi \cong 0.06$, $\eta \cong 1$, and, using the simple interpolating function V_2^{sc}, found that the contributions from V_2 and from V_2^{int} are equal within about 10%: sum rules 84 are saturated by the nucleon resonances alone.

Bloom and Gilman[19] carried out a much more extensive analysis considering the particular case $\xi = 0$. They used a slightly different interpolating function:

$$V_2^{BG} = \frac{1}{\nu(-q^2)} F_2\left(\frac{-q^2}{2|\nu| + b}\right)$$

and found that with $b = 1$ the sum rules are saturated in a remarkably local fashion: the interpolating function roughly averages out the resonance peaks.

This analysis was extended by Rittenberg and Rubinstein[20] to arbitrary values of ξ with an interpolating function of the type

$$V_2^{RR} = \frac{1}{\nu(a - q^2)}\left(1 + \frac{b}{2|\nu|}\right) F_2\left(\frac{a - q^2}{2|\nu| + b}\right)$$

with $a = 0.4$, $b = 1.5$. These authors again found that the sum rules are saturated locally: not only does the integral of the function V_2 across the resonance region equal the corresponding integral of the interpolating function, but also the equality is approximately valid peak by peak.

Unfortunately, the functions V_2^{BG} and V_2^{RR} are not causal. If sum rules 84 were really valid for the entire interval $-\infty < \nu < \infty$, we would have to conclude that the quantity V_2 is not causal either. It is highly desirable to repeat the analysis with a causal interpolating function. A causal function which closely resembles V_2^{RR} can be found in ref. 4.

11. STRONG LIGHT-CONE DOMINANCE

We take the evidence from inelastic electron scattering as sufficiently suggestive of the following general hypothesis.[4] Let us suppose that $V(q)$ is an amplitude describing some matrix element of a current commutator. The leading singularity structure of the current commutator on the light cone determines the behavior of $V(q)$ in the Bjorken limit. Let us suppose that this behavior is given by the scaling law

$$V(k+En) \to \frac{1}{E} F(kn,n) \tag{85}$$

We denote by $V^{int}(q)$ a causal interpolating function with the same behavior in the Bjorken limit. Causality then immediately implies the "superconvergence" relation

$$\int_{-\infty}^{\infty} dE[V(k+En) - V^{int}(k+En)] = 0 \tag{86}$$

The hypothesis of strong light-cone dominance now states that with a suitable choice of V^{int} this sum rule will be saturated locally, V^{int} then representing a smooth quasi-local average of V. If this is the case, the integral in Eq. 86 may be broken up into a set of small intervals such that for each one the area under the smooth interpolating function V^{int} equals the area under the actual curve V with its bumps and dips.

It is clear that strong light-cone dominance, which concerns the dependence of an amplitude on the mass, is very similar to the well-known duality property of hadronic on-shell amplitudes. In that case, the Regge representation approximating the amplitude in the high-energy region plays the role of the interpolating function. Its analytic continuation to the low-energy region also represents a quasi-local average of the absorptive part of the amplitude. As is true also of the concept of duality, the precise formulation of this notion is difficult. We wish to point out, however, that in contrast to duality strong light-cone dominance implies an interesting property of the amplitude in *coordinate space*. It is shown in ref. 4 that strong light-cone dominance essentially means that the function $\tilde{V}^{int}(x)$ not only reproduces the correct leading light-cone singularity of $\tilde{V}(x)$ but also actually reproduces $\tilde{V}(x)$ in a small neighborhood of the light cone in the sense that

$$\int dx f(x)[\tilde{V}(x) - \tilde{V}^{\text{int}}(x)] \cong 0$$

provided the testing function $f(x)$ is concentrated around the light cone with a width small compared to $(\Delta m)^{-1}$, where Δm represents an average spacing between resonances. (For a more detailed discussion of this interpretation the reader is referred to ref. 4.)

The consequences of this principle are clear. The function $V^{\text{int}}(q)$ *normalizes* the peaks of the actual function $V(q)$.

An example of this statement has been pointed out by Bloom and Gilman.[19] If one applies local saturation of the sum rules for V_2 to the elastic peak, one obtains the Drell-Yan[21] relation between the threshold behavior of $F_2(\xi)$ near $\xi = 1$ and the asymptotic behavior of the nucleon form factors. Similarly, the asymptotic behavior of the resonance form factors is normalized by the scaling function. More generally, the light cone normalizes the residues of one-particle poles, that is, normalizes on-shell quantities. In this way one finds that the light cone contains information about the behavior of amplitudes on the mass shell. (It should be noted that there is no such connection in general; additional assumptions beyond leading light-cone singularities are needed to connect the light cone and the mass shell. The strong light-cone dominance may serve as a general hypothesis which supplies this link.)

The consistence of strong light-cone dominance with other generally accepted requirements has been established[4] in the case of three-point functions by exhibiting a Veneziano-like model for the vertex whch satisfies these requirements. Work on the more interesting case of four-point amplitudes, in particular on the photo- and electroproduction of mesons, is under investigation.

ACKNOWLEDGMENT

Section 8 essentially reproduces a remark made by Professor Stichel in the discussion following this presentation. We are indebted to him as well for several comments concerning the contents of this chapter. We are also grateful to J. Gasser for helpful discussions concerning some of the material presented here. One of us (P.O.) would like to thank Professor A. Mercier and the Institut für theoretische Physik for kind hospitality during the past year.

APPENDIX A: A GENERALIZATION OF THE BOGOLIUBOV-VLADIMIROV THEOREM

The following statement is a precise version of that made in the text.

Statement 1. *A tempered distribution $V(q)$ which has a causal Fourier transform and vanishes identically in the region $a < q^2 < b \leqslant 0$ vanishes throughout the spacelike region $q^2 < 0$.*[23]

In order to verify this statement, we use the following theorem and lemma from the lectures of Wightman[22] on the Jost-Lehmann-Dyson representation.

Theorem (Dyson).   A tempered distribution $V(q)$ has a causal Fourier transform if and only if it is the value at $\sigma = 0$ of a (uniquely determined) tempered solution $V(q,\sigma)$ of the wave equation in five dimensions, which is even in σ:

$$\left\{ \frac{\partial^2}{\partial q_0^{\,2}} - \sum_{i=1}^{3} \frac{\partial^2}{\partial q_i^{\,2}} - \frac{\partial^2}{\partial \sigma^2} \right\} V(q,\sigma) = 0$$

$$V(q,\sigma) = V(q, -\sigma) \tag{A.1}$$

Lemma.   If $V(q,\sigma)$ is a tempered solution of wave equation A.1 and vanishes, together with all derivatives, on a timelike line segment, it vanishes throughout the causal diamond subtended by the line segment.

[In the Wightman lectures it is shown that $V(q,\sigma = 0)$ makes sense.]

   To prove statement 1, we simply apply the lemma after observing that the region $a < q^2 < b \leqslant 0$ contains many timelike line segments, upon which $V(q,\sigma)$ vanishes, together with all derivatives. [Derivatives with respect to σ vanish because $V(q,\sigma)$ is even and satisfies wave equation A.1.]

   The situation is illustrated in Figure 1 [in terms of the variables $q_0, |q_3|$ corresponding to the four-vector $q = (q_0, \vec{q}\,)$] for a particular line segment and the corresponding causal diamond projected on the surface $\sigma = 0$, $q_1 = q_2 = 0$. By considering all Lorentz transformations of the illustrated line segment and diamond, we find that $V(q)$ vanishes in the region $a' < q^2 < b'$, where $a' = -[(-a)^{1/2} + (b-a)^{1/2}]^2$ and $b' = -[(-a)^{1/2} - (b-a)^{1/2}]^2$, and repeat the argument. Since each repetition decreases a by at least $(b-a)$, we find that $V(q)$ vanishes for $-q^2 < b'$ and, using timelike line segments in this region, conclude that $V(q)$ vanishes for $q^2 < 0$.

   Combined with the Bogoliubov-Vladimirov theorem (which may itself

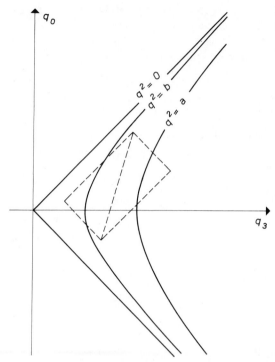

Figure 1. If the function $V(q)$ vanishes between $q^2 = a$ and $q^2 = b$, it vanishes in the dashed diamond and in all Lorentz transforms of it. Iteration of the argument implies that $V(q)$ vanishes for $q^2 < 0$.

be proved rigorously using techniques of the Wightman lectures), Statement 1 implies the following:

Statement 2. *A tempered distribution $V(q)$ which has a causal Fourier transform and vanishes identically in the region $a < q^2 < b \leqslant 0$ may be expressed in the form*

$$V(q) = \epsilon(q^0) \sum_{n=1}^{N} P_n(q) \rho_n(q^2)$$

where the $P_n(q)$ are polynomials in the components of q and the $\rho_n(q^2)$ vanish for $q^2 < 0$.

APPENDIX B: THE RELATION BETWEEN SCALING AND LIGHT-CONE SINGULARITIES

The following discussion of the remark below Eq. 21 of the text is based on the earlier treatment of Leutwyler and Stern.[1] The problem is to relate the asymptotic behavior of $R(k)$ in the Bjorken limit to local properties of

$\tilde{R}(x)$, the Fourier transform of $R(k)$. We study the function $r(E)$ defined in the text:

$$r(E) = \int d^4k R(k+En)\varphi(k)$$

where n is a fixed nonzero lightlike vector, $\varphi(k)$ a fixed testing function from $S(R^4)$, and $R(k)$ a tempered distribution. So defined, $r(E)$ is an infinitely differentiable function, polynomially bounded at infinity. Considering $r(E)$ as a distribution and computing its Fourier transform

$$\tilde{r}(\tau) = \int dE\, e^{i\tau E} r(E) \tag{B.1}$$

one finds (using the convolution theorem) for every testing function $w(\tau)$

$$\int d\tau\, w(\tau)\tilde{r}(\tau) = \int dx\, \tilde{R}(x)\tilde{\varphi}(x)w(n\cdot x) \tag{B.2}$$

an equation (equivalent to Eq. 22 of the text) that relates singularities of $\tilde{R}(x)$ in $x\cdot n$ to singularities of the one-dimensional distribution $\tilde{r}(\tau)$. We want to relate local singularities of $\tilde{r}(\tau)$ to the asymptotic behavior of its Fourier transform $r(E)$. The following two statements are immediate consequences of the Riemann-Lebesgue and Lebesgue dominated convergence theorems.

1. Suppose that $(d/d\tau)\tilde{r}(\tau)$ is an absolutely integrable function for each testing function $\varphi(k)$. Then $R(k)$ vanishes in the Bjorken limit:

$$\lim_{E\to\pm\infty} Er(E) = 0 \tag{B.3}$$

2. In the other direction, suppose that $r(E)$ is an absolutely integrable function [i.e., that $R(k)$ falls integrably fast in the Bjorken limit]. Then $\tilde{r}(\tau)$ is a continuous function of τ.

[Unfortunately, the words "integrably fast" cannot be dropped in statement 2: any function $f(E)$ which behaves as $(|E|\log|E|)^{-1}$ for large E satisfies $Ef(E)\to 0$, but has a Fourier transform which is unbounded at the origin.] Note that we have neither exploited the causality of $\tilde{R}(x)$ nor made use of support properties in momentum space. It is quite possible that these conditions strengthen the relation between light-cone singularities and the Bjorken limit.

REFERENCES and NOTES

1. H. Leutwyler and J. Stern, *Nucl. Phys.*, **B20**, 77 (1970).
2. Y. Georgelin, H. Leutwyler, and J. Stern, "Some Mathematical Aspects of Light Cone Physics," article to be published.

3. D. Stichel, contribution to *Ecole Internationale de la Physique des Particules Elementaires,* Basko Polje-Makarska, Yugoslavia, 1971.

4. J. Jersak, H. Leutwyler, and J. Stern, "The Light Cone and the Mass Shell," article to be published.

5. N. N. Bogoliubov and V. S. Vladimirov, *Nau. Dokl. Vys. Sh.,* **3**, 26 (1958). For a generalization to many variables see J. Bros, H. Epstein, and V. Glaser, *Commun. Math. Phys.,* **6**, 77 (1967).

6. R. Gatto, P. Menotti, and I. Vendramin, *Lettere Nuovo Cimento,* **4**, 79 (1972).

7. R. Jackiw, R. van Royen, and G. West, *Phys. Rev. D,* **2**, 2473 (1970). For an analysis of the relation between light-cone singularities and equal-time commutators see Y. Frishman and S. Yankielowicz, *Scaling Laws and Equal Time Commutators,* Weizmann Institute preprint (1972).

8. H. Leutwyler and J. Stern, *Phys. Letters,* **31B**, 458 (1970).

9. J. M. Cornwall, J. D. Corrigan, and R. E. Norton, *Phys. Rev. Letters,* **24**, 1141 (1970), and *Phys. Rev. D,* **3**, 536 (1971).

10. M. Damashek and F. J. Gilman, *Phys. Rev. D,* **1**, 1319 (1970); C. A. Dominguez, C. Ferro Fontan, and R. Suaya, *Phys. Letters,* **31B**, 365 (1970).

11. R. Rajaraman and G. Rajasekharan, *Phys. Rev. D,* **3**, 266 (1971).

12. M. Elitzur, *Phys. Rev. D,* **3**, 2166 (1971).

13. R. A. Brandt, M. Breidenbach, and P. Vinciarelli, *Regge Behavior of Electroproduction Structure Functions,* University of Maryland Technical Report 72-055, November 1971.

14. F. E. Close and J. F. Gunion, *Phys. Rev. D,* **4**, 742 (1971).

15. R. A. Brandt, W. -C. Ng, G. Preparata, and P. Vinciarelli, *Lettere Nuovo Cimento,* **2**, 937 (1971).

16. For a general treatment of this problem see W. Rühl, *Nuovo Cimento,* **68**, 235 (1970), and **69**, 231 (1970).

17. J. M. Cornwall and R. Jackiw, *Phys. Rev. D,* **4**, 367 (1971); H. Fritzsch and M. Gell-Mann, "Proceedings of the Coral Gables Conference on Fundamental Interactions at High Energy," University of Miami, 1971; H. Leutwyler and J. Stern, *Nucl. Phys.,* **B20**, 77 (1970); H. Leutwyler, "Superlocal Sources," in *Magic without Magic: John Archibald Wheeler,* ed. by J. Klauder, Freeman, San Francisco, 1972.

18. W. N. Cottingham, *Ann. Phys. (N.Y.),* **25**, 424 (1963).

19. E. D. Bloom and F. J. Gilman, *Phys. Rev. Letters,* **25**, 1140 (1970); *Phys. Rev. D,* **4**, 2901 (1971).

20. V. Rittenberg and H. Rubinstein, *Phys. Letters,* **35B**, 50 (1971); *Nucl. Phys.,* **B39**, 421 (1972).

21. S. Drell and T. M. Yan, *Phys. Rev. Letters,* **24**, 181 (1970).

22. A. S. Wightman, "Analytic Functions of Several Complex Variables," in *Relations de Dispersion et Particules Élémentaires,* ed. by C. de Witt and R. Omnes, Hermann, Paris, 1960.

23. This statement is a special case of the convex hull theorem [V. S. Vladimirov, D. A. N. CCCR **134**, 251 (1960); H. J. Borchers, *Nuovo Cimento,* **19**, 787 (1961)]. We are indebted to Professor Vladimirov for pointing this out to us.

CHAPTER 2

Tensor and Scalar Dominance of the Energy-Momentum Tensor

J. WESS

1. INTRODUCTION

The interaction of photons and gravitons is governed by symmetry principles. In the case of electrodynamics it is the gauge group that restricts the coupling of the photon to matter fields; in a theory of gravitation it is the group of general coordinate transformations. Photons and gravitons are massless, and both couple to conserved currents—the electric current and the energy-momentum tensor, respectively.

In the case of the electromagnetic interaction we have learned that the symmetry group can be successfully enlarged to include the isospin and chiral gauge groups, which are approximate symmetries. Moreover, the idea that the currents might be dominated by vector particles having appropriate quantum numbers has proved reasonably successful, in a certain energy range.

The question might be asked whether these ideas could be also applied to gravitational theories. Various attempts in this direction have been made.[1] It seems natural to extend the group of general coordinate transformations to include also conformal transformations. In such a theory the energy-momentum tensor and its trace play the role of currents, and dominance of the energy-momentum tensor by a spin-2 particle and its trace by a scalar particle would be the analog to vector and axial vector dominance.

In this chapter I present a scheme that allows us to formulate the ideas just mentioned in the framework of Lagrangian field theories. The universality of the gravitational coupling restricts the coupling of the spin-2 particle to other hadrons, and it is exactly this restriction on strong coupling that interests us. The couplings of the pseudoscalar mesons to the f, f', and σ mesons will serve as an example.

2. CONSERVATION AND TRACE IDENTITIES

We start with the assumption that Einstein's theory of gravitation should be valid in hadronic physics without any modifications at short distances. The laws describing the interaction of gravitons with hadrons must then be invariant under general coordinate transformations. These transformations will be called Einstein transformations.

We want to describe the laws of hadronic physics in terms of phenomenological hadronic fields ψ and an effective action A.[2] The gravitational field is described by the metric tensor $g_{\mu\nu}$. Because half-integer-spin fields are conveniently treated with the Vierbein formalism, we are going to use this formalism throughout,[3]

$$g_{\mu\nu} = e_{a\mu}e_\nu{}^a, \qquad e_{a\mu} = \delta_{a\mu} + \mu h_{a\mu} \tag{1}$$

The constant μ is related to the gravitational field. The hadronic fields are resolved into components ψ_a along the Vierbein fields, and any effective action must now be invariant under the Einstein transformations:

$$e_{a\mu}(x) = \frac{\partial x'^\rho}{\partial x^\mu} e'_{a\rho}(x')$$

$$\psi_a(x) = \psi'_a(x') \tag{2}$$

and local Lorentz transformations:

$$e'_{a\mu}(x) = L_a(x)_b e_{b\mu}(x)$$

$$\psi'_a(x) = L_a(x)_b \psi_b(x) \tag{3}$$

where L_{ab} is the representation of a Lorentz transformation.

The infinitesimal forms of these transformations are

$$\delta e_{a\mu} = \xi^\lambda \partial_\lambda e_{a\mu} + \partial_\mu \xi^\lambda e_{a\lambda}$$

$$\delta\psi = \xi^\lambda \partial_\lambda \psi \tag{4}$$

and

$$\delta e_{a\mu} = w_{ab} e_{b\mu}, \qquad w_{ab} = -w_{ba}$$

$$\delta\psi_a = \frac{i}{2} w_{ab} S^{ab} \psi_b \tag{5}$$

Einstein invariance of the action A gives rise to the *conservation identities*:[4]

$$-\partial_\mu(\tau^{a\mu} e_{a\lambda}) + \tau^{a\mu}\partial_\lambda e_{a\mu} - \frac{\delta A}{\delta\psi}\partial_\lambda\psi = 0 \tag{6}$$

where

$$-\tau^{a\mu} = \frac{\delta A}{\delta e_{a\mu}}$$

whereas local Lorentz invariance gives rise to the *symmetry identities*:

$$-\tau_a{}^\mu e_{b\mu} + \tau_b{}^\mu e_{a\mu} + i\frac{\delta A}{\delta\psi} S_{ab}\psi = 0 \tag{7}$$

Equations 6 and 7 represent the Ward identities for the irreducible vertices due to the invariance under general coordinate transformations, and they play a role analogous to that of the Ward identities derived from gauge invariance. Our effective action is assumed to rigorously satisfy these equations.

In addition we are going to consider a set of transformations which is assumed to play a role similar to that of the chiral gauge transformations. We shall call them Weyl transformations and shall assume that the effective action is approximately invariant under them. More precisely, we shall assume that there exists a scalar Goldstone boson σ, such that the Weyl symmetry is broken by the mass term of the σ-field only.

Under Weyl transformation we have

$$\delta e_{a\mu}(x) = \lambda(x) e_{a\mu}(x), \qquad \delta\sigma(x) = -\frac{1}{b}\lambda(x), \qquad \delta\psi = 0 \tag{8}$$

Here b is a universal constant which can be determined from the σ decay. We have assumed that all hadronic fields do not transform under Weyl transformations. This is possible because we can change the "weight" of a field by an admissible field transformation $\hat{\psi} = e^{db\sigma}\psi$, such that $\hat{\psi}$ has weight d: $\hat{\psi}' = e^{-d\Lambda}\hat{\psi}$ under Weyl transformations.

The Weyl transformation leads to the so-called *trace identities*:

$$-\tau^{a\mu}e_{a\mu} - \frac{1}{b}\frac{\delta A}{\delta\sigma} = \frac{\delta A}{\delta\lambda} \tag{9}$$

When restricted to flat space, an action which is Einstein invariant and Weyl invariant as well yields an action that is invariant under the fifteen-parameter conformal group. Moreover, in flat space $\tau^{a\mu}$ becomes the energy-momentum tensor of the hadrons, and Eq. 9 is then an equation for the trace of the energy-momentum tensor.

3. TENSOR AND SCALAR MESON DOMINANCE

Our aim is to solve the conservation identity (Eq. 6), the symmetry identity (Eq. 7), and the trace identity (Eq. 8) in such a way that the energy-momentum tensor and its trace are dominated by a tensor field and a scalar field. The tensor field will then be associated with the $f(1260)$ and the $f'(1514)$ mesons; the scalar field, with the $\epsilon(750)$ resonance.

The f meson is an SU(3) scalar, and we describe it by a hadronic Vierbein field: $u_a{}^\mu = \delta_{a\mu} - \lambda f_{a\mu}$. The constant λ enters universally in the strong interaction of the $f_{a\mu}$ field and can, for example, be determined from the decay width of f into two pions $(1/\lambda \sim 105$ MeV$)$. The f' meson is part of and SU(3) octet; we describe it by a tensor field f'_{ab}. The ϵ meson is an SU(3) singled; we will identify it with the Goldstone boson σ.

The transformation properties of f, f', and σ are, respectively, as follows:

Einstein transformations:

$$\delta u_a{}^\mu = \xi^\lambda \partial_\lambda u_a{}^\mu - \partial_\lambda \xi^\mu u_a{}^\lambda$$

$$\delta f'_{ab} = \xi^\lambda \partial_\lambda f'_{ab} \tag{10}$$

$$\delta\sigma = \xi^\lambda \partial_\lambda \sigma$$

Local Lorentz transformations:

$$\delta u_a{}^\mu = w_{ab}u_b{}^\mu, \qquad w_{ab} = -w_{ba}$$

$$\delta f'_{ab} = w_{ac}f'_{cb} + w_{bc}f'_{ac} \tag{11}$$

$$\delta\sigma = 0$$

Weyl transformations:

$$\delta u = 0, \qquad \delta f = 0$$

$$\delta \sigma = -\frac{1}{b} \lambda(x)$$

(12)

We shall solve identities 6, 7, and 9 in terms of local effective Lagrangians; this corresponds to an approximation of the one-particle irreducible vertices with polynomials of low order in the momenta. The conservation and symmetry identities imply that the effective action has to be invariant under Einstein and local Lorentz transformations. The dominance idea means that the graviton should not couple directly to the phenomenological fields ψ of the hadrons, but only through the intermediary of the tensor fields f and f'. Therefore the bulk of the Lagrangians for strong interaction should not depend on the metric tensors $g_{\mu\nu}$; Einstein and local Lorentz invariance has to be achieved by using the hadronic Vierbein field $u_a{}^\mu$ instead of $e_{a\mu}$, the gravitational one.

Scalar meson dominance is achieved if it is only the mass term of the σ-field that breaks Weyl invariance. We shall therefore decompose an effective action as follows:

$$\mathsf{A} = A\left\{\psi, f'_{ab} u_a{}^\mu\right\} + W\left\{\sigma, e_{a\mu}\right\} - \tfrac{1}{2} m_\sigma{}^2 \sigma^2 + W\left\{u_a{}^\mu, e_{a\mu}, \sigma\right\} \qquad (13)$$

The part $A\{\psi, f', u\}$ describes the strong interactions of the hadronic fields. It is independent of $e_{a\mu}$ because we do not want any direct coupling. It is also independent of the σ-field because all the hadronic fields are weightless, and therefore a dependence on the σ-field would break Weyl invariance. $A\{\psi, f', u\}$ will, among other interactions, contain the kinetic part for the u- and f'-fields and also the interaction that forces an f–f' mixing. We shall discuss this in the following.

The action $W\{\sigma, e_{a\mu}\}$ contributes to the kinetic part of the σ-field. Because the σ-field and the gravitational field are the only ones with weights different from zero, both have to enter W in order to make it Einstein, local Lorentz, and Weyl invariant.

We find the invariant action:

$$W\left\{\sigma, e_{a\mu}\right\} = \eta^2 \int d^4x \sqrt{-g}\, \left(\tfrac{1}{2} g^{\mu\nu} \partial_\mu e^{-b\sigma} \partial_\nu e^{-b\sigma} + \tfrac{1}{12} R(e_{a\mu}) e^{-2b\sigma}\right) \qquad (14)$$

The term with the contracted Rieman tensor must be added for Weyl invariance.

The part of the action $W\{u_a{}^\mu, e_{a\mu}, \sigma\}$ has to fulfill the following requirements. It must describe the interaction of the f meson with the gravitational field, that is, it has to contain a coupling term of the form $e_{a\mu}u^{a\mu}$. It has to be Einstein, local Lorentz, and Weyl invariant. Finally, when all couplings are turned off, a mass term of the Pauli-Fierz form should remain:

$$-\tfrac{1}{2}m_f^2[\,f_{ab}f^{ba} - (f_a{}^a)^2]$$

in order to describe a spin-2 particle without ghosts.

These requirements allow four different choices.[2] We choose the action:

$$W\{u_a{}^\mu, e_{a\mu}, \sigma\} = \frac{m^2}{\lambda^2}\int d^4x\,(3u - uu_a{}^\mu e_{a\mu}e^{b\sigma} + ee^{4b\sigma})\qquad(15)$$

where $e = -\det e_{a\mu}$, $u = -\det u_{a\mu}$. This has the simplest form for the graviton coupling.

The "dominance" idea becomes transparent if we compute the energy-momentum tensor and its trace from action 13 and restrict it to flat space. We remember that

$$\left.\frac{\delta A}{\delta e_{a\mu}}\right|_{e_{a\mu}=\delta_{a\mu}} = -\theta_{a\mu}$$

is the energy-momentum tensor for the matter fields. From the trace identity there follows, as a consequence of the equations of motion $(\delta A/\delta\sigma = 0)$,

$$\theta_{aa} = -\frac{1}{b}m_\sigma^2\sigma\qquad(16)$$

If we compute $(\delta A/\delta e_{a\mu})|_{e_{a\mu}=\delta_{a\mu}}$ from Eqs. 15 and 14, and if we keep only terms linear in the hadron fields, we find the "dominance" relation:

$$\theta_{ab} = -\frac{m^2}{\lambda}\left(f_{ab} - \delta_{ab}f + \frac{3b}{\lambda}\delta_{ab}\sigma\right) - \tfrac{1}{3}\eta^2 b(\partial_a\partial_b - \delta_{ab}\Box)\sigma\qquad(17)$$

The field f_{ab} entering these equations is not yet the "physical" field, describing the spin-2 meson. A transformation on the field is required in order to separate the f-, f'-, and σ-fields. This will be done in the next section.

4.   CURRENT MIXING OF f, f', AND σ MESONS

As an example of $A\{\psi, f', u\}$ we want to discuss an action that is suitable to account for the known facts about a system consisting of a pseudoscalar octet and the f, f', and σ mesons. This action should also be consistent with the requirements listed above. We shall need a kinetic part for the f- and f'-fields and a term that leads to a mixing of f and f' as it is observed. Because the mixing term should be part of an Einstein invariant, it seems natural to choose current mixing, that is, to introduce mixing through the kinetic part and not through the mass part. A suitable action is:

$$A\{\psi,f',u\} = -\frac{1}{2\lambda^2}\int d^4x\, uR(u)$$

$$+\frac{x}{2\lambda}\int d^4x\, uf'^{\mu\nu}\left[R_{\mu\nu}(u)-\tfrac{1}{2}u_{\mu a}u_{\nu a}R(u)\right]+A\{f',u\}$$

$$(18)$$

where $A\{f'\}$ is an Einstein-invariant action that reduces to the Pauli-Fierz action for a spin-2 field in the case $u_a{}^\mu=\delta_{a\mu}$.

When we now add all the contributions of Eqs. 14, 15, and 18 to the action, we find that all terms in Eq. 13 linear in the fields cancel. The contribution quadratic in the fields is:

$$A^{\text{lin}}=f'_{\mu\nu}K_{\mu\nu,\rho\sigma}f'_{\rho\sigma}-\tfrac{1}{2}m'^2\left[f'_{\mu\nu}f'_{\nu\mu}-(f'_{\nu\nu})^2\right]$$

$$+f_{\mu\nu}K_{\mu\nu,\rho\sigma}f_{\rho\sigma}-\tfrac{1}{2}m^2\left[f_{\mu\nu}f_{\nu\mu}-(f_{\nu\nu})^2\right]$$

$$+xf'_{\mu\nu}K_{\mu\nu,\rho\sigma}f_{\rho\sigma}-\frac{3b}{\lambda}m^2\sigma f_{aa}+\frac{6b^2}{\lambda^2}m^2\sigma^2$$

$$+\frac{\eta^2 b^2}{2}\partial_\mu\sigma\partial_\mu\sigma-\tfrac{1}{2}m_\sigma{}^2\sigma^2 \qquad (19)$$

where $K_{\mu\nu,\rho\sigma}$ is an abbreviation for the kinetic term in the Pauli-Fierz Lagrangian:

$$K_{\mu\nu,\rho\sigma}=\tfrac{1}{2}(\delta_{v\sigma}\partial_\rho\partial_\mu+\delta_{\mu\sigma}\partial_\rho\partial_\nu-\delta_{\mu\rho}\delta_{v\sigma}\square-\delta_{\rho\sigma}\partial_\nu\partial_\mu-\delta_{\mu\nu}\partial_\rho\partial_\sigma+\delta_{\mu\nu}\delta_{\rho\sigma}\square) \qquad (20)$$

Action 19 contains various bilinear couplings. They have to be separated by a suitable field transformation. If we transform:

$$\hat{f}_{\mu\nu}=C_T f_{\mu\nu}-S'_T f'_{\mu\nu}-\frac{b}{\lambda}C_T\delta_{\mu\nu}\sigma+\frac{b}{\lambda}\left(\frac{2}{m^2}C_T-S'_T\frac{x}{m'^2}\right)\partial_\mu\partial_\nu\sigma$$

$$\hat{f}'_{\mu\nu}=S_T f_{\mu\nu}+C'_T f'_{\mu\nu}-\frac{b}{\lambda}S_T\delta_{\mu\nu}\sigma+\frac{b}{\lambda}\left(\frac{2}{m^2}S_T+\frac{x}{m'^2}C'_T\right)\partial_\mu\partial_\nu\sigma$$

$$(21)$$

we find:

$$A^{\text{lin}} = \hat{f}'_{\mu\nu} K_{\mu\nu,\rho\sigma} \hat{f}'_{\rho\sigma} - \tfrac{1}{2} m_f'^2 \left(\hat{f}'_{\mu\nu} \hat{f}'_{\nu\mu} - \hat{f}'^2_{\nu\nu} \right)$$

$$+ \hat{f}_{\mu\nu} K_{\mu\nu,\rho\sigma} \hat{f}_{\rho\sigma} - \tfrac{1}{2} m_f^2 \left(\hat{f}_{\mu\nu} \hat{f}_{\nu\mu} - \hat{f}_{\nu\nu}^2 \right) + \tfrac{1}{2} \partial_\mu \sigma \partial_\mu \sigma - \tfrac{1}{2} m_\sigma^2 \sigma^2 \quad (22)$$

if $\eta^2 = 1/b^2 + 6/\lambda^2$.

This shows that the fields $\hat{f}$ and $\hat{f}'$ have to be interpreted as fields describing the physical particles f and f' with masses m_f and m'_f, respectively. The meanings of several constants in Eqs. 21 and 22 have to be explained:

$$C_T = \frac{m}{m_f} \cos\varphi, \qquad S_T = \frac{m}{m'_f} \sin\varphi$$

$$C'_T = \frac{m'}{m'_f} \cos\varphi, \qquad S'_T = \frac{m'}{m_f} \sin\varphi$$

$$\frac{1}{m^2} = \frac{(\cos\varphi)^2}{m_f^2} + \frac{(\sin\varphi)^2}{m_f'^2}, \qquad \frac{1}{m'^2} = \frac{(\sin\varphi)^2}{m_f^2} + \frac{(\cos\varphi)^2}{m_f'^2}$$

$$x = 2mm' \sin\varphi \cos\varphi \left(\frac{1}{m'^2} - \frac{1}{m_f^2} \right)$$

All constants are expressible in terms of the physical masses m_f and m'_f and in terms of the mixing angle φ. We can compute m' from the Okubo-Gell-Mann mass formula for the spin-2 octet: $m'^2 = \tfrac{1}{3}(4m_{K^*}^2 - m_{A2}^2)$. This allows us to determine the mixing angle φ; the value $\tan\varphi = 0.58$ seems to be reasonable.

Solving Eqs. 21 for $f_{\mu\nu}$ and $f'_{\mu\nu}$, we find:

$$f_{\mu\nu} = \left(\frac{m_f}{m} \right)^2 C_T \hat{f}_{\mu\nu} + \left(\frac{m_{f'}}{m} \right)^2 S_T \hat{f}'_{\mu\nu} + \frac{b}{\lambda} \partial_{\mu\nu}\sigma - \frac{2}{m^2} \frac{b}{\lambda} \partial_\mu \partial_\nu \sigma$$

$$f'_{\mu\nu} = -\left(\frac{m_f}{m'} \right)^2 S'_T \hat{f}_{\mu\nu} + \left(\frac{m_{f'}}{m'} \right)^2 C'_T \hat{f}'_{\mu\nu} - \frac{bx}{\lambda m'^2} \partial_\mu \partial_\nu \sigma \quad (23)$$

If we now express $f_{\partial\nu}$ in formula 17 in terms of the physical fields $\hat{f}$ and $\hat{f}'$, we find the "dominance" equation:

$$-\theta_{\mu\nu} = \frac{m_f^2}{\lambda} C_T \hat{f}_{\mu\nu} + \frac{m_{f'}^2}{\lambda} S_T \hat{f}'_{\mu\nu} + \frac{1}{3b} (\partial_\mu \partial_\nu - \delta_{\mu\nu} \Box)\sigma + \cdots \quad (24)$$

The coupling of the field $f_{\mu\nu}$ to all the other hadronic fields is universal.

Let us now investigate the couplings of $f_{\mu\nu}$ and $f'_{\mu\nu}$ to a system of a pseudoscalar octet represented by a SU(3) matrix M. The action should be:

$$\mathsf{A}\{M,f,f'\} = \tfrac{1}{2}\operatorname{tr}\partial_\mu M \partial_\nu M u_a{}^\mu u^{a\nu} u$$

$$-\tfrac{1}{2}\mu^2\operatorname{tr}MMu - gf'^{\mu\nu}\operatorname{tr}\lambda_8\partial_\mu M\partial_\nu Mu \qquad (25)$$

The constant g is arbitrary and characterizes the coupling of the spin-2 particle to the pseudoscalar octet. If we keep only terms linear in f, this action becomes:

$$\mathsf{A}^{\text{lin}}\{M,f,f'\} = -\lambda f_{\mu\nu}\operatorname{tr}\{\partial_\mu M\partial_\nu M + \tfrac{1}{2}\delta_{\mu\nu}(\mu^2 MM - \partial_\rho M\partial_\rho M)\}$$

$$- gf'_{\mu\nu}\operatorname{tr}\lambda_8\partial_\mu M\partial_\nu M \qquad (26)$$

We have to substitute expressions 23 for $f_{\mu\nu}$ and $f'_{\mu\nu}$ in order to obtain the coupling of the physical particles $\hat{f}_{\mu\nu}$, $f'_{\mu\nu}$, and σ to the pseudoscalar mesons. If we put the pseudoscalar particles on mass shell, we derive the following σ-M-M coupling from Eq. 26:

$$\mathsf{A}_{\sigma MM} = -b(\Box - \tfrac{1}{2}\mu^2)\sigma\operatorname{tr}MM + \frac{b}{2}\frac{g}{\lambda}\frac{S_T C'_T}{m'^2}\left(\frac{m_f^2}{m_f'^2} - 1\right)\operatorname{tr}[\lambda_8 M^2\Box^2\sigma] \qquad (27)$$

The first part is exactly what we would have obtained in a theory without tensor dominance.[5] It should be noted that the part of $f_{\mu\nu}$ with the derivatives on σ does not contribute to the effective action if the pseudoscalar mesons are on mass shell. This is the case because $f_{\mu\nu}$ couples essentially to the energy-momentum tensor of the hadronic fields, which is conserved in the limit of flat space. If the σ meson is also put on mass shell, Eq. 27 becomes:

$$\mathsf{A}_{\sigma MM} = +b(\tfrac{1}{2}\mu^2 + m_\sigma^2)\operatorname{tr}M^2\sigma - \frac{b}{2}\frac{m_\sigma^4}{m'^2}\left(1 - \frac{m_f^2}{m_f'^2}\right)\frac{g}{\lambda}S_T C'_T\operatorname{tr}\lambda_8 M^2\sigma \qquad (28)$$

In a moment we shall see that from the requirement that the f'-π-π coupling be zero there follows $g/\lambda = -\sqrt{3}\,(m'/m)\tan\varphi$. With this assumption Eq. 28 yields the following σ-π-π coupling:

$$\mathsf{A}_{\sigma\pi\pi} = b\left[\tfrac{1}{2}\mu^2 + m_\sigma^2\left(1 + \frac{1}{2}\frac{m_\sigma^2}{m^2}\right)\left(1 - \frac{m_f^2}{m_f'^2}\right)S_T^2\right]\sigma\vec{\pi}^2 \qquad (29)$$

With a mixing angle $\tan\varphi = 0.58$ we find that the contribution of the $\square^2$-σ-$\vec{\pi}^2$ coupling to Eq. 29 is negligible. Therefore, it does not change the analysis of Ellis.[6]

Finally, we find the following predictions for the f-f' pseudoscalar interaction:

$$A = -\left(g_{f\pi\pi}\hat{f}_{\mu\nu} + g_{f'\pi\pi}\hat{f}'_{\mu\nu} \right)\partial_\mu\vec{\pi}\partial_\nu\vec{\pi}$$

$$-\left(g_{fKK}\hat{f}_{\mu\nu} + g_{f'KK}\hat{f}'_{\mu\nu} \right)\left(\partial_\mu K^+\partial_\nu K^- + \partial_\mu\bar{K}^0\partial_\nu K^0 \right)$$

$$-\left(g_{f\eta\eta}\hat{f}_{\mu\nu} + g_{f'\eta\eta}\hat{f}'_{\mu\nu} \right)\partial_\mu\eta\partial_\nu\eta \tag{30}$$

where the coupling constants can be expressed in terms of λ, g, the mixing angle ρ, and the physical masses of the spin-2 particles. We find, for example,

$$g_{f'\pi\pi} = m_f'^2\left(\lambda\frac{S_T}{m^2} + \frac{1}{\sqrt{3}}g\frac{C_T'}{m'^2} \right) \tag{31}$$

If we assume that $g_{f'\pi\pi} = 0$, we conclude that

$$\frac{g}{\lambda} = -\sqrt{3}\,\frac{m'}{m}\tan\varphi \tag{32}$$

This determines g in terms of the universal constant λ.

The other constants of interest are:

$$g_{f\pi\pi} = \lambda\left(\frac{m_f}{m}\right)^2 C_T\left(1 + \frac{m_f^2}{m_f'^2}\frac{S_T'^2}{C_T'^2} \right)$$

$$g_{fKK} = \lambda\left(\frac{m_f}{m}\right)^2 C_T\left(2 - \frac{m_f^2}{m_f'^2}\frac{S_T'^2}{C_T'^2} \right) \tag{33}$$

$$g_{f'KK} = 3\lambda\left(\frac{m_f'}{m}\right)^2 S_T$$

The universal constant λ can be determined from the f-π-π width. If we assume $\Gamma_{f\pi\pi} = 130$ MeV, we predict that $\Gamma_{fKK} = 7.3$ MeV, $\Gamma_{f'KK} = 35$ MeV. The experimental values are

$$\Gamma_{fKK}^{\exp} \sim 7.5 \text{ MeV}, \qquad \Gamma_{fKK}^{\exp} \sim 30\text{–}80 \text{ MeV}$$

These values can be compared with predictions from mass mixing:[6]

$$\Gamma_{fKK} = 4.6 \text{ MeV}, \qquad \Gamma_{f'KK} = 30 \text{ MeV}$$

Thus it seems that the idea of σ, f, f' mixing and tensor dominance of the energy-momentum tensor is not in obvious disagreement with experimental data, as far as we have analyzed them here.

ACKNOWLEDGMENT

This contribution is based on work done in collaboration with B. Zumino.

REFERENCES

1. V. I. Ogievetsky and I. V. Polubarinov, *Ann. Phys. (N.Y.)*, **35**, 167 (1965); C. I. Isham, A. Salam, and S. Strathdee, Trieste Preprint IC/70/108 (1970); P. G. O. Freund and Y. Nambu, *Phys. Rev.*, **174**, 1741 (1968); G. Mack and A. Salem, *Ann. Phys. (N.Y.)*, **53**, 174 (1969); B. Renner, *Phys. Letters*, **33B**, 599 (1970).
2. B. Zumino, in *Lectures on Elementary Particles and Fields* (1970 Brandeis University Summer Institute), Vol. 2, MIT Press, Cambridge, Mass., 1971.
3. J. Wess, *Springer Tracts in Modern Physics*, Springer-Verlag, Berlin, Vol. 60, p. 1.
4. B. Zumino, Symposium held at the Max Planck-Institut für Physik und Astrophysik, Munich, June 1971.
5. K. Raman, Middletown, Conn. 06457, unpublished article.
6. J. Ellis, *Nucl. Phys.*, **B22**, 478 (1970).

CHAPTER 3

Bjorken Scaling
and Scale-Invariant
Quantum Field Theories

B. SCHROER

1. INTRODUCTION

There is hardly any recent endeavor in high-energy physics that has enriched the insight into quantum field theory (QFT) more than the search for a deeper understanding of the Bjorken scaling law. Most of the problems of renormalization theory and the short-distance behavior of renormalized field theories have been with us ever since the early years of the Feynman-Schwinger-Dyson-Bogoliubov renormalization framework of the 1950s. For a long time, however, the connection between renormalized QFT and the "real world" of experimental high-energy physics was too weak to stimulate the enthusiasm necessary to solve hard problems. This situation has changed in a remarkable way. Physicists are now developing powerful machinery in order to solve the problems of short-distance behavior, scale invariance, anomalies, non-Abelian gauge theories, and so on. A particularly fruitful algorithm which allows a unified treatment of all these problems is the normal product (NP) algorithm. This formalism, which constitutes a generalization of the BPH renormalization theory, will be discussed in Section 3. In our special context of scale invariance, it easily allows to identify a scale-invariant renormalizable QFT as a "Gell-Mann/Low limit" of an ordinary renormalizable QFT. It also yields a proof that the scale limit implies conformal invariance, a statement which hitherto was derived by formal (unrenormalized or classical field theory) manipulations[1] only.

The recognition that scale invariance implies conformal invariance is very helpful because the usefulness of conformal symmetry in connection with the Bjorken scaling law has been amply demonstrated[2]. We will make some new comments on this point in Section 2.

The material will be presented in three sections. In Section 2 we will accept conformal invariance and show to what extent it can be used for understanding Bjorken scaling. Section 3 introduces the NP algorithm and its applications for deriving conformal symmetry. Section 4 surveys the use of the NP algorithm for studying the scale properties of short-distance expansion as postulated by Wilson.[3]

2. THE USEFULNESS OF CONFORMAL SYMMETRY

The conformal group, a fifteen-parameter extension of the Poincaré group, is defined by considering in addition to the well-known Poincaré transformation the dilatation or scale transformation:

$$x' = \lambda x \tag{1a}$$

and the special conformal transformation:

$$x' = \frac{x - b \cdot x^2}{\sigma(x)}$$

where

$$\sigma(x) = 1 - 2bx + b^2 x^2 = \left(\det \frac{\partial x'}{\partial x} \right)^{-1/4} \tag{1b}$$

This group, which has the characterizing property that it leaves the infinitesimal Minkowski distance invariant up to an x-dependent scale factor, first entered classical physics in the context of Maxwell's theory.[4] The best-known classical consequence of the symmetry is the fact that an illuminated sphere is optically seen as a (rotated) sphere by a moving observer.[5] Formally all Lagrangians without derivative couplings (exception: the well-known derivative terms coming from the minimal electromagnetism or the minimal Yang-Mills couplings to $s = 0, 1$ fields have this symmetry) lead to conformal symmetry. In quantum theory an invariance should be implemented by a unitary operator:

$$U(b)\varphi(x)U^+(b) = [\sigma(b,x)]^{-d} M(b,x)\varphi(x') \tag{2}$$

Here d is the dimension of the field, that is, the d in

$$U(\lambda)\varphi(x)U^+(\lambda) = \lambda^d\varphi(\lambda x)$$

and $M(b,x)$ is a matrix acting on the components of φ. The M fulfills (this follows from the group property of Eq. 2) the relation

$$M(b,x)M\left[b', \frac{x-bx^2}{(b,x)}\right] = M(b+b',x) \tag{3}$$

which is typical of a nonlinear finite-dimensional realization of the conformal group (σ is a scalar realization). The M may be explicitly determined either by using the group theoretical commutation relations of the generators of Eq. 1b with the rest of the Poincaré group (as well as the known Poincaré transformation properties of fields), or by using free-field Lagrangians and working out the infinitesimal transformation properties belonging to Eq. 1b which leave the "action" invariant.[6] For a vector we obtain

$$M_\nu^\mu(b,x) = \sigma(b,x)\frac{\partial x_\nu'}{\partial x_\mu} \tag{4}$$

From the mathematical aspects of Eq. 2 it is readily apparent that, except for free fields and their local functions (i.e., for the Borchers class of the free field), such a $U(b)$, respectively its infinitesimal generator K_μ, does not exist. The physical origin of this *impossibility* of having "strong conformal invariance" is the phenomenon of reverberation.[7] We say that a zero-mass field reverberates, if its commutator, respectively anticommutator, has the following property:

$$[\varphi(x),\varphi(y)]_\mp = \begin{cases} 0 & (x-y)^2<0 \\ \neq 0 & (x-y)^2=0 \text{ and } (x-y)^2>0 \end{cases} \tag{5}$$

The terminology comes from classical field theory, where, for example, the free wave equation in an odd-numbered space-time dimension does not fulfill Huygens' principle (propagation on the light cone) but rather "reverberates" inside the forward cone. For an even space-time dimension the phenomenon of reverberation comes about via dimensionless interactions of massless fields, as, for example, in the Thirring model.[8] It is easily established that anomalous dimension $d\neq$ integer necessarily leads to reverberation.

In all these cases one still can expect the validity of *weak conformal invariance* (WCI), which means the conformal symmetry of the analytically continued vacuum expectation values. Conformal transformations lead out of the first Riemann sheet, that is, the invariance holds on a multisheeted Riemann surface. The physical boundary prescription is not left invariant unless the field is a free one. For all recent investigations on conformal symmetry (in the Polyakov-Migdal program,[9] the Ferrara-Gatto-Grillo[2] approach to operator expansions, etc.) WCI is sufficient. The situation is quite different in the theory of critical flucuations, where conformal invariance (i.e., Euclidean conformal symmetry), if valid at all, would be strong.[10] Keeping this in mind, one may with impunity compute as if formula 2 would be valid.

Conformal symmetry is peculiar also in that it prefers certain local fields to others. Let $\varphi(x)$ be a free charged scalar field. Then $\partial_\mu \varphi$ is not a conformal invariant vector field (unless dim $\varphi = 0$, which happens for free fields in two-dimensional space-time), but rather $[K_\lambda, \partial_\mu \varphi(0)] = 2g_{\lambda\mu}\varphi$. It is easy to see that, by combining φ and $\partial_\mu \varphi$ to a five-dimensional field φ with a dimension d which is a diagonal matrix one may introduce dimensionally mixed objects for which the infinitesimal conformal transformation reads as follows:

$$[K_\lambda, \varphi(0)] = \chi_\lambda \varphi(0) \equiv \delta_\lambda \varphi(0) \tag{6}$$

with χ_λ = nilpotent matrix. However important, physical fields, especially those which are Noether currents of internal symmetries, must be conformally invariant in the sense of Eq. 2, that is, $\chi_\lambda = 0$. This is, for example, the case for the free-field current, $j_\mu(x) = i:\varphi^+(x) \overleftrightarrow{\partial}_\mu \varphi(x):$ or the free improved energy-momentum tensor,[6] $\theta_{\mu\nu}$. Conformal invariance gives interesting and useful restrictions on the vacuum expectation values,[9] respectively the light-cone expansion of the product of two operators.[2] In general, however, it does not permit derivation of the Bjorken scaling law, which states that the light-cone singularity of the matrix element of two currents between one-nucleon states is a canonical light-cone singularity.

In order to see how much can be said solely on the basis of conformal symmetry let us imagine a theory of scalar or pseudoscalar gluons (say π mesons) interacting with $s = \frac{1}{2}$ particles. According to Polyakov and Migdal,[9] the structure of the three-point function is determined by conformal symmetry. For the scalar particle we have (leaving out the $i\epsilon$ prescription)

$$\langle T\varphi^+(x_1)j_\mu(x_2)\varphi(x_3)\rangle = g\frac{1}{(x_1-x_2)^2}\overset{\leftrightarrow}{\partial}_\mu^{x_2}\frac{1}{(x_2-x_3)^2}\left[\frac{1}{(x_1-x_3)^2}\right]^{d-1}$$

(7)

Note that the only assumption in addition to conformal invariance is that $\dim j_\mu = 3$. The validity of the Ward identity for the three-point function, that is, current conservation, is a result, not an input.[9]

Because of anomalous dimension the ordinary Lehmann-Symanzik-Zimmerman (LSZ) scattering theory does not apply to the conformal invariant limit (it would formally lead to a vanishing asymptotic field, as seen from the two-point function). For the class of pseudoscalar gluon theories which remain free of infrared divergences for $m_{\rm gl}\to 0$, Symanzik has presented arguments that the limiting (all masses $\to 0$) Gell-Mann/Low theory for "nonexceptional momenta" has finite vertex function on the zero-mass shell. For ordinary particle theories it is known that the LSZ limit is identical to the mass shell values of the vertex functions (amputated Green function). In the zero-mass limit we therefore define the scattering amplitudes with the help of vertices according to:

$$\langle T\varphi(x_1)\cdots\varphi(x_n)\rangle \overset{\rm LSZ}{\longrightarrow} (p_i^2-m^2)G(p_1\cdots p_n)|_{p_i^2=m^2}$$

$$=\Gamma(p_1\cdots p_n)|_{p_i^2=m^2}\overset{\rm Gell\text{-}Mann/Low}{\underset{m\to 0\ \rm limit}{\longrightarrow}}\Gamma(p_1\cdots p_n)|_{p_i^2=0} \quad (8)$$

In this case the dimension of the scattering amplitude is $\dim\Gamma = 4-4d$. The last statement is a result following directly from the definition

$$\Gamma(p_1\cdots p_n) = \prod_i\Delta_F^{-1}(p_i)G(p_1\cdots p_n)$$

For the conformal invariant vertex corresponding to Eq. 7 we obtain

$$\dim\Gamma_\mu(p_1,p_2) = 3-2d \quad (9)$$

leading to Migdal's[9] decrease of the form factor as $[(p_1-p_2)^2]^{1-d}$. An explicit computation shows that the mass shell restriction exists and gives absolute convergence of the Fourier transform in the range $1<d<2$. Note, however, that the conformal theory cannot be taken seriously for exceptional momenta $p_1 = p_2$. This is the reason why in the case of Bjorken scaling, where we have exceptional momenta, the scaling law cannot be obtained by considering the S-matrix aspects of the conformal invariant limit. This limit is useful *only for abstracting the light-cone singularity*, not for answering questions involving particle states. In other words, the singularities of the conformal limit may tell us why we have Bjorken scaling, but the limiting Green function cannot be used to obtain a theory of the structure function.

Let us now look at what conformal symmetry has to say about the light-cone singularity of the four-point function. Since Ward's identity:

$$\partial_{x_2}{}^{\mu}\langle 0|T\varphi^+(x_1)j_{\mu}(x_2)j_{\nu}(x_3)\varphi(x_4)|0\rangle$$

$$= \delta(x_1 - x_2)\langle 0|T\varphi^+(x_2)j_{\nu}(x_3)\varphi(x_4)|0\rangle$$

$$- \delta(x_4 - x_2)\langle 0|T\varphi^+(x_1)j_{\nu}(x_3)\varphi(x_4)|0\rangle \qquad (10)$$

has to be maintained, the general conformally symmetric solution has the form

$$\langle 0|T\varphi^+(x_1)j_{\mu}(x_2)j_{\nu}(x_3)\varphi(x_4)|0\rangle = C\frac{1}{(x_1-x_2)^2}\overleftrightarrow{\partial}_{\mu}^{x_2}\frac{1}{(x_2-x_3)^2}\overleftrightarrow{\partial}_{\nu}^{x_3}$$

$$\times \frac{1}{(x_3-x_4)^2}\left[\frac{1}{(x_1-x_4)^2}\right]^{d-1} + (\mu\leftrightarrow\nu, x_2\leftrightarrow x_3)$$

$+$ general conformal invariant solution of homogeneous equation   (11)

Clearly the particular solution of the inhomogeneous equation has the canonical light-cone singularity. It is, up to the last factor (which takes care of the anomalous dimension of the field), the free-field expression, that is, the type of singular behavior desired by Gell-Mann and Fritzsch.[11] However, the homogeneous solution, which we can take from the work of Boulware, Brown, and Peccei[12] (up to a small modification due to the anomalous dimension), contains two arbitrary harmonic ratios and hence, without using further dynamical information, may lead to any light-cone singularity.

Thus it is clear from this consideration, as well as from other discussions of conformal invariance,[2] that the problem cannot be decided by purely group theoretical considerations. For the gluon model at hand there are two ways of obtaining dynamical information: either by studying the details of the Polyakov-Migdal[9] bootstrap program (i.e., Bethe-Salpeter structures), as advocated by Mack and Todorov[13] and by Symanzik,[14] or by investigating normal product expansions of operator products for the Gell-Mann/Low limiting theory. Neither approach has been carried through, and therefore the problem is still open. We will touch on the second approach in the following sections.

Canonical light cone behavior has a good chance to be true in the scale-invariant (Gell-Mann/Low) limit of a vector gluon model. The argument is as follows. In the scale-invariant Gell-Mann/Low limit the (isoscalar) gluon current must have dimension 3, and hence the field $G_{\mu\nu}$ related to g_μ by

$$\partial^\nu G_{\nu\mu} = g_\mu \tag{12}$$

has dimension 2. The resulting two-point function is that of a free field, and hence $G_{\mu\nu}(x)$ will be zero on the gauge-invariant factor space generated by applying the set of all gauge-invariant operators to the vacuum. In particular, any Wightman-function $\langle 0|G_{\mu_1\nu_1}(x_1)\cdots G_{\mu_n\nu_n}(x_n) X|0\rangle$, where X is a product of gauge-invariant operators [e.g., the SU(3) vector or pseudovector current], fulfills the free-field equation in $x_1,\ldots,x_n$. This means that the bilinear gauge-invariant quantities, as, for example, $\bar\psi\,\gamma_\mu\lambda_i\psi$, must decouple from the field. It is very plausible that the interacting spinor field differs from a free field[16] only by a (complicated) operator gauge transformation. In this case one could understand the above free-field behavior. The SU(3) currents would (apart from their normalization) be free currents, and the Gell-Mann/Low limiting theory has the light-cone algebra envisaged by Gell-Mann and Fritzsch.[11] The isoscalar gluon current itself vanishes in this limit. Note that this simple argument leading to Bjorken scaling does not hold if there is an admixture of a pseudoscalar gluon. Only the vector gluon would decouple in the conformal limit!

By the same token the conformal invariant limit of full quantum electrodynamics (QED)(if it exists) would lead to a vanishing current. Hence, if this possibility is realized in nature, Bjorken scaling ceases to be true in the conformal regime of QED. The high-energy region for this regime is presumably the region in which the effective electromagnetic coupling becomes comparable to the effective strong coupling in the present scaling region.

Also let us mention a final "strange" property of scale-invariant theories. For fields with integer (and sufficiently high) dimension the time-ordered Green functions are not always scale invariant, even though the Wightman functions are. Consider, for example, the time ordering of a two-point function of a conserved current:

$$\langle j_\mu(x) j_\nu(y)\rangle = C\left(g_{\mu\nu}\partial^2 - \partial_\mu\partial_\nu\right)\left[\frac{1}{(\xi^2 - i\epsilon\xi)}\right]^2 \tag{13}$$

Clearly the spectral function belonging to $1/(\xi^2 - i\epsilon\xi)^2$ is $\rho = $ const. The necessary subtraction for the time ordering cannot be made at $x^2 = 0$ because of the infrared divergence of the subtracted integral. One easily sees that there is no scale-invariant subtraction. Hence in such a case a measurement of the time-ordered two-point function* could reveal a scale-breaking log behavior even though the underlying operator theory is scale invariant—note that, according to our previous remarks, this cannot happen if the current is coupled to a vector meson.

3. THE NORMAL PRODUCT ALGORITHM

The NP algorithm as an extension of the BPH[17] renormalization framework was proposed by Zimmermann.[18] Lowenstein[19] subsequently demonstrated that this formalism leads to a universal and cutoff-independent finite treatment of quantized Noether currents, soft symmetry breakings, and the construction of a renormalized energy tensor, as well as a straightforward derivation of the Gell-Mann/Low renormalization[20] group equations and the Callan-Symanzik[25] equations. The problem of gauge invariance and anomalies is also most convincingly dealt with in this framework.[21] Here we will briefly consider the derivation of conformal symmetry in the scale limit of a renormalized field theory.[22]

We remind the reader that the starting point for these considerations is the Gell-Mann/Low perturbation formula for Green functions:

$$\langle 0|TA(x_1) \cdots A(x_n)|0\rangle = \text{``finite part''} \langle \Phi_0|TA_0(x_1) \cdots A(x_n)e^{i\int L_I d^4x}|\Phi_0\rangle_V$$

(14)

where $|\Phi_0\rangle = $ Fock vacuum, $A_0 = $ free field, and $V = $ omission of vacuum bubbles.

For reasons of simplicity we consider here a neutral scalar self-intracting theory with $L_I = -(g/4!)A^4$. "Finite part" stands for the BPH prescription, which leads to the unitary, causal, renormalized Green functions. In order to obtain the properly normalized Green functions, we add the well-known finite counterterms to the Lagrangian:

$$L_I \to L_{I\,\text{eff}} = L_I + \frac{1}{2}aA^2 + \frac{1}{2}b\partial_\mu A \partial^\mu A + \frac{c}{4!}A^4$$

(15)

where a, b, and c are determined as finite power series in g.

*Measurable, for example, in higher-order electromagnetic ee scattering.

This R operation can be generalized in order to construct arbitrary local functions of the fields (i.e., the entire Borchers class,[23]) for example,

$$\langle 0| TN_2[A^2](x)A(x_1)\cdots A(x_n)|0\rangle$$

$$= \text{FP}\langle \Phi_0| T{:}A_0{}^2(x){:}A_0(x_1)\cdots A_0(x_n)e^{i\int L_{\text{eff}}}|\Phi_0\rangle \qquad (16)$$

It is clear that the momentum space Feynman graphs of Eq. 16 differ from Eq. 14 only in the presence of an additional external two-vertex. Hence all that is necessary is to define a new R operation for primitive subgraphs containing this new vertex. According to how many Taylor subtractions are used, we index the local function of A^2 and call it a normal product of different degrees. The lowest possible index agrees by definition with the canonical dimension of the operator product. These normal products obey four rules.

1. Equation of motion:

$$\partial^2\langle 0| TA(x)\prod_i A(x_i)|0\rangle = -\frac{1}{3!}\frac{g-c}{1+b}\langle 0| TN_3[A^3](x)\prod_i A(x_i)|0\rangle$$

$$-\frac{m^2-a}{1+b}\langle 0| TA(x)\prod_i A(x_i)|0\rangle$$

$$-\frac{i}{1+b}\sum_1^N \delta(x-x_k)\langle 0| T\prod_i A(x_i)|0\rangle$$

$$\qquad (17)$$

2.

$$\partial_\mu\langle 0| TN_\delta[M](x)\prod_i A(x_i)|0\rangle = \langle 0| TN_{\delta+1}[\partial_\mu M](x)\prod_i A(x_i)|0\rangle \qquad (18)$$

where M is a monomial in the field.

3. Equation of motion inside a normal product:

$$\partial^2\langle 0| N_{\delta-2}[AB](x)\prod_i A(x_i)|0\rangle$$

$$= \langle 0| TN_\delta\left[\left(-\frac{1}{3!}\frac{g-c}{1+b}A^3 - \frac{m^2-a}{1+b}A\right)B\right](x)\prod_i A(x_i)|0\rangle$$

$$-i\sum_1^N \delta(x-x_k)\langle 0| TB(x)A(x_1)\cdots \hat{A}(x_k)\cdots A(x_N)|0\rangle \qquad (19)$$

Here B stands for $A(x)$, $\partial_0 A$, or an arbitrary spatial derivative with $\dim B < \delta - 3$.

4. *Zimmermann's identity, which relates an N with a high δ to an N with a lower δ–example (to be understood inside the Green function):*

$$N_4[A^2] = N_2[A^2] - rN_4[\partial_\mu A \, \partial^\mu A] - sN_4[A\partial^2 A] - \frac{t}{3!2}N_4[A^4]$$

where

$$r = -\tfrac{1}{8}\langle 0|TN_2[A^2](0)\widetilde{\partial_\mu A}(0)\,\widetilde{\partial^\mu A}(0)|0\rangle^{\text{prop}}$$

$$s = -\tfrac{1}{8}\langle 0|N_2[A^2](0)\tilde{A}(0)\widetilde{\partial^2 A}(0)|0\rangle^{\text{prop}} \qquad (20)$$

$$t = \tfrac{1}{2}\langle 0|TN_2[A^2](0)\tilde{A}^4(0)|0\rangle^{\text{prop}}$$

These properties of normal products constitute the NP algorithm. They incorporate the structural properties of BPH renormalization in a condensed form. With the help of the integrals over certain normal products (again inside Green functions)

$$\Delta_1 = \frac{i}{2}\int d^4x\, N_4[A^2](x)$$

$$\Delta_2 = \frac{i}{2}\int d^4x\, N_4[\partial_\mu A \, \partial^\mu A](x)$$

$$\Delta_3 = \frac{i}{4!}\int d^4x\, N_4[A^4](x) \qquad (21)$$

$$\Delta_0 = \frac{i}{2}\int d^4x\, N_2[A^2](x)$$

one can express the renormalized Schwinger action principle (or rather a special version) as follows:

$$W = i\int N_4[\mathsf{L}](x)\, d^4x = \text{action}$$

$$\delta\mathsf{L} = \delta\epsilon\frac{\partial\mathsf{L}}{\partial\epsilon}, \qquad \mathsf{L} = \mathsf{L}_0 + \mathsf{L}_{\text{eff}} \qquad (22)$$

$$\delta G^{(N)}(p_1\cdots p_n) = \langle 0|T\delta W\tilde{A}(p_1)\cdots\tilde{A}(p_N)|0\rangle \qquad (23)$$

This principle, which is a consequence of the NP algorithm, states, for example, that

$$\frac{\partial G^N}{\partial m^2} = (\text{linear combination of } \Delta_i) G^{(N)}, \qquad i = 1, 2, 3$$

(24)

$$\frac{\partial G^{(N)}}{\partial g} = (\text{linear combination of } \Delta_i) G^{(N)}$$

In order to go to the zero-mass limit, one has to normalize the Green function off shell[24] at $p^2 = \mu$. Then $\partial/\partial\mu^2$ is another linear combination of the Δ_i. It is now easy to see that the number of fields N is also expressible as such a linear combination (counting identity of Lowenstein). These relations, together with the integrated Zimmermann identity (Eq. 20), constitute five relations between three Δ_i's. Hence there must be two relations between the Δ_0, N, and the three differentiations (Eq. 24) (including $\partial/\partial\mu^2$). These relations can be chosen as the Callan-Symanzik[25] equation:

$$\left(m^2 \frac{\partial}{\partial m^2} + \mu^2 \frac{\partial}{\partial\mu^2} + \beta \frac{\partial}{\partial g} + N\gamma \right) G^{(N)} = \alpha m^2 \Delta_0 G^{(N)}$$

(25)

and the Gell-Mann/Low[24] renormalization group equation:

$$\left(\mu^2 \frac{\partial}{\partial\mu^2} + \sigma \frac{\partial}{\partial g} + N\tau \right) G^{(N)} = 0$$

(26)

Asymptotic scale invariance is equivalent to the existence of an "eigenvalue" of β:

$$\exists g_0 \quad \text{with} \quad \beta(g_0) = 0$$

(27)

Symanzik[27] has shown that the asymptotic theory is (up to normalization factors) equal to the Gell-Mann/Low limiting theory, which is defined as the $m^2 \to 0$ theory at a zero of

$$G_{as} = G_{GML}$$

(28)

Note that the conditions $\beta = 0$ or $\sigma = 0$ transcend perturbation theory; that is, we have to postulate the existence of the NP algorithm (which was originally abstracted from every order renormalized perturbation theory) outside perturbation theory.

Conformal invariance as a result of scale invariance is demonstrated if we can show the Gell-Mann/Low theory has a vanishing trace of an improved energy-momentum tensor. Let us breifly indicate that this is indeed the case. The renormalized canonical energy-momentum tensor is known[18] to have the form:

$$\theta_{\mu\nu}(x) = N_4\left[\theta_{\mu\nu}^{eff}\right](x) \tag{29a}$$

with $L = L_0 + L_{eff}$, and θ^{eff} belonging to $L_0 + L_{eff}$, that is,

$$\theta_{\mu\nu} = (1+b)N_4[\partial_\mu A \, \partial_\nu A]$$

$$-g_{\mu\nu}\left\{\frac{1}{2}N_4[\partial_\mu A \, \partial^\mu A] - \frac{1}{2}(m^2-a)N_4[A^2] - \frac{1}{4!}(g-c)N_4[A^4]\right\} \tag{29b}$$

We construct an "improved" energy-momentum tensor:[26]

$$\hat{\theta}_{\mu\nu} = \theta_{\mu\nu} + f(\partial_\mu \delta_\nu - g_{\mu\nu}\partial_\alpha \partial^\alpha)N_2[A^2] \tag{30}$$

It is now a matter of straightforward computation, using Zimmermann's identity, to show that for

$$f = -\frac{1+b}{6}(2\gamma_0+1) + \frac{m^2 s}{6}, \qquad \gamma_0 = \gamma(g_0) \tag{31}$$

we obtain

$$\hat{\theta}_\mu^{\ \mu} = -\alpha m^2 N_2[A^2] \tag{32}$$

In the asymptotic region N_2 is "soft" (i.e., can be neglected). One can also see that this right-hand side has smooth infrared properties, that is, vanishes in the Gell-Mann/Low limit (this would not be true for the $N_4[A^2]$!). Hence in this particular model we have the following: scale invariance→conformal invariance.

   A similar consideration holds for other renormalizable models. For vector meson models the two-point function of the vector meson current vanishes in the scale limit as a result of the Callan-Symanzik equations.

4.   DOES BJORKEN SCALING PREFER CERTAIN MODELS?

In Section 2 we saw that pure isoscalar vector gluon models lead to Bjorken scaling for the octet currents. The crucial question is whether this property is shared by other models.[28] Although we have no definite results on this problem, we would like to outline how the NP algorithm in principle permits us to answer this question. For this purpose we have to remind the reader in what manner a Wilson expansion is obtained in this framework.

Consider first the operator product of two fields. By using the N_2, this may be written as follows:[18]

$$A(x+\xi)A(x-\xi) = E_0(\xi) + E_1(\xi) \cdot N_2[A^2(x)] + R(x,\xi) \qquad (33)$$

Here R has the form:

$$R(x,\xi) = N_2[A(x+\xi)A(x-\xi)] - N_2[A^2(x)] \qquad (34)$$

where $N_2[A(x_1)A(x_2)]$ is a straightforward bilocal generalization of the local normal product (this has light-cone singularities in perturbation theory!). Also, E_0 and E_1 can be expressed in terms of the Green function of A. A Taylor expansion of $R(x,\xi)$ in ξ would lead to a divergent local operator, for example, $N_2[\partial_\mu A(x)\partial^\mu A(x)] = \infty$. The reason is that the index is smaller than the smallest δ permitted by the naive dimension of the object inside the bracket. Therefore one must first shift the index by using Zimmermann's identity for the bilocal product before performing the Taylor expansion. This identity has the form

$$N_2[A(x+\xi)A(x-\xi)] = N_\delta[A(x+\xi)A(x-\xi)] + \Sigma F_n(\xi)O_n(x) \qquad (35)$$

where the O_n are existing (i.e., finite) normal products of monomials of A, and the F_n are coefficients whose derivatives have singularities. By pushing the δ high enough, one obtains the Wilson expansion to any desired order. In an (asymptotically) scale-invariant theory, the singularities of the coefficient functions are determined by rules involving the dimensions of the normal products that multiply these coefficients. Note that the index of an N is generally *not* the dimension of this N in the scale limit. The true dimension has to be determined by deriving the Callan-Symanzik versus renormalization group equations for the normal products. Therefore one needs to study the connection between the coefficient $\tau(A)$ entering the Callan-Symanzik equation for the basic field and the $\tau(N)$ appearing in that of the normal product. Using the NP algorithm of the massive Thirring model, as recently considered by Lowenstein and Gomez,[26] it is possible, for example, to determine the anomalous dimension of $N_1[\bar\psi\psi]$.

In order to apply these ideas to Bjorken scaling one has to use the indicated methods for electromagnetic currents. The simplest model would be an $A^{+2}A^2$ self-coupling for a charged scalar field. In this case the conserved current turns out to be

$$j_\mu(x) = N_3\left[A^+ \overset{\leftrightarrow}{\partial}_\mu A\right](x)$$

Here j_μ has the dimension 3 in the scale-invariant limit. The next step is the construction of the normal products which appear in the Wilson expansion of two currents. The last step is the investigation of their scaling behavior via the Callan-Symanzik equation— in particular, the determination of their "anomalous dimension" in terms of the anomalous dimension of the field.

Since the content of Bjorken scaling has been analyzed in terms of restrictions on the dimensions of operators appearing in the Wilson expansion, the problem in the title of this chapter can, in principle, be answered in every renormalizable model.

REFERENCES and NOTES

1. G. Mack and A. Salam, *Ann. Phys.*., **53**, 174 (1969); D. Gross and J. Wess, *Phys. Rev. D*, **2**, 753 (1970).

2. S. Ferrara, R. Gatto, and A. F. Grillo, *Springer Tracts in Modern Physics*, Vol. 67, Springer-Verlag, Berlin.

3. K. Wilson, *Phys. Rev. D*, **3**, 1818 (1971).

4. E. Cunningham, *Proc. Math. Soc. (London)*, **8**, 77 (1910); H. Bateman, *ibid.*, **8**, (1910).

5. J. Terrel, *Phys. Rev.*, **88**, 179 (1952).

6. S. Coleman and R. Jackiw, *Ann. Phys.*, **67**, 552 (1971).

7. M. Hortaćsu, R. Seiler, and B. Schroer, article to be published in *Phys. Rev. D*, May or June 1971.

8. K. Johnson, *Nuovo Cimento*, **20**, 773 (1961); B. Klaiber, *Lectures in Theoretical Physics: High Energy and Particle Physics*, ed. by W. E. Brittin and A. O. Barut, Gordon and Breach, New York, 1968, Vol. XB.

9. A. M. Polyakov, *JETP Letters*, **12**, 538 (1971); A. A. Migdal, *Phys. Letters*, **37B**, 98, 386 (1971).

10. B. Schroer, "Scaling Laws and Scale Invariance in Statistical Mechanics and Relativistic Quantum Field Theory," lecture delivered at the IV Symposio Brasileiro De Fisica Teorica, January 1972. An expanded version will be issued in the near future.

11. H. Fritzsch and M. Gell-Mann, "Proceedings of the Coral Gables Conference on Fundamental Interactions at High Energy," University of Miami, 1971.

12. D. G. Boulware, Lowell S. Brown, and R. D. Peccei, *Phys. Rev. D*, **2**, 293 (1970).

13. G. Mack and J. T. Todorov, Trieste Preprint IC/71/139 (October 1971); see Chapter 5 in this volume.

14. K. Symanzik, private communication.

15. S. Ferrara, R. Gatto, A. F. Grillo, and G. Parisi, *Phys. Letters*, **38B**, 333 (1972).

16. See, for example, K. Johnson, *Proceedings of the Symposium on Basic Questions in Elementary Particle Physics, June 1971, Dedicated to W. Heisenberg.*

17. N. N. Bogoliubov and D. V. Shirkov, *Introduction to the Theory of Quantized Fields*, Interscience, New York, 1959; K. Hepp, lectures given at Les Houches (1970), to be published.

18. W. Zimmermann, in *Lectures on Elementary Particles and Fields* (1970 Brandeis University Summer Institute), Vol. 2, ed. by S. Deser, M. Grisaru, and H. Pendleton, MIT Press, Cambridge, Mass., 1971.

19. J. H. Lowenstein, *Phys. Rev. D*, **4**, 228 (1971).

20. J. H. Lowenstein, to be published.

21. J. H. Lowenstein and B. Schroer, University of Pittsburgh Preprint NYO-3829-88 (1972), to be published in *Phys. Rev. D*.

22. B. Schroer, *Lettere Nuovo Cimento*, **2**, 887 (1971).

23. See, for example, R. F. Streater and A. S. Wightman, *PCT, Spin and Statistics and All That*, Benjamin, New York, 1964.

24. M. Gell-Mann and F. Low, *Phys. Rev.*, **95**, 1300 (1954).

25. C. G. Callan, Jr., *Phys. Rev. D*, **2**, 1541 (1970); K. Symanzik, *Commun. Math. Phys.*, **18**, 227 (1970).

26. This tensor is slightly different from the one given in ref. 6, which is soft in the free-field case.

27. K. Symanzik, *Commun. Math. Phys.*, **23**, 49 (1971).

28. Using a stronger assumption whose validity has not been established in renormalized perturbation theory (respectively in the Gell-Mann/Low limit), one can give a derivation of the Bjorken scaling law: G. Mack, *Nucl. Phys.*, **B35**, 592 (1971).

CHAPTER 4

General Consequences
of Conformal Algebra

S. Ferrara
R. Gatto
A. F. Grillo
G. Parisi

1. INTRODUCTION

In this chapter we summarize a series of results which follow from conformal algebra, assumed to be an approximate (in a specific sense) or exact symmetry of quantum field theory. By approximate validity of invariance under the conformal algebra we mean the following: the theory is not invariant under infinitesimal conformal transformations, but it exhibits invariance in its limiting light-cone behavior. Although such a definition of approximate invariance is not complete in an axiomatic sense, we find it convenient to exploit its "kinematical" consequences.

In particular, we discuss, in Section 2, the implications of covariance under the conformal algebra on the leading light cone singularities in terms of operator product expansions. The imposition of covariance then leads to a well-defined expression for each contributing irreducible conformal tensor and, rather interestingly, exhibits causality in an explicit form. Applications can be given to forward and nonforward matrix elements, the latter ones connected to the asymptotic behaviors of form factors. In discussing the consequences of full conformal covariance, that is, covariance unrestricted to the leading light-cone limits, it is convenient to use the manifestly covariant six-dimensional formalism for the O(4,2) algebra. A summary of the formalism, together with a brief introduction to conformal algebra and its representations, can be found in the Appendix.

The restrictions of conformal algebra on vacuum expectation values are given in Section 3a, where the usefulness of the "shadow-operator" technique is also illustrated. Two-point and three-point functions are intimately connected to the conformal covariant operator product expansion discussed in Section 3b. This fact leads to a consistency relation between the coefficients of the operator product expansion and the normalization of two- and three-point functions. Physically relevant consequences of this relation have been recently explored. The restrictions on the four-point function are separately dealt with in Section 3c, where an expression is derived that exhibits explicitly the conformal covariant structure. The problem of the four-point function is related to that of product expansions for three local operators. Canonical scaling, as implied by extrapolation of the experimental results on deep inelastic scattering, shows specific features which allow for the derivation of a special result valid in that case, namely, the existence of an infinite number of local conservation laws. The theorem explicitly poses the dilemma between two theoretical alternatives: (1) the parton model; and (2) renormalization of dimension (experiment then requires "small" renormalization, and thus a complex theoretical problem arises). The theorem is, however, derived on the assumption of absence of spontaneous breaking, which might be considered as a third alternative.

The theorem of canonical scaling and its implications are discussed in Section 4. Finally, in Section 5 we examine the special situation occurring in two space-time dimensions. The interest is twofold: first, the existence of explicitly soluble models in two dimensions; second, the possibility of connection with the duality formalisms. Such possibility is clearly speculative at this stage. Nevertheless the mathematical analogies are intriguing and suggestive, and we hope that further work will shed additional light on this point.

2. CONFORMAL COVARIANT LIGHT-CONE EXPANSION

The possible relevance of the algebraic concept of scale invariance was suggested by Wilson[1] in connection with operator product expansions. The extension from dilatations to the entire conformal algebra may be justified on the basis of a number of reasons (none of them, however, compelling). (1) Lagrangian field theories, which are formally invariant under dilatations, are often invariant also under special conformal transformations. For instance, a sufficient (but not necessary) condition is the absence of derivative couplings. (2) Conformal transformations leave the light-cone invariant. (3) The conformal algebra provides for a natural homogenization of the inhomogeneous Poincaré algebra.

The algebraic implications of conformal invariance on the light cone were studied, in ref. 2, within the formalism, using equal-time commutators. The requirement of covariance under the infinitesimal generators of SU(2,2) can be imposed directly on an operator product expansion on the light cone.[3] To such purpose one has first to analyze the transformation properties of the infinite set of local operators which provide a basis for the operator expansion.

It will be interesting to illustrate as a preliminary step two aspects of light-cone expansions which finally turn out to be connected to conformal invariance. They are (a) causality, and (b) translation invariance on a Hermitian basis.

Let us consider the expansion

$$A(x)B(0) = \sum_n c_n(x)O_n(x) \tag{1}$$

where $c_n(x)$ are c-number functions and $O_n(x)$ form a complete set, extending the concepts and definitions of Wilson's work.[1] When we commute with some arbitrary local operator $C(y)$, we obtain

$$[A(x),C(y)]B(0) + A(x)[B(0),C(y)] = \sum_n c_n(x)[O_n(0),C(y)] \tag{2}$$

One notes that for y_μ spacelike, that is, for $y^2 < 0$, each commutator $[O_n(0), C(y)]$ vanishes. Hence, taking $y^2 < 0$, each term on the right-hand side vanishes, whereas on the left-hand side $[B(0),C(y)]$ vanishes, but not necessarily the first term $[A(x),C(y)]B(0)$. The latter term vanishes if, in addition, $(x-y)^2 < 0$, which, on the light cone, amounts to requiring $y^2 < 2xy$. There is no paradox, because of the infinite summation on the right-hand side. However, it would be better to have an improved operator product expansion which formally exhibits the causality properties in each of its terms. This is the problem we have indicated under (a).

Let us now show what the problem specified under (b) is. Again let us consider a light-cone expansion[4] of the form

$$A(x)B(0) = (-x^2 + i\epsilon x_0)^{-\gamma} \sum_n x^{\alpha_1} \cdots x^{\alpha_n} O_{\alpha_1 \cdots \alpha_n}(0) \qquad (3)$$

The tensor $O_{\alpha_1 \cdots \alpha_n}$ are symmetric traceless tensors. They can always be chosen to be Hermitian. The commutator $[A(x), B(0)]$ has then the correct support required by causality. On Eq. 3 one makes a number of algebraic steps. One first translates by $-x$, then changes x into $-x$, expands $O_{\alpha_1 \cdots \alpha_n}(x)$ in a power series around $x = 0$, and finally takes the Hermitian conjugate. The expression obtained can be compared with the expression started from, Eq. 3, and one discovers that for consistency the following infinite set of relations must be satisfied:

$$O_{\alpha_1 \cdots \alpha_n}(x) = \sum_{m=0}^{n} \frac{(-1)^m}{(n-m)!} \partial_{\alpha_{m+1}} \cdots \partial_{\alpha_n} O_{\alpha_1 \cdots \alpha_m}(x) \qquad (4)$$

It is interesting that, for $n =$ odd, Eq. 4 tells that $O_{\alpha_1 \cdots \alpha_n}$ is a sum of derivative operators (which therefore have vanishing forward matrix elements).

It turns out that the imposition, on the general operator product expansion on the light cone, of the requirement of covariance under infinitesimal special conformal transformations results in a very stringent set of limitations.[3] They essentially amount to fixing the relative coefficients in the expansion of each derivative term $\partial_{\alpha_{m+1}} \cdots \partial_{\alpha_n} O_{\alpha_1 \cdots \alpha_m}(x)$ with respect to the nonderivative term $O_{\alpha_1 \cdots \alpha_m}(x)$. The expansion including such restrictions is found to exhibit a very compact form in terms of a confluent hypergeometric function. An interesting circumstance then becomes apparent: the two problems that we have mentioned under the headings (a) and (b) above are in fact automatically solved with the new form of operator product expansion, essentially reducing to some known properties of the confluent hypergeometric function. In other words, the imposition of conformal invariance directly eliminates the two problems of causality support and translation invariance on a Hermitian basis (the reverse, however, is not true). We have already discussed why the imposition of conformal symmetry on the light cone seems to be a reasonable requirement. At this stage one is working within well-defined limitations: (1) one deals only with infinitesimal conformal transformations, and (2) the symmetry is supposed to hold only on the light cone, not necessarily for the complete theory. It will be convenient to deal with a slightly more general situation than is usually assumed. For two scalar local operators A, B of dimensions $-l_A, -l_B$ we write our conformal light-cone expansion as

$$A(x)B(0) \approx (x^2 - i\epsilon x_0)^{-(1/2)(l_A+l_B)} \sum_{n=0}^{\infty} (x^2 - i\epsilon x_0)^{(1/2)(l_n-n)}$$

$$\cdot c_n^{AB} x^{\alpha_1} \cdots x^{\alpha_n} \phi[(\tfrac{1}{2})(l_A - l_B + l_n + n), l_n + n; x\partial] O_{\alpha_1 \cdots \alpha_n}(0)$$

$$(5)$$

where $O_{\alpha_1 \cdots \alpha_n}(x)$ are local, Lorentz irreducible, $(\tfrac{1}{2}n, \tfrac{1}{2}n)$ tensors, of dimensions $-l_n$, satisfying $[K_\lambda, O_{\alpha_1 \cdots \alpha_n}(0)] = 0$ (K_λ generates special conformal transformations); $\phi(a, c; x)$ is the confluent hypergeometric function (see ref. 5, p. 248); and the expansion coefficients c_n^{AB} satisfy

$$c_n^{AB} = (-1)^n c_n^{BA} \qquad (6)$$

Equation 4 follows only from translation invariance and hermiticity of the basis. For $l_n - n = 1$ (where l is fixed), as presumably happens in the expansion for $j_\mu(x)j_\nu(0)$,[6] the x^2 dependence in Eq. 5 factorizes out, and one regains an expansion of the kind in Eq. 3 except that all derivative operators have been formally summed up by means of the hypergeometric function ϕ. The relation among derivative and nonderivative operators implied by Eq. 3 is automatically satisfied in models based on free quark commutators.[6] These models correspond to special choices of $O_{\alpha_1 \cdots \alpha_n}$ and c_n^{AB} in Eq. 5, for two currents: the summed-up expansion corresponds to a bilocal operator. We also note that the invariance (by construction) under infinitesimal conformal transformations of the improved expansion, for arbitrary dimensions, eliminates any hope that canonical dimensions could follow only from such an invariance.

Having written down our expansion, we come back to the causality restriction. Equation 5 can formally be written as

$$A(x)B(0) \approx (x^2 - i\epsilon x_0)^{-(1/2)(l_A+l_B)} \sum_{n=0}^{\infty} (x^2 - i\epsilon x_0)^{(1/2)(l_n-n)} \tilde{c}_n^{AB} x^{\alpha_1} \cdots x^{\alpha_n}$$

$$\cdot \int_0^1 du\, u^{(1/2)(l_A-l_B+l_n+n)-1} (1-u)^{(1/2)(l_B-l_A+l_n+n)-1} O_{\alpha_1 \cdots \alpha_n}(ux) \qquad (7)$$

$$\tilde{c}_n^{AB} = c_n^{AB} \frac{\Gamma(l_n+n)}{\Gamma[\tfrac{1}{2}(l_A-l_B+l_n+n)]\Gamma[\tfrac{1}{2}(l_B-l_A+l_n+n)]} \qquad (8)$$

Commuting with $C(y)$, one obtains, on the right, commutators $[O_{\alpha_1\cdots\alpha_n}(ux), C(y)]$, $0<u<1$, which vanish for $(ux-y)^2<0$ or $y^2<2uxy$, when x is on the light cone. The term on the left, $[A(x), C(y)]B(0)+A(x)[B(0), C(y)]$, certainly vanishes if $y^2<0$ and $(x-y)^2<0$, or $y^2<2xy$. Clearly, if $y^2<2uxy$ holds, $0\leqslant u\leqslant 1$, then both $y^2<0$ and $y^2<2xy$ hold, and vice versa: q.e.d.

We next verify that translation invariance holds automatically. We repeat the steps leading to Eq. 4. We translate Eq. 5 by $-x$, change x into $-x$, and take the Hermitian conjugate, obtaining

$$B(x)A(0) \approx \left(x^2-i\epsilon x_0\right)^{-(1/2)(l_A+l_B)} \sum_{n=0}^{\infty} \left(x^2-i\epsilon x_0\right)^{(1/2)(l_n-n)}$$

$$\cdot (-1)^n c_n{}^{AB} x^{\alpha_1} \cdots x^{\alpha_n} \phi[\tfrac{1}{2}(l_A-l_B+l_n+n), l_n+n; -x\partial] O_{\alpha_1\cdots\alpha_n}(x)$$

$$(9)$$

However, using the Kummer transformation $\phi(a,c;x)=\phi(c-a,c;-x)e^x$, we have

$$\phi[\tfrac{1}{2}(l_A-l_B+l_n+n), l_n+n; -x\partial] O(x)$$

$$= \phi[\tfrac{1}{2}(l_B-l_A+l_n+n), l_n+n; x\partial] e^{-x\partial} O(x)$$

$$= \phi[\tfrac{1}{2}(l_B-l_A+l_n+n), l_n+n; x\partial] O(0)$$

Recalling also Eq. 6, we see that Eq. 9 is identical to Eq. 5 except for the interchange $A\leftrightarrow B$: q.e.d.

We note that for $A=B$ Eq. 6 tells that $c_n{}^{AA}=0$ for n odd, as we know in particular from discussion of Eq. 4.

The result in Eq. 5 can be obtained by application of the Jacobi identities of conformal algebra on the expansion

$$A(x)B(0) = \sum_{\substack{n=0 \\ x^2\to 0}}^{\infty} \left(\frac{1}{x^2}\right)^{(1/2)(l_A+l_B+n-l_n)} \sum_{m=n}^{\infty} c_{nm}{}^{AB} x^{\alpha_1}\cdots x^{\alpha_m} O^{nm}{}_{\alpha_1\cdots\alpha_m}(0) \quad (10)$$

where the families of Hermitian operators

$$O^{nm}{}_{\alpha_1\cdots\alpha_m}(0) = \left[\cdots\left[O^{(n)}{}_{\alpha_1\cdots\alpha_n}(0), P_{\alpha_{n+1}}\right], \cdots P_{\alpha_m}\right](i)^{m-n} \quad (11)$$

together contribute a complete set for expansion on the light cone. Each family (i.e., fixed n) transforms irreducibly under the conformal algebra in space-time.[3] In the representation, $O^{(n)}_{\alpha_1 \cdots \alpha_n}(0)$ is the lowest-dimension operator for which $K_\lambda = 0$. Note that P_λ and K_λ are dimension-raising and dimension-lowering operators, respectively, within each irreducible representation. Commuting both sides of Eq. 10 with the generators of special conformal transformation K_λ, one obtains

$$-i[A(x)B(0), K_\lambda] = \sum_{n=0}^{\infty} \left(\frac{1}{x^2} \right)^{(1/2)(l_A + l_B + n - l_n)}$$

$$\times \sum_{m=n}^{\infty} c_{nm}^{AB} \left\{ 2 \left(l_A + m - \frac{l_A + l_B + n - l_n}{2} \right) \right.$$

$$\left. \times x_\lambda x^{\alpha_1} \cdots x^{\alpha_n} - x^2 \sum_{i=1}^{m} g_\lambda^{\alpha_i} x^{\alpha_1} \cdots x^{\hat{\alpha_i}} \cdots x^{\alpha_n} \right\} O^{nm}_{\alpha_1 \cdots \alpha_m}(0)$$

$$= -i \sum_{n=0}^{\infty} \left(\frac{1}{x^2} \right)^{(1/2)(l_A + l_B + n - l_n)}$$

$$\times \sum_{m=n}^{\infty} c_{nn}^{AB} x^{\alpha_1} \cdots x^{\alpha_n} [O^{nm}_{\alpha_1 \cdots \alpha_m}(0), K_\lambda]$$

where

$$i[O^{nm}_{\alpha_1 \cdots \alpha_m}(0), K_\lambda] = -(m-n)(2l_n + m - n - 1) S_{\{\alpha\}} g_{\alpha_m \lambda} O^{nm-1}_{\alpha_1 \cdots \alpha_n, \alpha_{n+1} \cdots \alpha_{m-1}}(0)$$

$$- (m-n)(m-n-1) S_{\{\alpha\}} \left(g_{\alpha_m \lambda} O^{nm-1}_{\alpha_1 \cdots \alpha_n, \alpha_{n+1} \cdots \alpha_{m-1}}(0) \right.$$

$$\left. - g_{\alpha_{m-1} \alpha_m} O^{nm-1}_{\alpha_1 \cdots \alpha_n, \alpha_{n+1} \cdots \alpha_{m-2} \lambda} \right) + 2(m-n) n S_{\{\alpha\}}$$

$$\times \left[g_{\alpha_1 \alpha_m} O^{nm-1}_{\alpha_2 \cdots \alpha_m \lambda, \alpha_{n+1} \cdots \alpha_{m-1}}(0) - g_{\lambda \alpha_1} O^{nm-1}_{\alpha_2 \cdots \alpha_n \alpha_m, \alpha_{n+1} \cdots \alpha_{m-1}}(0) \right] \quad (12)$$

From the structure of the commutator given by Eq. 11 it is manifest that the leading terms on the light cone, which are proportional to x_λ, arise from these terms in the commutator (Eq. 12) which are proportional to $g_\lambda{}^{\alpha_i}$. Their symmetrization with respect to the $\{\alpha\}$ indices gives

$$-2(m-n)(l_n+m-1)S_{\{\alpha_i\}}g_{\alpha_i\lambda}O_{\alpha_1\cdots\hat{\alpha}_i\cdots\alpha_m}^{nm-1}(0) \qquad (13)$$

Inserting Eq. 13 into the commutator (Eq. 11), we obtain

$$-i[A(x)B(0),K_\lambda] = \sum_{n=0}^{\infty}\left(\frac{1}{x^2}\right)^{(1/2)(l_A+l_B+n-l_n)}$$

$$\times \sum_{m=n}^{\infty}c_{nm}{}^{AB}2\left(l_A+m-\frac{l_A+l_B+n-l_n}{2}\right)x_\lambda x^{\alpha_1}\cdots x^{\alpha_m}O_{\alpha_1\cdots\alpha_m}^{nm}(0)$$

$$= \sum_{n=0}^{\infty}\left(\frac{1}{x^2}\right)^{(1/2)(l_A+l_B+n-l_n)}\sum_{m=1}^{\infty}c_{nm}{}^{AB}b(n,m)x_\lambda x^{\alpha_1}\cdots{}^{\alpha_{m-1}}O_{\alpha_1\cdots\alpha_{m-1}}^{nm-1}(0)$$

$$\qquad (14)$$

where $b(n,m)=(m-n)(l_n+m)$.

Equation 14, by comparing equal power in x, gives rise to the recurrence relation

$$c_{n,n+k-1}^{AB}[\tfrac{1}{2}(l_A-l_B+l_n+n)+k-1] = c_{n,n+k}^{AB}k(l_n+n+k-1) \qquad (15)$$

giving the solution

$$c_{n,n+k}^{AB} = \frac{\Gamma[\tfrac{1}{2}(l_A-l_B+l_n+n)+k]\Gamma(l_n+n)}{k!\,\Gamma[\tfrac{1}{2}(l_A-l_B+l_n+n)]\Gamma(l_n+n+k)}c_{n,n}^{AB} \qquad (16)$$

Equation 16 brings about, by Taylor expansion, the confluent hypergeometric function

$$\phi[\tfrac{1}{2}(l_A-l_B+l_n+n);l_n+n;x\partial] = \sum_{k=0}^{\infty}\frac{c_{n,n+k}^{AB}}{c_{n,n}^{AB}}(x\cdot\partial)^k \qquad (17)$$

Let us consider some implications of the expansion on physically relevant matrix elements of the massive theory.

For forward matrix elements, such as those occurring, for instance, in deep inelastic scattering, we have

$$\langle p|A(x)B(0)|p\rangle \underset{x^2\to0}{\sim} \sum_n\left(\frac{1}{x^2}\right)^{(1/2)(l_A+l_B-\tau_n)}c_n{}^{AB}x^{\alpha_1}\cdots x^{\alpha_n}\langle p|O_{\alpha_1\cdots\alpha_n}(0)|p\rangle$$

since derivative operators do not contribute. Then we see that canonical Bjorken scaling implies that $l_n = l + n$, with $l = 2$, on inequivalent irreducible representations of conformal algebra.

Bjorken scaling therefore constitutes dynamical information on the spectrum of such representations. One can also see this by explicit computation of the quadratic Casimir operator:

$$C_1 = M^{\mu\nu}M_{\mu\nu} + 2PK - 2D^2 + 8D = 2n(n+2) + 2l_n(l_n - 4)$$

We remark that the previous analysis clarifies the kinematical role of conformal algebra. We see that scaling in the deep inelastic limit is a dynamical information not contained in conformal symmetry.

A simplest case of nonforward matrix element is the off-shell form factor[7]

$$W_\mu(x,p) = \langle 0|J_\mu(x)\phi(0)|p\rangle \tag{18}$$

where ϕ is a local field, and J_μ is a conserved current. Let us consider the light-cone limit of this vertex and assume, according to Brandt and Preparata,[4] that this limit is related to the asymptotic behavior of the corresponding on-shell form factor. Then we can use conformal symmetry on the light cone and write

$$W_\mu(x,p) \underset{x^2 \to 0}{\sim} \langle 0|T\big(J_\mu(x)\phi(0)\big)|p\rangle \underset{x^2 \to 0}{}$$

$$\sim (p\cdot\partial\partial_\mu - p_\mu\Box) \sum_n \left(\frac{1}{-x^2 + i\epsilon}\right)^{(1/2)(l-\tau_n)} (xp)^{n-1} \int_0^1 du f_n(u)e^{iupx} \tag{19}$$

By Fourier transforming we have, for $-q^2 \to \infty$ and $\omega = 2m_\pi\nu/q^2$ fixed,

$$W_\mu(p,q) = \big(p_\mu q^2 - p\cdot q q_\mu\big) \sum_n c_n (q^2)^{(1/2)(l-\tau_n)-2} (\omega)^{-(1/2)(l+\tau_n)}$$

$$\cdot (\omega-1)^{l-2}\theta(\omega-1) \,_2F_1\left(\frac{l-d_n}{2}, \frac{d_n+l-4}{2}+l; l-1; 1-\frac{1}{\omega}\right) \tag{20}$$

The important point of Eq. 20 is that the threshold limit $\omega \to 1$ relevant to the mass shell is just

$$W_2(q^2,s) \underset{\omega \to 1}{\sim} s^{l-2} \sum_n c_n(q^2)^{l-(1/2)(1+\tau_n)} \tag{21}$$

$[s = q^2(1 - \omega)]$, so that for the pion form factor we have

$$F(q^2) = \operatorname{Im} G^{-1}(s) W_2(q^2,s) \underset{q^2 \to \infty}{\sim} \sum_n (q^2)^{l-(1/2)(1+\tau_n)} \tag{22}$$

and the s dependence in Eq. 22 exactly cancels the inverse propagator, giving an unambiguous result in this limit.

From Eq. 22 we see that each term corresponds to a different light-cone singularity. Hence, if we assume light-cone dominance, the term with the smallest-decreasing behavior dominates the form factor. As $\tau_n \geqslant 2$ we see that, if $l \leqslant 2$,

$$F(q^2) \underset{-q^2 \to \infty}{\sim} \left(\frac{1}{q^2}\right)^{l-1} \tag{23}$$

However, if $l > 2$, the operator of smallest twist τ_n $(\tau_n = 1 - n)$, such that $\tau_n < 1$, dominates the form factor.

This is what happens, under these assumptions, in the case of the canonical quark model, where $l_\pi = 3$ and $\tau = 2$ for the axial current, and we find

$$F_\pi(q^2) \underset{-q^2 \to \infty}{\sim} \left(\frac{1}{q^2}\right)^{3/2} \tag{24}$$

while the full conformal invariant result would give, as pointed out by Migdal, $(1/q^2)^2$, a behavior corresponding to the π-field contribution to the operator product.

3. CONSEQUENCES OF FULL CONFORMAL INVARIANCE

a. Vacuum Expectation Values

We shall use the covariant formalism developed in the Appendix. It will be convenient, however, to also make use in some case of the corresponding space-time formulation.

Let us start with the simplest case of the two-point function. Consider the vacuum expectation values (VEV) of two (conformal) scalar fields of dimension l_A, l_B, respectively:

$$\langle 0|A(\eta)B(\eta')|0\rangle = F(\eta\cdot\eta') \qquad (25)$$

(Equation 25 obviously follows from invariance under $O(4,2)$ transformations.) With the previously derived parametrization of the six-dimensional cone $\eta^2 = 0$ [where $\eta_A = (x_\mu, k)$] the homogeneity conditions

$$\eta^A \partial_A F(\eta\cdot\eta') = -l_A F(\eta\cdot\eta')$$
$$\eta'^A \partial_A' F(\eta\cdot\eta') = l_B F(\eta\cdot\eta') \qquad (26)$$

are consistent only if $l_A = l_B$ [from Eq. A.30, $\eta\cdot\eta' = -\frac{1}{2}kk'(x-x')^2$].
We thus obtain the unique solution

$$F(\eta\cdot\eta') = c_{AB}(\eta\cdot\eta')^{-l_A}, \qquad l_A = l_B$$
$$= 0, \qquad l_A \neq l_B \qquad (27)$$

or on space-time

$$F\left[(x-x')^2\right] = c'_{AB}\left[\frac{1}{(x-x')^2}\right]^{l_A}, \qquad l_A = l_B$$
$$= 0, \qquad l_A \neq l_B \qquad (28)$$

The generalization of selection rule 27 to the two-point function of two irreducible tensor fields is given by the following:

VEV selection rule.   The VEV

$$\langle 0|\psi_{A_1\cdots A_n}(\eta)\phi_{B_1\cdots B_m}(\eta')|0\rangle = F_{A_1\cdots A_n B_1\cdots B_m}(\eta, \eta') \qquad (29)$$

is nonvanishing if and only if $l_A = l_B$ and $n = m$, where $-l_{A_1}, -l_B$ are the degrees of homogeneity of the two tensor fields.
    Proof. The scalar function

$$F(\eta\cdot\eta') = \eta'^{A_1}\cdots\eta'^{A_m}\eta^{B_1}\cdots\eta^{B_m}F_{A_1\cdots A_n B_1\cdots B_m}(\eta, \eta') \qquad (30)$$

is homogeneous of degree $-l_A + m$, $-l_B + n$ in k and k', respectively, so that Eq. 30 is consistent only for

$$l_A - l_B = m - n \qquad (31)$$

The scalar (Eq. 30) is the contribution to the VEV (Eq. 29) of the covariant

$$\eta_{A_1}\cdots\eta_{A_n}\eta'_{B_1}\cdots\eta'_{B_m}(\eta\cdot\eta')^{-l_A-n} \tag{32}$$

which, by itself, satisfies the correct trace and transversality conditions with fixed homogeneity degree for l_A, l_B related by Eq. 31. The whole set of allowed covariants is obtained from Eq. 32 by performing one of the following operations:

1. Permutations of η and η'.
2. Substitution of an arbitrary number of couples (η, η') with g_{AB}.
3. Substitution of an equal number of (η, η) and (η', η') couples with a corresponding number of symbols g_{AB}.

This concludes the proof; in fact, we can transform into space-time, using Eq. A.38:

$$\langle 0|O_{\alpha_1\cdots\alpha_n}(x)O_{\beta_1\cdots\beta_m}(x')|0\rangle = k^{l_A}k'^{l_B}(e^{-ik\pi})^{A_1\cdots A_n}_{\alpha_1\cdots\alpha_n}$$

$$\cdot(e^{-ix'\pi})^{B_1\cdots B_m}_{\beta_1\cdots\beta_m}\langle 0|\psi_{A_1\cdots A_n}(\eta)\phi_{B_1\cdots B_m}(\eta')|0\rangle \tag{33}$$

On the other hand, transformation 33 on the coordinates can be seen to give in general

$$(e^{-ix\pi})^{A_1\cdots A_n}_{\alpha_1\cdots\alpha_n}\overline{\eta}_{A_1}\cdots\overline{\eta}_{A_n} = \overline{k}^n(\overline{x}-x)_{\alpha_1}\cdots(\overline{x}-x)_{\alpha_n}$$

so that the covariants defined above, satisfying the supplementary, traceless, and symmetry conditions, do not contribute to Eq. 33 unless $n = m$; in fact, consider as an example the leading light-cone contribution to the VEV (Eq. 29), which comes out from the covariant

$$\eta'_{A_1}\cdots\eta'_{A_n}\eta_{B_1}\cdots\eta_{B_m}F'(\eta\cdot\eta')$$

On the basis of homogeneity arguments, $O(4,2)$ covariance implies that $l_A - l_B = n - m$ [and then $F'(\eta\cdot\eta')\sim(\eta\cdot\eta')^{-l_B-n}$], which turns out to be consistent with Eq. 31 only for $m = n$ and then $l_A = l_B$.

In particular, one has

$$\langle 0|j_\mu(x)j_\nu(0)|0\rangle = c\left(\frac{1}{x^2}\right)^{l_j+1}\left(x_\mu x_\nu - \tfrac{1}{2}x^2 g_{\mu\nu}\right)$$

(34)

$$\langle 0|\theta_{\mu\nu}(x)\theta_{\rho\sigma}(0)|0\rangle = c'\left(\frac{1}{x^2}\right)^{l_\theta+2}$$

$$\times\left[4x_\mu x_\nu x_\rho x_\sigma - x^2\left(x_\mu x_\sigma g_{\nu\rho} + x_\nu x_\sigma g_{\mu\rho} + x_\mu x_\rho g_{\nu\sigma} + x_\nu x_\rho g_{\mu\sigma}\right)\right.$$

$$\left. + \tfrac{1}{2}x^4\left(g_{\mu\rho}g_{\nu\sigma} + g_{\nu\rho}g_{\mu\sigma} - \tfrac{1}{2}g_{\mu\nu}g_{\rho\sigma}\right)\right]$$

Note that the Ward identities expressing local conservation are automatically satisfied for $l_j = 3$, $l_\theta = 4$.

For the general n-point function (scalars for simplicity) one has

$$\langle 0|A_1(\eta_1)\cdots A_n(\eta_n)|0\rangle = F_n(\eta_1\cdots\eta_n)$$

(35)

where F_n depends on the $n(n-1)/2$ scalar products $\eta_1\cdot\eta_2\cdots\eta_{n-1}\cdot\eta_n$. Moreover F_n verifies the n-constraints:

$$\eta^i\partial_{A_i}F_n(\eta_1\cdot\eta_2\cdots\eta_{n-1}\cdot\eta_n) = -l_{A_i}F_n(\eta_1\cdot\eta_2\cdots\eta_{n-1}\cdot\eta_n)$$

(36)

so that it depends only on $[n(n-1)/2]-n = n(n-3)/2$ independent variables.* As a consequence, the three-point function is completely determined and turns out to be

$$F_3(\eta_1\cdot\eta_2,\eta_1\cdot\eta_3,\eta_2\cdot\eta_3) = c_{123}(\eta_1\cdot\eta_2)^{-(1/2)(l_{A1}+l_{A2}-l_{A3})}$$

$$\cdot(\eta_1\cdot\eta_3)^{-(1/2)(l_{A1}+l_{A3}-l_{A2})}(\eta_2\cdot\eta_3)^{-(1/2)(l_{A2}+l_{A3}-l_{A1})}$$

(37)

or, on space-time,

$$\langle 0|A_1(x_1)A_2(x_2)A_3(x_3)|0\rangle = c'_{123}\left[\frac{1}{(x_1-x_2)^2}\right]^{(1/2)(l_{A1}+l_{A2}-l_{A3})}$$

$$\left[\frac{1}{(x_1-x_3)^2}\right]^{(1/2)(l_{A1}+l_{A3}-l_{A2})}\left[\frac{1}{(x_2-x_3)^2}\right]^{(1/2)(l_{A2}+l_{A3}-l_{A1})}$$

(38)

*This holds only for $n \leqslant 6$. For $n \geqslant 6$ the number of independent variables is obviously $4n - 15$.

One similarly has

$$\langle 0|J_\mu(x)A(y)B(0)|0\rangle = c_{JAB}\left[\frac{1}{(x-y)^2}\right]^{(1/2)(l_J+l_A-l_B+1)}$$

$$\cdot\left(\frac{1}{x^2}\right)^{(1/2)(l_J+l_B-l_A+1)}\left(\frac{1}{y^2}\right)^{(1/2)(l_A+l_B-l_J+1)}\left[x^2(x-y)_\mu - (x-y)^2 x_\mu\right]$$

$$\tag{39}$$

$$\langle 0|\theta_{\mu\nu}(x)A(y)B(0)|0\rangle = c_{\theta AB}\left[\frac{1}{(x-y)^2}\right]^{(1/2)(l_\theta+l_A-l_B+2)}$$

$$\cdot\left(\frac{1}{x^2}\right)^{(1/2)(l_\theta+l_B-l_A+2)}\left(\frac{1}{y^2}\right)^{(1/2)(l_A+l_B-l_\theta+2)}$$

$$\cdot\left\{x^4(x-y)_\mu(x-y)_\nu + (x-y)^4 x_\mu x_\nu\right.$$

$$\left. - x^2(x-y)^2[(x-y)_\mu x_\nu + x_\mu(x-y)_\nu] - \tfrac{1}{4}x^2 y^2(x-y)^2 g_{\mu\nu}\right\}$$

$$\tag{40}$$

The Ward identities associated with vertices 39 and 40 give the following selection rule:

$$\langle 0|J_\mu(x)A(y)B(0)|0\rangle = 0 = \langle 0|\theta_{\mu\nu}(x)A(y)B(0)|0\rangle \tag{41}$$

unless $l_A = l_B$.

Equation 41 is a particular case of the general selection rule valid for conserved irreducible four-tensors, $O_{\alpha_1\cdots\alpha_n}(x)$ (and then $l_n = 2+n$):

$$\langle 0|O_{\alpha_1\cdots\alpha_n}(x)A(y)B(0)|0\rangle = 0 \quad \text{unless} \quad l_A = l_B \tag{42}$$

Conformal covariant VEV's were discussed in various cases by Polyakov,[8] Migdal,[9] Schreier,[10] and Ferrara, Gatto, and Grillo.[11] The treatment reported here follows that of Ferrara et al.

In the study of VEV's and operator product expansions in a conformal covariant theory it is useful to make use of the following (vertex graph) identity[12] for time-ordered three-point functions (scalar field for simplicity):

$$\langle 0|T(A(x)B(y)C(z))|0\rangle = \int d^4t \langle 0|T(A(x)B(y)C^*(t))|0\rangle$$

$$\times \langle 0|T(C(t)C(z))|0\rangle \qquad (43)$$

where $C^*(t)$ is a conventional operator of dimensions $l_c^* = 4 - l_c$. The operators A, B, C satisfy $[A(0), D] = il_A A(0)$, and so on, and $[A(0), K_\lambda] = 0$, and so on. They transform according to irreducible representations labeled by the Casimir operator:

$$C_1 = M_{\mu\nu}M^{\mu\nu} + 2PK - 2D^2 + 8iD = 2l(l-4) \qquad (44)$$

(the other Casimir operators vanish). Note that C_1 is invariant under $l \leftrightarrow 4 - l$. In this sense l_c^* is conjugate to l_c. Equation 43 is the basic ingredient for the *shadow-operator formalism*,[13] which allows for the derivation of simple conformal covariant parametrizations of the n-point functions. Equation 43 is nothing but the application of the following representation to the three-point function (Eq. 38):

$$\left[\frac{1}{(x-y)^2}\right]^{(1/2)(l_A + l_B - l_C)} \left[\frac{1}{(y-z)^2}\right]^{(1/2)(l_C + l_B - l_A)} \left[\frac{1}{(x-z)^2}\right]^{(1/2)(l_C + l_A - l_B)}$$

$$= (\text{const.}) \left[\frac{1}{(x-y)^2}\right]^{(1/2)(l_A + l_B - l_C^*)} \int d^4t \left[\frac{1}{(t-x)^2}\right]^{(1/2)(l_C^* + l_A - l_B)}$$

$$\left[\frac{1}{(t-y)^2}\right]^{(1/2)(l_C^* + l_B - l_A)} \left[\frac{1}{(t-z)^2}\right]^{l_C}$$

$$(45)$$

Equation 46 is graphically represented as follows (integration over internal points is understood):

$$(46)$$

Note also the obvious identities:

$$(47)$$

The general form of the vertex identity for tensors is

$$\langle 0|T\left(O_{\alpha_1\cdots\alpha_n}(x_1)P_{\beta_1\cdots\beta_m}(x_2)Q_{\gamma_1\cdots\gamma_j}(x_3)\right)|0\rangle$$

$$= \int d^4\xi \langle 0|T\left(O_{\alpha_1\cdots\alpha_n}(x_1)P_{\beta_1\cdots\beta_m}(x_2)Q^{*\bar{\gamma}_1\cdots\bar{\gamma}_j}(x_3)\right)|0\rangle$$

$$\cdot \langle 0|T\left(Q_{\bar{\gamma}_1\cdots\bar{\gamma}_s}(\xi)Q_{\gamma_1\cdots\gamma_j}(x_3)\right)|0\rangle$$

$$(48)$$

The conformal covariance of Eq. 48 can easily be checked using the coordinate inversion R and the transformation property of any conformal tensor ($[O_{\alpha_1\cdots\alpha_n}(0), K_\lambda] = 0$) under R.

Apart from a sign one can define R as

$$Rx_\mu = \frac{x_\mu}{x^2} \equiv \left(\frac{1}{x}\right)_\mu, \qquad R^2 = I \tag{49}$$

Then it is easy to show that

$$RM_{\mu\nu}R = M_{\mu\nu}, \qquad RDR = -D \tag{50}$$

$$RP_\mu R = K_\mu \tag{51}$$

where K_μ generate the four-parameter Abelian subalgebra of the special conformal transformations.

From Eqs. 49, 50, and 51 it follows that covariance (invariance) under the conformal algebra is equivalent to covariance (invariance) under the Poincaré algebra + dilatation and R. On space-time it is easier to impose covariance under the operator R than under the complicated action of special conformal transformations; therefore it is natural to investigate the action of this operation on conformal irreducible tensors. To this purpose we note that

$$\frac{\partial}{\partial x_\mu} = \frac{1}{x^2} M_{\mu\nu}(x) \frac{\partial}{\partial(Rx_\nu)} \tag{52}$$

where

$$M_{\mu\nu}(x) = g_{\mu\nu} - 2\frac{x_\mu x_\nu}{x^2} \tag{53}$$

For arbitrary conformal tensor fields we have

$$RO_{\alpha_1\cdots\alpha_n}(x) = \left(\frac{1}{x^2}\right)^{l_n} M_{\alpha_1}{}^{\beta_1}(x)\cdots M_{\alpha_n}{}^{\beta_n}(x) O_{\beta_1\cdots\beta_n}\left(\frac{1}{x}\right) \tag{54}$$

We write some remarkable properties of the "metric" matrix[14] $M_{\mu\nu}(x)$:

$$M_{\mu\nu}(x) = M_{\mu\nu}\left(\frac{1}{x}\right) \tag{55}$$

$$M_{\mu\sigma}(x)M_\nu{}^\sigma(x) = g_{\mu\nu} \tag{56}$$

$$M_{\mu\nu}(x)x^\nu = -x_\mu \tag{57}$$

$$M_{\mu\nu}(x-y) = M_\mu{}^\rho(x)M_\nu{}^\sigma(y)M_{\rho\sigma}\left(\frac{1}{y}-\frac{1}{x}\right) \tag{58}$$

Using coordinate-inversion symmetry, one can easily verify the following general conformal covariant ansatz:[13]

$$\langle 0|O_{\alpha_1\cdots\alpha_n}(x)O_{\beta_1\cdots\beta_n}(0)|0\rangle = C_n\left(\frac{1}{x^2}\right)^{l_n} M_{\alpha_1\beta_1}(x)\cdots M_{\alpha_n\beta_n}(x) - \text{traces} \tag{59}$$

$$\langle 0|O_{\alpha_1\cdots\alpha_n}(x)B(y)G(z)|0\rangle = C\left[\frac{1}{(y-z)^2}\right]^{(1/2)(l_B+l_C-\tau_n)}$$

$$\times \left[\frac{1}{(x-y)^2}\right]^{(1/2)(\tau_n+l_B-l_C)}\left[\frac{1}{(x-z)^2}\right]^{(1/2)(\tau_n+l_C-l_B)}$$

$$\left[\left(\frac{1}{z-x}\right)_{\alpha_1}+\left(\frac{1}{x-y}\right)_{\alpha_1}\right]\cdots\left[\left(\frac{1}{z-x}\right)_{\alpha_n}+\left(\frac{1}{x-y}\right)_{\alpha_n}\right] - \text{traces}$$

$$\tag{60}$$

b.   Conformal Covariant Operator Product Expansion

We limit ourselves for simplicity to the expansion of a product $A(x)B(x')$, where $A(x), B(x)$ are two Lorentz scalars with $K_\lambda = 0$, that is, satisfying $[A(0), K_\lambda] = 0$, and the same for $B(0)$ (conformal scalars). In the covariant six-dimensional formalism with coordinates η_A $(A = 0, 1, 2, 3, 5, 6)$ the general form of the expansion is

$$A(\eta)B(\eta') = \sum_{n=0}^{\infty} E_n(\eta \cdot \eta') D^{(n)A_1 \cdots A_n}(\eta, \eta') \psi_{A_1 \cdots A_n}(\eta') \qquad (61)$$

where $D^{(n)A_1 \cdots A_n}(\eta, \eta')$ is an "orbital" tensor operator defined over $\eta^2 = 0 = \eta'^2$ and regular at $\eta \cdot \eta' = 0$, $E_n(\eta \cdot \eta')$ is a c-number of the form

$$E_n(\eta \cdot \eta') = \gamma_n(\eta \cdot \eta')^{(1/2)(\lambda_A + \lambda_B - \lambda_n - n)}$$

and $\psi_{A_1 \cdots A_n}(\eta)$ are irreducible tensor representations of SU(2,2) (the spinor group associated with $O_{4,2}$), homogeneous of degree $\lambda_n = -l_n$, containing Lorentz tensors of maximum order n, and satisfying supplementary conditions $\eta^{A_1} \psi_{A_1 \cdots A_n}(\eta) = 0$ and $\partial^{A_1} \psi_{A_1 \cdots A_n}(\eta) = 0$.

We observe that we have taken, for simplicity, each irreducible representation $\psi_{A_1 \cdots A_n}(\eta)$ without multiplicity. Obviously, in general, a sum over the same tensor representation (with possible different degrees of homogeneity) is understood.

The expansion in Eq. 61 is manifestly conformal covariant on the hypercones $\eta^2 = 0$ and $\eta'^2 = 0$. The most general form of the operator $D^{(n)A_1 \cdots A_n}(\eta \cdot \eta')$ can be shown to be

$$D^{(n)A_1 \cdots A_n}(\eta \cdot \eta') = \sum_{m=0}^{n} \eta^{A_1} \cdots \eta^{A_{n-m}} \eta'^{A_{n-m+1}} \cdots \eta'^{A_n} \overset{(n,m)}{D}(\eta, \eta') c_{nm} \qquad (62)$$

where c_{nm} are constants and $D^{(n,m)}(\eta, \eta')$ is a differential operator defined on $\eta^2 = 0 = \eta'^2$ and homogeneous of degree $h = \frac{1}{2}(\lambda_A - \lambda_B + \lambda_n - n) + m$ in k/k' ($\lambda_A, \lambda_B, \lambda_n$ are the degrees of homogeneity of A, B and $\psi_{A_1 \cdots A_n}$, and we recall that $x_\mu = k^{-1}\eta_\mu, k = \eta_5 + \eta_6$). The operator $D^{(n,m)}$ is uniquely given as formal power

$$D^{(n,m)}(\eta, \eta') = D^h(\eta, \eta') \qquad (63)$$

where

$$D(\eta, \eta') = \eta \cdot \eta' \Box_6' - 2\eta \cdot \eta'(1 + \eta' \cdot \partial') \qquad (64)$$

Indeed, $D(\eta,\eta')$ is the only operator defined on the hypercones and homogeneous of degree 1 in k/k'. We note that the two terms in $D(\eta,\eta')$, Eq. 64, both contain a term proportional to $\partial/\partial\eta'^2$, and their sum is indeed the only combination which remains well defined on $\eta'^2=0$. It can be rewritten as

$$D(\eta,\eta') = (\eta\cdot\eta')^{-1}\eta^A\eta^C g^{BD}L'_{AB}L'_{CD} \tag{65}$$

where $L'_{AB}=i(\eta'_A\partial'_B-\eta'_B\partial'_A)$ are the orbital generators of $O_{4,2}$. For $D^h(\eta,\eta')$ one can prove the representation[15]

$$D^h(\eta,\eta') = \left(\frac{k}{k'}\right)^h(-2)^h\frac{\Gamma(l_n-l+h)}{\Gamma(-h)\Gamma(l_n-1)}$$

$$\int_0^1 du\, u^{-h-1}(1-u)^{l_n+h-1}\exp\left[u(x-x')\partial'\right]_0$$

$$\times F_1\left[l_n-1;-\left(\frac{x-x'}{2}\right)^2\Box'u(1-u)\right] \tag{66}$$

Equation 66 is meant as a formal operator expression with all derivatives located at the right and acting to the right. Using Eq. 66, one has for the expansion in Eq. 61

$$A(x)B(x') = \sum_{n=0}^{\infty}\left[\frac{1}{(x-x')^2}\right]^{(1/2)(l_A+l_B+n-l_n)}c_n^{AB}$$

$$\times\int_0^1 du\, u^{(1/2)(l_A-l_B+l_n+n)-1}\cdot(1-u)^{(1/2)(l_B-l_A+l_n-n)-1}$$

$$\times\exp\left[u(x-x')\partial'\right]_0 F_1\left[l_n-1;\left(\frac{x-x'}{2}\right)^2\Box'u(1-u)\right]$$

$$\cdot x^{A_1}\cdots x^{A_n}\psi dA_1\cdots A_n(x') \tag{67}$$

where $\eta^A=kx^A$ and $\psi_{A_1\cdots A_n}(x)=k^{l_n}\psi_{A_1\cdots A_n}(\eta)$.

The tensors $O_{A_1\cdots A_n}(x)$, which transform according to the conformal algebra in space-time, are given (see Appendix) by

$$O_{A_1\cdots A_n}(x) = [\exp(-ix\cdot\pi)\psi]_{A_1\cdots A_n}(x) \tag{68}$$

where the "internal generator" $\pi_\mu = S_{6\mu} + S_{5\mu}$ acts as

$$(\pi_\mu O)_{A_1 \cdots A_n}(0) = i \sum_{i=1}^{n} \{ (g_{6A_i} + g_{5A_i}) O_{A_1 \cdots A_i \cdots A_n \mu}(0)$$

$$- g_{\mu A_i} [O_{A_1 \cdots \hat{A_i} \cdots A_n 6}(0) + O_{A_1 \cdots A_i \cdots A_n 5}(0)] \} \quad (69)$$

(the notation $O_{A_1 \cdots \hat{A_i} \cdots A_n}$ means that A_i is omitted), and the components $O_{\alpha_1 \cdots \alpha_j xx \cdots}$ (where x is 5 or 6) can be obtained through the supplementary conditions (Eq. A41)

$$O_{\alpha_1 \cdots \alpha_{n-k} 66 \cdots}(x) = 2^{-k} \frac{\Gamma(l_n - 2 - n)}{\Gamma(l_n - 2 - n + k)} \partial_{\mu_1} \cdots \partial_{\mu_k} O^{\mu_1 \cdots \mu_k}_{\alpha_1 \cdots \alpha_{n-k}}(x) \quad (70)$$

(the substitution 5↔6 does not change the value on account of the first supplementary condition). The covariant product in Eq. 67 can be written as

$$x^{A_1} \cdots x^{A_n} \psi_{A_1 \cdots A_n}(x') = \sum_{J=0}^{n} \binom{n}{J} \frac{\Gamma(l_n - 2 - n)}{\Gamma(l_n - 2 - n + J)} [-\tfrac{1}{2}(x - x')^2]^J$$

$$\cdot (x - x')^{\alpha_1} \cdots (x - x')^{\alpha_J} \partial'_{\mu_1} \cdots \partial'_{\mu_J} O^{\mu_1 \cdots \mu_J}_{\alpha_1 \cdots \alpha_{n-J}}(x')$$

$$(71)$$

One obtains $[x_u^A = (1 - u)x_\mu \tfrac{1}{2}[1 + (1 - u)^2 x^2], \tfrac{1}{2}[1 - (1 - u)^2 x^2]$

$$A(x)B(0) = \sum_{n=0}^{\infty} \left(\frac{1}{x^2} \right)^{(1/2)(l_A + l_B + n - l_n)} c_n^{AB}$$

$$\times \int_0^1 du\, u^{(1/2)(l_A - l_B + l_n + n) - 1} \cdot (1 - u)^{(1/2)(l_B - l_A + l_n - n) - 1} x_u^{A_1} \cdots x_u^{A_n}$$

$$\cdot \times \left\{ {}_0F_1 \left[l_n - 1; \frac{-x^2}{4} u(1 - u) \cdot (u^{-2}\Box + 2iu^{-1}\pi \cdot \partial - \pi^2) \right] O \right\}_{A_1 \cdots A_n} (ux)$$

$$(72)$$

The expansion obtained, Eqs. 67 and 72, is conformally covariant, as it is evident from its derivation from the form in Eq. 61. The form obtained here is particularly interesting since it reduces directly to the light-cone expansion, Eq. 7. At $x^2 = 0$ the $_0F_1$ function becomes $_0F_1(l_n - 1; 0) = 1$, and one can write

$$x^{A_1} \cdots x^{A_n} \psi_{A_1 \cdots A_n}(x') = (x - x')^{\alpha_1} \cdots (x - x')^{\alpha_n} O_{\alpha_1 \cdots \alpha_n}(x')$$

Nonleading terms in x^2 can be obtained simply by expanding $_0F_1$ in power series in x^2.

Finally we show how the covariant expansion can be derived from the three-point function. We limit ourselves to the scalar contribution to the expansion (for simplicity), and write

$$A(x)B(0) = \left(\frac{1}{x^2}\right)^{(1/2)(l_A + l_B - 1)} C_{ABO} \int_0^1 du \, u^{(1/2)(l_A - l_B + 1) - 1} (1 - u)^{(1/2)(l_B - l_A + 1) - 1}$$

$$\times \cdot \exp(ux \cdot \partial) \, _0F_1\left[l_n - 1; \frac{-x^2}{4} \square u(1 - u)\right] O(0)$$

$$(73)$$

On the other hand we know that (Eq. 38),

$$\langle 0|C(y)A(x)B(0)|0\rangle = C_{ABC}\left[\frac{1}{(y - x)^2}\right]^{(1/2)(l_C + l_A - l_B)}$$

$$\times \left(\frac{1}{x^2}\right)^{(1/2)(l_A + l_B - l_C)} \left(\frac{1}{y^2}\right)^{(1/2)(l_C + l_B - l_A)} \quad (74)$$

We use the identity[6]

$$\left(\frac{1}{y^2}\right)^{(1/2)(l_C + l_B - l_A)} \left[\frac{1}{(y - x)^2}\right]^{(1/2)(l_C + l_A - l_B)} \propto \int_0^1 du \, u^{(1/2)(l_C + l_A - l_B) - 1}$$

$$\cdot (1 - u)^{(1/2)(l_C + l_B - l_A) - 1} [(y - ux)^2]^{-l_C}\left[1 + x^2 \frac{u(1 - u)}{(y - ux)^2}\right]^{-l_C}$$

$$= \int_0^1 du \, u^{(1/2)(l_C + l_A - l_B) - 1} (1 - u)^{(1/2)(l_C + l_B - l_A) - 1}$$

$$\sum_{h=0}^{\infty} \frac{1}{h!} \frac{\Gamma(l_C + h)}{\Gamma(l_C)} (-x^2)^h [u(1 - u)]^h \left[\frac{1}{(y - ux)^2}\right]^{l_C + h} \quad (75)$$

We next note that

$$\langle 0|\Box^h C(x)C(y)|0\rangle \propto \Box^h\left[\frac{1}{(x-y)^2}\right]^{l_C} C_{CC}$$

$$= 4^h \frac{\Gamma(l_C+h)\Gamma(l_C-1+h)}{\Gamma(l_C)\Gamma(l_C-1)}\left[\frac{1}{(y-x)^2}\right]^{l_C+h}\cdot C_{CC} \tag{76}$$

$$C_{CC}\left[\frac{1}{(y-ux)^2}\right]^{l_C+h} = \exp[ux\cdot\partial](\tfrac{1}{4})^h\frac{\Gamma(l_C)\Gamma(l_C-1)}{\Gamma(l_C+h)\Gamma(l_C-1+h)}$$

$$\times \langle 0|C(y)\Box^h O(0)|0\rangle \tag{77}$$

One has $l = l_C$ from the selection rule of the conformal algebra on two-point function.

The contribution in Eq. 74 thus comes from the expansion

$$C_{AB}{}^C\int_0^1 du\, u^{(1/2)(l_C+l_A-l_B)-1}(1-u)^{(1/2)(l_C+l_B-l_A)-1}\exp(ux\cdot\partial)$$

$$\sum_{h=0}^\infty \frac{1}{h!}\frac{\Gamma(l_C-1)}{\Gamma(l_C-1+h)}\left(\frac{-x^2}{4}\right)^h[u(1-u)\Box^h C(0)]$$

$$= C_{AB}{}^C\int_0^1 du\, u^{(1/2)(l_C+l_A-l_B)-1}(1-u)^{(1/2)(l_C+l_B-l_A)-1}$$

$$\cdot\exp(ux\cdot\partial)\,_0F_1\left[l_C-1;\frac{-x^2}{4}u(1-u)\Box\right]C(0)$$

which coincides with that in Eq. 73, provided $C_{ABC} = C_{AB}{}^C C_{CC}$. For A and B electromagnetic currents and C axial current one obtains Adler's anomaly in terms of electroproduction and annihilation parameters as recently shown by Crewther.[34]

c.   The Four-Point Function

The study of the conformal covariant four-point function is strictly related to the problem of the conformal covariant Wilson expansion of three local operators, say $A(x), B(y), C(z)$. In fact, consider the product $A(x)B(y)C(z)$ and the expansion

$$A(x)B(y) = \sum_n f_n^{AB}(x,y,\partial_y) O_n(y) \tag{78}$$

We have

$$A(x)B(y)C(z) = \sum_n f_n^{AB}(x,y,\partial_y) O_n(y)C(z) \tag{79}$$

and, expanding again, we obtain

$$A(x)B(y)C(z) = \sum_{nm} f_n^{AB}(x,y,\partial_y) f_m^{O_nC}(y,z,\partial_z) D_n(z) \tag{80}$$

Using the selection rule (see Eq. 29) on the conformal covariant two-point function, we see that Eq. 80 is entirely equivalent to the conformal covariant expansion of the four-point function; in fact, multiplying both sides of Eq. 80 by $D(t)$ and taking the vacuum expectation value, we obtain

$$\langle 0|A(x)B(y)C(z)D(t)|0\rangle = \sum_n f_n^{AB}(x,y,\partial_y) f_0^{OC}(y,z,\partial_z) W(z-t)$$

$$\tag{81}$$

or

$$\langle 0|A(x)B(y)C(z)D(t)|0\rangle = \sum_n W_n(x,y,z,t) \tag{82}$$

The study of Eq. 82 will be the object of investigation in the present section. For what concerns the constraints that conformal covariance puts on the n-point correlation function, we recall that there are $N = n(n-3)/2$ independent harmonic ratios:

$$x_{ijhk} = \frac{(x_i - x_h)^2 (x_j - x_k)^2}{(x_i - x_k)^2 (x_j - x_h)^2} \tag{83}$$

For $n=4$ we have $N=2$, and we can always write the four-point function of four conformal scalars as

$$W_0(xyzt) = \langle 0 | A(x) B(y) C(z) D(t) | 0 \rangle$$

$$= \left[\frac{1}{(x-y)^2} \right]^{l_B} \left[\frac{1}{(x-z)^2} \right]^{(1/2)(l_A - l_B + l_C - l_D)}$$

$$\left[\frac{1}{(x-t)^2} \right]^{(1/2)(l_A - l_B + l_D - l_C)} \left[\frac{1}{(z-t)^2} \right]^{(1/2)(l_D + l_C + l_B - l_A)} f(\rho, \eta)$$

$$(84)$$

where

$$\rho = \frac{(x-t)^2 (y-z)^2}{(x-y)^2 (z-t)^2}, \qquad \eta = \frac{(x-z)^2 (y-t)^2}{(x-y)^2 (z-t)^2} \tag{85}$$

In Eq. 84, l_A, l_B, l_C, l_D are the scale dimensions of the local operators A, B, C, D, respectively, and we have assumed $[A(0), K_\lambda] = 0$ and analogous formulas for B, C, D.

We can now insert a Wilson expansion for $A(x) B(y)$. Note that, because of the selection rules of conformal algebra, only those operators survive which appear both in the expansion of $A(x) B(y)$ and in that of $C(z) D(t)$.

As a consequence the contribution of a local conformal irreducible tensor operator $O_{\alpha_1 \cdots \alpha_n}(x)$ to the four-point function can be evaluated explicitly. For example, consider a local scalar operator $O(x)$; then the conformal operator expansion is

$$A(x) B(0) = \left(\frac{1}{x^2} \right)^{(1/2)(l_A + l_B - 1)}$$

$$\times \int_0^1 du \, f_{ABO}{}^{(u)} \, {}_0F_1 \left[l - 1; \frac{-x^2}{4} u(1-u) \Box \right] O(ux)$$

$$(86)$$

where

$$f_{ABO}(u) = u^{(1/2)(l_A - l_B + 1) - 1} (1 - u)^{(1/2)(l_B - l_A + 1) - 1} \tag{87}$$

Inserting into Eq. 84, we obtain

$$W_0(x,y,z,t) = \left[\frac{1}{(x-y)^2}\right]^{(1/2)(l_A+l_B-1)}\left[\frac{1}{(z-t)^2}\right]^{(1/2)(l_C+l_D-1)}$$

$$\cdot \int d^4p\,\theta(p^2)\theta(p_0)\int_0^1\int_0^1 du\,dv\,\exp\{ip[ux+(1-u)y-vz-(1-v)t]\}$$

$$\cdot[uv(1-u)(1-v)(x-y)^2(z-t)^2]^{1-(1/2)l}J_{l-2}[(-p^2u(1-u)(x-y)^2)^{1/2}]$$

$$\cdot J_{l-2}[(-p^2v(1-v)(z-t)^2)^{1/2}] \tag{88}$$

for x,y,z,t all spacelike to each other. Carrying out five of the six integrations, we arrive at the manifestly conformal covariant expression:[17]

$$W_0(x,y,z,t) = \left[\frac{1}{(x-y)^2}\right]^{(1/2)(l_A+l_B-1)}\left[\frac{1}{(z-t)^2}\right]^{(1/2)(l_C+l_D-1)}$$

$$\left[\frac{1}{(x-t)^2}\right]^{(1/2)(l_A-l_B+1)}\left[\frac{1}{(y-z)^2}\right]^{(1/2)(l_C-l_D+1)}$$

$$\times\left[\frac{1}{(y-t)^2}\right]^{(1/2)(l_B-l_A-l_C+l_D)}\cdot\rho^{(1/2)(l_A-l_B+1)}$$

$$\times\int_0^1 d\sigma\,\sigma^{(1/2)(l_A-l_B-l_C+l_D)-1}(1-\sigma)^{(1/2)(l_B-l_A-l_C+l_D)-1}\cdot\left(\frac{\rho}{\sigma}+\frac{\eta}{1-\sigma}\right)^{(1/2)(l_D-l_C-1)}$$

$$\times {}_2F_1\left[\tfrac{1}{2}(1+l_D-l_C),\tfrac{1}{2}(1+l_C-l_D);l-1;\left(\frac{\rho}{\sigma}+\frac{\eta}{1-\sigma}\right)^{-1}\right] \tag{89}$$

It can be shown that another suitable form in which to write Eqs. 88 and 89 is the following:

$$W_0(x,y,z,t) = \left[\frac{1}{(x-y)^2}\right]^{(1/2)(l_A+l_B)} \left[\frac{1}{(z-t)^2}\right]^{(1/2)(l_C+l_D)}$$

$$\cdot \int_0^1 \int_0^1 du\,dv\, f_{AB}(u) f_{CD}(v) \lambda_t^{-1} {}_2F_1\left[\tfrac{1}{2}(l+1), \tfrac{1}{2}; l-1; \lambda_t^{-2}\right]$$

$$(90)$$

where

$$f_{AB}(u) = u^{(1/2)(l_A-l_B)-1}(1-u)^{(1/2)(l_B-l_A)-1}$$

$$(91)$$

and analogously for $f_{CD}(v)$. Here

$$\lambda_+ = -\tfrac{1}{2}\left[uv(1-u)(1-v)(x-y)^2(z-t)^2\right]^{-1/2}$$

$$\cdot\left[(y-t)^2(1-u)(1-v)\pm u(1-v)(x-t)^2 + v(1-u)(z-y)^2 \pm uv(x-z)^2\right]$$

$$(92)$$

In order to obtain the contribution of an exchanged operator of spin n [traceless $(n/2, n/2)$ symmetric tensor] it is more useful to start with the vertex graph identity, Eq. 48, which gives

$$W_{n,l_n}(x,y,z,t) = \int d^4\xi \langle 0|A(x)B(y)O_{\alpha_1\cdots\alpha_n}(\xi)|0\rangle$$

$$\times \langle 0|O^{*\alpha_1\cdots\alpha_n}(\xi)C(z)D(t)|0\rangle$$

$$= \left[\frac{1}{(x-y)^2}\right]^{(l_A+l_B-\tau_n)/2} \left[\frac{1}{(z-t)^2}\right]^{(l_C+l_D-\tau_n^*)/2}$$

$$\times \int d^4\xi \left[\left(\frac{1}{x-\xi}\right)_{\alpha_1} + \left(\frac{1}{\xi-y}\right)_{\alpha_1}\right] \cdots \left[\left(\frac{1}{x-\xi}\right)_{\alpha_n} + \left(\frac{1}{\xi-y}\right)_{\alpha_n}\right]$$

$$\times \left[\left(\frac{1}{\xi-z}\right)^{\alpha_1} + \left(\frac{1}{t-\xi}\right)^{\alpha_1}\right] \cdots \left[\left(\frac{1}{\xi-z}\right)^{\alpha_n} + \left(\frac{1}{t-\xi}\right)^{\alpha_n}\right] - \text{traces}$$

$$(93)$$

where we have used the conformal covariant prescription for the vertex $\langle 0|A(x)B(y)O_{\alpha_1 \cdots \alpha_n}(\xi)|0\rangle$.[13]

Equation 93 can be rewritten as

$$W_{n,l_n}(x,y,z,t) = \left[\frac{1}{(x-y)^2} \right]^{(l_A+l_B)/2} \left[\frac{1}{(z-t)^2} \right]^{(l_C+l_D)/2}$$

$$\times \int d^4\mu(\xi z t) \left[\frac{(\xi-y)^2}{(\xi-x)^2} \right]^{(l_A-l_B)/2} \left[\frac{(\xi-t)^2}{(\xi-z)^2} \right]^{(l_C-l_D)/2}$$

$$\times \Lambda^{l_n}(xy,zt) C_n^1 \left[-\Omega_\xi(xy,zt) \right] \tag{94}$$

where we have defined

$$-\Omega_\xi(xy,zt) = \cos\widehat{xy} = \frac{1}{2\left[(x-y)^2(z-t)^2 \right]^{1/2}}$$

$$\times \left\{ X^{yt,xz}(x-z)^2 + X^{xz,yt}(y-t)^2 - X^{xy,tz}(y-z)^2 - X^{yz,xt}(x-t)^2 \right\}$$

$$X^{x_1 x_2, x_3 x_4} = \left[\frac{(\xi-x_1)^2(\xi-x_2)^2}{(\xi-x_3)^2(\xi-x_4)^2} \right]^{1/2}$$

$$\Lambda_\xi(xy,zt) = \left[\frac{(\xi-t)^2(\xi-t)^2(x-y)^2}{(\xi-x)^2(\xi-y)^2(z-t)^2} \right]^{1/2}$$

$$d\mu(\xi z t) = \left[\frac{(z-t)^2}{(\xi-z)^2(\xi-t)^2} \right]^2 d^4\xi$$

and C_n' is a Gegenbauer polynomial.

We observe that Eq. 94 is manifestly conformal covariant. In fact it is manifestly inversion invariant as it transforms properly under R

$$Rx_i = \frac{x_i}{x^2}; \quad RA(x_i) = \left(\frac{1}{x_i^2} \right)^{l_i} A_i(Rx_i)$$

Moreover using the property $C_n^i(x) = (-1)^n C_n^i(-x)$, one obtains the reflection properties

$$W_{n,l_n}(xyzt, \Delta_{AB}, \Delta_{CD}) = (-1)^n W_n(yxzt, -\Delta_{AB}, \Delta_{CD})$$

$$= (-1)^n W_n(xytz, \Delta_{AB}, -\Delta_{CD})$$

$$= W_n(yxtz, -\Delta_{AB}, -\Delta_{CD}) \qquad (95)$$

The general four-point function for four conformal scalar operators can now be expanded in terms of generalized partial waves, where each partial wave amplitude corresponds to a term as in Eq. 94. One obtains

$$\langle 0|A(x)B(y)C(t)D(t)|0\rangle = \left[\frac{1}{(x-y)^2}\right]^{(l_A+l_B)/2}\left[\frac{1}{(z-t)^2}\right]^{(l_C+l_D)/2}$$

$$\sum_{n,l_n}\int d^4\mu(\xi zt)\left[\frac{(\xi-y)^2}{(\xi-x)^2}\right]^{\Delta_{AB}/2}\left[\frac{(\xi-t)^2}{(\xi-z)^2}\right]^{\Delta_{CD}/2}$$

$$\times \Lambda_\xi^{l_n}(xy,zt)C_n^1(-\Omega_\xi(xy,zt)) \qquad (96)$$

Summation over n, l_n (to be supposed as a complete set of conformal quantum numbers) suggests a manifestly conformal covariant representation for the scattering amplitude

$$\langle 0|A(x)B(y)C(z)D(t)|0\rangle = \left[\frac{1}{(x-y)^2}\right]^{(l_A+l_B)/2}\left[\frac{1}{(z-t)^2}\right]^{(l_C+l_D)/2}$$

$$\int d^4\mu(\xi zt)\left[\frac{(\xi-y)^2}{(\xi-x)^2}\right]^{(l_A-l_B)/2}\left[\frac{(\xi-t)^2}{(\xi-z)^2}\right]^{(l_C-l_D)/2}$$

$$\times g(\Lambda_\xi(xy,zt),\Omega_\xi(xy,zt)) \qquad (97)$$

where g is arbitrary function of the two-variables Λ_ξ, Ω_ξ. Manifest invariance follows from the fact that

$$Rg = g \tag{98}$$

and that the other factors of the right-hand side of Eq. 97 just reproduce the transformation properties of the left-hand side.

As a final step let us consider a particular example in which $W_0(x,y,z,t)$ can be explicitly evaluated. Consider the case $l_A = l_B$, $l_C = l_D$ (but $l_A \neq l_C$) and the contribution of a conformal operator with $l = 2$ (scalar current). In this case the integral in Eq. 89 can easily be evaluated, and we get

$$W_0(x,y,z,t) = \left[\frac{1}{(x-y)^2} \right]^{l_A - 1} \left[\frac{1}{(z-t)^2} \right]^{l_c - 1} \frac{1}{(x-t)^2} \frac{1}{(y-z)^2}$$

$$\times \rho \frac{1}{[\eta^2 + \rho^2 + 1 - 2(\rho + \eta + \eta\rho)]^{1/2}}$$

$$\times \left[\log \frac{\eta - \rho + 1 - i\sqrt{\eta^2 + \rho^2 + 1 - 2(\rho + \eta + \eta\rho)}}{\eta - \rho + 1 + i\sqrt{\eta^2 + \rho^2 + 1 - 2(\rho + \eta + \eta\rho)}} \right.$$

$$\left. - \log \frac{\eta - \rho - 1 - i\sqrt{\eta^2 + \rho^2 + 1 - 2(\rho + \eta + \eta\rho)}}{\eta - \rho - 1 + i\sqrt{\eta^2 + \rho^2 + 1 - 2(\rho + \eta + \eta\rho)}} \right] \tag{99}$$

In the limit $(x-y)^2 \to 0$ $[(z-t)^2 \to 0]$ we have

$$W_0(x,y,z,t) = \left[\frac{1}{(x-y)^2} \right]^{l_A - 1} \left[\frac{1}{(z-t)^2} \right]^{l_c - 1}$$

$$\times \frac{1}{(x-z)^2(y-t)^2 - (x-t)^2(y-z)^2} \log \frac{(x-t)^2(y-z)^2}{(x-z)^2(y-t)^2} \tag{100}$$

4.   CANONICAL SCALING AND CONFORMAL INVARIANCE

It is well known that exact "scaling" implies that in the light-cone expansion of $j_\mu(x)j_\nu(0)$, where $j_\mu(x)$ is the electromagnetic current, there appears an infinite sequence of local operators $O_{\alpha_1 \cdots \alpha_n}(x)$ which are symmetric and traceless and each of which has scale dimensions $l_n = 2 + n$. Within the currently accepted theoretical frame[1] one is dealing in the scaling limit with a scale-invariant operator scheme, the skeleton theory. Such a scheme may exhibit conformal invariance, beyond scale invariance.[2, 3, 14]

A sequence of general mathematical properties (to be reported below) of an exact (not spontaneously broken) conformal covariant theory then shows that each of the tensors of the above family is divergenceless,[18] that is, the skeleton theory possesses an infinite number of local conservation equations, to which one can think of associating an infinite number of conserved charges. Or, alternatively, strict conformal invariance does not apply to the skeleton theory.

We consider irreducible conformal tensor fields $O_{\alpha_1 \cdots \alpha_n}(x)$, which behave under the stability subalgebra at $x = 0$ as follows:

$$[O_{\{\alpha\}}(0), M_{\mu\nu}] = \Sigma\{{}^{\beta}_{\alpha}\}O_{\{\beta\}}(0),$$

$$[O_{\{\alpha\}}(0), D] = ilO_{\{\alpha\}}(0), \qquad [O_{\{\alpha\}}(0), K_\mu] = 0 \tag{101}$$

where l is the scale dimension and Σ is an irreducible tensor representation for $M_{\mu\nu}$. The irreducible representation to which $O_{\alpha_1 \cdots \alpha_n}$ belongs is thus characterized by n and l. We now state the following theorem:[3]

Degeneracy Theorem.   The divergence, $\partial^{\alpha_1}O_{\alpha_1 \cdots \alpha_n}$, of an irreducible conformal tensor field $O_{\alpha_1 \cdots \alpha_n}$, of order n and scale dimension l_n equal to $2 + n$, is an irreducible conformal tensor field.

Proof. Since $O_{\alpha_1 \cdots \alpha_n}$ is symmetric and traceless, one obtains that $[\partial^{\alpha_1}O_{\alpha_1 \cdots \alpha_n}(0), K_\mu]$ is proportional to $(l_n - 2 - n)O_{\mu\alpha_2 \cdots \alpha_n}(0)$ and thus vanishes for $l_n = 2 + n$. We call this theorem a degeneracy theorem because it originates from the degeneracy, for $l_n = 2 + n$, of the representation of the stability algebra from which the irreducible tensor representation is induced; namely, $O_{\alpha_1 \cdots \alpha_n}$ and $\partial^{\alpha_1}O_{\alpha_1 \cdots \alpha_n}$ behave irreducibly under the stability subalgebra (but not under the full algebra) and are both annihilated by K_λ.

We note the following corollary.

Corollary.   *A conserved irreducible conformal tensor has $l_n = 2 + n$.*

From Section 3a we recall the following result:

Orthogonality Theorem. The vacuum expectation value of the product of two irreducible conformal tensor fields:

$$W_{\alpha_1\cdots\beta_m}(x) = \langle 0|O^{(n)}_{\alpha_1\cdots\alpha_n}(x)O^{(m)}_{\beta_1\cdots\beta_m}(0)|0\rangle \qquad (102)$$

vanishes unless $n = m$ and $l_n = l_m$, in an exactly (not spontaneously) broken) conformal covariant theory.

From the degeneracy theorem and the orthogonality theorem we derive the following corollary:

Corollary. *An irreducible conformal tensor field $O_{\alpha_1\cdots\alpha_n}$ with $l_n = 2 + n$ is necessarily conserved.*

Proof. From the degeneracy theorem $\partial^{\alpha_1}O_{\alpha_1\cdots\alpha_n}$ satisfies

$$[\partial^{\alpha_1}O_{\alpha_1\cdots\alpha_n}(0), K_\lambda] = 0$$

and has dimension $3 + n$. Then, from the orthogonality theorem,

$$\langle 0|\partial^{\alpha_1}O_{\alpha_1\cdots\alpha_n}(x)O_{\beta_1\cdots\beta_n}(y)|0\rangle = 0$$

Therefore

$$\langle 0|\partial^{\alpha_1}O_{\alpha_1\cdots\alpha_n}(x)\partial^{\beta_1}O_{\beta_1\cdots\beta_n}(y)|0\rangle = 0$$

Well-known arguments then imply that $\partial^{\alpha_1}O_{\alpha_1\cdots\alpha_n}(x) = 0$.

It is now straightforward to apply the above results to the physical situation. The set $O_{\alpha_1\cdots\alpha_n}$, of dimensions $l_n = 2 + n$ and $K_\lambda = 0$, is required from the observed scaling,[3] namely, the most singular part of the product $j_\mu(x)j_\nu(0)$ when $x^2 \to 0$ can be expanded in terms of such operators. From the assumption that the skeleton theory is conformal invariant it then follows that $\partial^{\alpha_1}O_{\alpha_1\cdots\alpha_n}(x) = 0$ for each n.

The conclusion of an infinite set of local conservation equations for the skeleton theory may turn out to be physically unacceptable, or in any case too strong a limitation. Among the various alternatives that can be taken in such a case, one which seems to us rather suggestive is a spontaneously broken conformal invariance of the skeleton theory. We have stressed that the failure of the orthogonality theorem in this case invalidates the derivation of the infinite conservation laws. On a still more conjectural ground it may be imagined that $SU(3) \times SU(3)$ remains spontaneously broken in the skeleton limit, implying spontaneous breaking of scale in this limit.

At first sight the existence of an infinite number of conserved quantities seems to be too strong a limitation for an interacting theory. This is not so obvious, however, because the O'Raifertaigh[19] theorem and its generalizations cannot be applied in the absence of a mass gap. Nevertheless it can still be proved that in some cases the existence of this infinite number of conserved quantities implies free-field theory.[20]

We shall restrict ourselves to a $g\varphi^4$ theory. We have

$$[O_{0\mu_2\cdots\mu_N}(x),\varphi(y)]\delta(x_0-y_0) = C_N\delta^4(x-y)[\partial_{\mu_2}\cdots\partial_{\mu_N}\varphi(y) - \text{traces}]$$

$$+ \text{Schwinger terms} \qquad (103)$$

We stress that Eq. 103 may not be valid in a two-dimensional world where twist zero operators are present. For this reason our conclusions will not be valid in the two-dimensional Thirring model.

The constant C_N cannot be zero; otherwise also the three-point function

$$\langle 0|O_{\mu_1\mu_N}(x)\phi^+(y)\phi(z)|0\rangle \qquad (104)$$

vanishes identically as discussed in Section 3b.

Such a possibility must be excluded as it implies the vanishing of $Q_{\mu_1\cdots\mu_N}$. Indeed the Green functions of N fields φ and $O_{\mu_1\cdots\mu_N}$ are proportional[21] to Eq. 104. If Eq. 104 vanishes, they also vanish.

In the absence of spontaneous breaking the charge

$$Q_{\mu_2\cdots\mu_N}(t) = \int d^4x\, \delta(x_0-t) O_{0\mu_2\cdots\mu_N}(x) \qquad (105)$$

is time independent, and it is the generator of an exact symmetry.

Although we are in a zero-mass theory, we are still able to prove that the Goldstone phenomenon cannot occur. We use a generalization of the Goldstone theorem due to Symanzik;[22] he has shown that, if a symmetry is spontaneously broken, the Wightman functions of the generating current satisfy the following cluster property:

$$\lim_{\lambda\to\infty}\lambda^3 \langle 0|O_{\mu_1\cdots\mu_N}(y+\lambda a)\phi(x')\cdots\phi^+(x^k)|0\rangle \neq 0 \qquad (106)$$

where a is a spacelike vector.

This is impossible in a conformal invariant theory. From the general form of the conformal covariant N-point Wightman function (see Section 3a) it follows that for generical points the right-hand side of Eq. 106 is always of order λ^{-2l+3} or less (l is the dimension of the operator $O_{\mu_1\cdots\mu_N}$).

We have thus proved that the operator O_{μ_1, μ_N} generates a "good" symmetry, and therefore the following equation must be valid:

$$0 = \langle 0 | [Q_{\mu_2 \cdots \mu_N}, \phi(x') \cdots \phi^+(x^k)] | 0 \rangle$$

$$= \left[C_N \frac{\partial}{\partial x_{\mu_2}^1} \cdots \frac{\partial}{\partial x_{\mu_N}^1} + \cdots + \frac{\partial}{\partial x_{\mu_2}^k} \cdots \frac{\partial}{\partial x_{\mu_N}^k} - \text{traces} \right]$$

$$\times \langle 0 | \phi(x^1) \cdots \phi^+(x^k) | 0 \rangle \tag{107}$$

All the Wightman functions must satisfy this infinite set of independent differential equations. Writing explicitly all these constraints, we find that the connected part of the four-point Wightman function is zero.

Similar results can be obtained also for the other connected Wightman functions. The theory is therefore free.

It is remarkable that the occurrence of only canonical singularities in the product of two currents on the light cone implies that the skeleton theory is free, and therefore the strength and the operatorial form of the light-cone singularities are the same as in free-field theory.[6] Small renormalization of dimensions, compatible with the experimental limits for scaling, would be a way of avoiding such a conclusion. We also recall that our result has been proved only on the assumption of no spontaneous breaking of conformal symmetry.

5. CONFORMAL ALGEBRA IN TWO SPACE-TIME DIMENSIONS

The interest in the study of conformal algebra in two space-time dimensions comes essentially from two sources: first, from the known availability of soluble models in such a case; second, from a similarity with the algebraic properties of dual models which seems rather suggestive.

It will be useful to introduce conformal transformations in D dimension by direct definition and to study their properties.[14] In a D-dimensional pseudo-Euclidean space-time ($D-1$ space dimensions), conformal transformations are defined as those leaving the flat metric invariant, apart from multiplication by a scalar function of the coordinates:

$$g'_{\mu\nu}(x') = \frac{\partial x^\lambda}{\partial x'^\mu} \frac{\partial x^\rho}{\partial x'^\nu} g_{\lambda\rho} = \Lambda(x) g_{\mu\nu} \tag{108}$$

where the first equality is simply the definition of the transformed metric tensor. Their name is due to the fact that they leave the cosine of infinitesimal angles

$$\cos\phi = \frac{dx^{\mu}\,dy_{\mu}}{(dx^2\,dy^2)^{1/2}}$$

invariant.

Equation 108 gives, for infinitesimal changes

$$x'_{\mu} \cong x_{\mu} + \delta x_{\mu}, \qquad \Lambda(x) \cong 1 - \lambda(x)$$

the differential equation

$$\partial_{\mu}\delta x_{\nu} + \partial_{\nu}\delta x_{\mu} = \lambda(x)g_{\mu\nu} \qquad (109)$$

From a different point of view, it is easy to show that Eq. 109 follows from the requirement of the conservation of the Noether current associated with a transformation

$$\partial^{\mu}(\theta_{\mu\nu}\delta x^{\nu}) = \theta_{\mu\nu}\partial^{\mu}\delta x^{\nu} = 0 \qquad (110)$$

if and only if this current is generated by a symmetric and *traceless* energy-momentum tensor $\theta^{\mu\nu}$.[23] This can be easily seen by decomposing $\partial_{\mu}\delta x_{\nu}$ into irreducible components.

For the generating function $\lambda(x)$ one finds the equation[14]

$$[(D-2)\partial_{\mu}\partial_{\nu} + g_{\mu\nu}\Box]\lambda(x) = 0 \qquad (111)$$

which in turn implies, if $D \neq 2$,

$$\partial_{\mu}\partial_{\nu}\lambda(x) = 0 \qquad (112)$$

This means that $\lambda(x)$ is a linear function of x, so that Eq. 109 implies that δx_{μ} can at most be a quadratic function, giving

$$\delta x_{\mu} = \delta a_{\mu} + \delta\omega_{\mu\nu}x^{\nu} + x_{\mu}\delta\rho + (x^2\delta c_{\mu} - 2x_{\mu}\delta c \cdot x) \qquad (113)$$

Conformal transformations are thus seen to form a group depending on $(D+2)(D+1)/2$ parameters, which contains the Poincaré group as a subgroup (the vector δa_{μ} and the antisymmetric tensor $\delta\omega_{\mu\nu}$), the dilatation subgroup ($\delta\rho$), and the subgroup of special conformal transformations (δc_{μ}).

From Eq. 111 it is evident that the case $D=2$ is a special one, implying only

$$\Box\lambda(x)=0 \tag{114}$$

As a last point, note that in the definition of Eq. 108 is contained also the finite transformation R giving coordinate inversion, already defined in Section 4.

The solution of Eq. 109 for $D=2$ is simply given by

$$\delta x_\mu = m_\mu g(u) + n_\mu h(v) \tag{115}$$

where

$$u = n_\mu x^\mu, \qquad n_\mu = (1,1)$$
$$v = m_\mu x^\mu, \qquad m_\mu = (1,-1) \tag{116}$$

and $h(u)$ and $g(v)$ are arbitrary functions of u and v, respectively; the group of conformal transformations turns out to be infinite dimensional.

It is interesting to note that a general coordinate transformation such that

$$u = x^0 + x^1 \rightarrow f(u) \tag{117}$$

$$v = x^0 - x^1 \rightarrow f(v) \tag{118}$$

is indeed a conformal transformation, when conformal transformations are defined as transformations which take lightlike events, $(x_1 - x_2)^2 = 0$, into lightlike events. In fact, if

$$(u_1 - u_2)(v_1 - v_2) = 0$$

holds, then also

$$[f(u_1) - f(u_2)][g(v_1) - g(v_2)] = 0$$

holds.

To every infinitesimal transformation an infinitesimal generator can be associated:

$$T(\delta x_\nu) = \int d\sigma_\mu \theta^{\mu\nu} \delta x_\nu$$

which can be decomposed into two terms depending only on u and v, respectively.

Let us consider only the u part of the group. In order to study the commutation relations of the generators a model is needed for the commutator of the energy-momentum tensor; this can be taken, for example, from the free Thirring model, as we shall soon see. The relevant result[24] is the following commutator:

$$[T^u(h), T^u(h')] = T^u(h, h') + \Delta(h, h') \tag{119}$$

(and a similar relation for the v part), where we define

$$[h, h'](u) = h(u)\frac{d}{du}h'(u) - \left[\frac{d}{du}h(u)\right]h'(u) \tag{120}$$

and $\Delta(h, h')$ is a c-number functional of h, h'.

It is interesting to note that, by choosing the following basis:

$$h(u) = u^{1-n}, \qquad h'(u) = u^{1-m}$$

$$[T_n, T_m] = (m - n)T_{n+m} + c - \text{number} \tag{121}$$

one obtains an algebra formally identical with the gauge algebra of the dual models.[25]

It should be mentioned that the algebra of Eq. 119 can be obtained also by quantizing a four-dimensional field theory on a lightlike plane.[26]

In the Thirring model[27] we have

$$\partial\psi(x) = g:j(x)\psi(x): \tag{122}$$

and the conserved currents

$$j_\mu(x) = :\psi(x)\gamma_\mu\psi(x): \tag{123}$$

$$j_\mu^5(x) = :\psi(x)\gamma_5\gamma_\mu\psi(x): = \epsilon_\mu^\nu j_\nu(x) \tag{124}$$

The currents satisfy ($\square = 4\partial_\mu\partial_\nu$)

$$\square j_\mu(x) = 0, \qquad \square j_\mu^5(x) = 0 \tag{125}$$

One defines

$$j_+(u) = j_0(x) + j_1(x), \qquad j_-(v) = j_0(x) - j_2(x) \tag{126}$$

with commutation relations

$$[j_+(u), j_+(u')] = ic\delta'(u - u') \tag{127a}$$

$$[j_-(v), j_-(v')] = ic\delta'(v - v') \tag{127b}$$

$$[j_+(u), j_-(v')] = 0 \tag{127c}$$

The stress tensor can be chosen as

$$\theta_{\mu\nu}(x) = :j_\mu(x)j_\nu(x): - \tfrac{1}{2}g_{\mu\nu}:j_\alpha(x)j^\alpha(x): \tag{128}$$

which is conserved, symmetric, and traceless.

In general, for $\theta^{\mu\nu}$ satisfying

$$\partial_\mu\theta^{\mu\nu} = 0, \qquad \theta^{\mu\nu} = \theta^{\nu\mu}, \qquad \theta_\mu{}^\mu = 0$$

one has

$$\theta_{00} + \theta_{01} = \theta^+(u) \tag{129}$$

$$\theta_{00} - \theta_{01} = \theta^-(v) \tag{130}$$

and

$$L(f) = \tfrac{1}{2}\int d^1x[\theta^+(u)f_+(u) + \theta^-(v)f_-(v)] = L^+ + L^- \tag{131}$$

Conditions 129 are fulfilled, since (c depends on the coupling constant)

$$\theta_{00} + \theta_{01} = \frac{1}{2c} :j_+(u)j_+(u): \tag{132}$$

$$\theta_{00} - \theta_{01} = \frac{1}{2c} :j_-(v)j_-(v): \tag{133}$$

The operator $L^\pm(f)$ can be written as

$$L^\pm(f) = \int dx_\pm f_\pm(x_\pm):j_\pm(x_\pm)j_\pm(x_\pm): \tag{134}$$

where $x_+ = u$, $x_- = v$.

From the commutation relations 127 one derives formally

$$[L_n^\pm, L_m^\pm] = (m-n)L_{n+m}^\pm + c(n)\delta_{n,-m} \tag{135a}$$

$$[L_n^+, L_m^-] = 0 \tag{135b}$$

In Eq. 135a $c(n)$ is a c-number depending on n. Furthermore

$$[L_n^\pm, j_+(x)] = \frac{d}{dx_\pm}[x_\pm^{1-n}j_\pm(x_\pm)] \tag{136}$$

expressing the well-known fact that $j_\pm$ have dimensions 1. Equation 136 is to be interpreted in the sense of distributions.

The generators $L_1^\pm, L_0^\pm, L_{-1}^\pm$ satisfy the commutation relation of the algebra

$$O(2,2) \sim O(2,1) \otimes O(2,1) \qquad (137)$$

which is the two-dimensional restriction of the $O(4,2)$ conformal algebra on Minkowski space-time. These generators coincide, of course, with those defined by Dell'Antonio, Frishman, and Zwanziger.[28]

It is interesting to consider the general structure of the $[\theta, \theta]$ commutators in a conformal invariant theory in two dimensions:

$$[\theta^\pm(x_\pm), \theta^\pm(x'_\pm)] = c\delta'''(x_\pm - x'_\pm) + \delta'(x_\pm - x'_\pm)\Theta^\pm(x_\pm, x'_\pm) \qquad (138)$$

and to observe that the homogeneous part of the algebra of Eq. 135 arises from the bilocal operator $\Theta(u, u')$, whereas the c-number part comes from the disconnected c-number Schwinger term in the $[\theta, \theta]$ commutator. Such a c-number term does not contribute to the Poincaré subalgebra. However, the homogeneous part of the algebra is essentially model independent, the only relevant requirement being that the lightlike restriction $\theta(u)$ of the bilocal operator $\Theta(u, u')$ coincide with the stress tensor, as implied by Poincaré invariance. On the other hand, $c(n)$ in Eq. 135a is quite model dependent. In the Thirring model it is given by

$$c(n) = \tfrac{1}{12}n(n^2 - 1) \qquad (139)$$

If we look at the structure of the algebra in Eq. 135, we find that it contains three homogeneous subalgebras:

Subalgebra	Generators
$O(2,2)$	$L_i^\pm$ for $i = 0, \pm 1$
$G^\uparrow$	$L_i^\pm$ for $i = +1, 0, -1, -2, \ldots, -\infty$
$G^\downarrow$	$L_i^\pm$ for $i = -1, 0, +1, +2, \ldots, +\infty$

We have

$$G^\uparrow \cap G^\downarrow = O(2,2) \qquad (140)$$

Recalling our previous discussion, we note that only $G^\uparrow$ is obtained by considering coordinate transformations which can be Taylor expanded at $x_\mu = 0$. Enlargement to G can be obtained provided that under the operation R of coordinate inversion

$$\theta^+(u) \to \frac{1}{|u|^4}\theta^+\left(\frac{1}{u}\right) \qquad (141)$$

as would follow from invariance under R. Then we easily see that

$$RL_n^\pm R^{-1} = L_{-n}^\pm \tag{142}$$

recovering the property

$$RG^\uparrow R^{-1} = G^\downarrow \tag{143}$$

and one obtains the full conformal algebra $G = G^\uparrow \cap G^\downarrow$.

It is interesting to verify the conformal covariance of the operator product expansion in the Thirring model.

The commutation relations of $j_\mu(x)$ with $\psi(x)$ and $\bar\psi(x)$ are

$$[j_+(u), \psi(u', v')] = -(a + \bar a\gamma_5)\psi(u', v')\delta(u' - u) \tag{144a}$$

$$[j_-(u), \psi(u', v')] = -(a - \bar a\gamma_5)\psi(u', v')\delta(v' - v) \tag{144b}$$

where $a, \bar a$ are determined in terms of the coupling constant g from consistency with the equation of motion and from the spinor properties of ψ. From Eqs. 144 and 122 we get

$$[L_n^\pm, \psi(x)] = x_\pm^{1-n}\frac{\partial}{\partial x_\pm}\psi(x) + \frac{\lambda^2}{8\pi c}(1-n)x_\pm^{-n}\psi(x) \tag{145}$$

(in the sense of distributions), where λ depends on a and $\bar a$ (see ref. 28).

We can now discuss the operator product expansion in the Thirring model. Dell'Antonio, Frishman, and Zwanziger have derived[28]

$$\psi_1(u, v)\psi_1^+(u', v') = (u - u_0)^\alpha (v - v_0)^\beta : \exp\left[\gamma\int_u^{u'} j_+(\xi)\,d\xi + \delta\int_v^{v'} j_-(\eta)\,d\eta\right] : \tag{146}$$

with α, β, γ, and δ functions of the coupling constant g. One can check that expansion 146 is covariant under the infinite-dimensional algebra of L_n.

We recall that for a conformal covariant operator product expansion in four-dimensional space-time we obtained (Section 4)

$$A(x)B(0) = \sum_n (x^2)^{(-1/2)(l_A + l_B - l_n + n)} x^{\alpha_1}\cdots x^{\alpha_n}$$

$$\times \int_0^1 du\, f_n(u, x\partial, x^2\Box)O_{\alpha_1\cdots\alpha_n}(ux) \tag{147}$$

where f_n are known transcendental functions, and $O_{\alpha_1 \cdots \alpha_n}(0)$ are taken to belong to representations such that

$$[O_{\alpha_1 \cdots \alpha_n}(0), K_\lambda] = 0 \tag{148}$$

In spite of the occurrence, in a two-dimensional space-time, of the infinite set of operators L_n which can connect different inequivalent representations of the $O(2,2)$ algebra, the light-cone expansion for such a case is not uniquely determined, because of the appearance of an infinite number of representations of the (infinite-dimensional) conformal algebra. As we have already said, Eq. 146 is, however, explicitly conformal covariant.

A final result we want to prove is that, in spite of the formal invariance of the theory under the algebra of the L_n generators, the vacuum cannot be invariant under L_n for $n = 2, \ldots, \infty$. We assume the commutators (see Eq. 136)

$$[L_n, j_+(u)] = \frac{d}{du}[u^{1-n}j_+(u)] \tag{149}$$

and that j_+ satisfies the free-field equation. Let us consider the Wightman function

$$\langle 0|j_+(u_1)j_+(u_2)|0\rangle \tag{150}$$

which is necessarily of the form $(u_1 - u_2)^\alpha$.

If $L_n|0\rangle = 0$ and $L_n{}^+|0\rangle = 0$, we have

$$\langle 0|[L_n, j_+(u_1)j_+(u_2)]|0\rangle = 0$$

giving

$$(1-n)[u_1^{-n} + u_2^{-n}] + \alpha(u_1 - u_2)^{-1}(u_1^{1-n} - u_2^{1-n}) = 0 \tag{151}$$

which is satisfied for $n = 1$ with any α, and for $n = 0$ and $n = -1$ provided $\alpha = -2$. Then necessarily $L_n|0\rangle \neq 0$ or $\langle 0|L_n \neq 0$ for $n = 2, \ldots, \infty$, and only the $O(2,2)$ subalgebra can be a symmetry of the vacuum (and α is fixed equal to -2, as required by scale invariance).

APPENDIX: CONFORMAL ALGEBRA (SUMMARY)

The conformal generators J_{AB} $(A, B = 0, 1, \ldots, 6)$ satisfy the commutation relations

$$[J_{AB}, J_{CD}] = i(g_{AD}J_{BC} + g_{BC}J_{AD} - g_{AC}J_{BD} - g_{BD}J_{AC}) \tag{A.1}$$

where g_{AB} is diagonal with $g_{AA} = (+---,-+)$. One has $J_{AB} = -J_{BA}$, giving a total of fifteen independent generators. In terms of the $IO(3,1)$ generators $M_{\mu\nu}, P_{\mu}$, plus the new generators D and K_{μ}, one has the correspondence

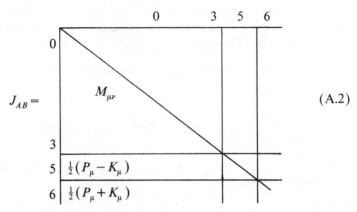

$$(A.2)$$

The algebra satisfied by the generators, Eq. A.1, is the $O(4,2)$ algebra. It is isomorphic to the spinor algebra $SU(2,2)$. Written in terms of $M_{\mu\nu}$, P_{μ}, D, and K_{μ}, the commutation relations in Eq. A.1 become as follows.

Poincaré subalgebra:

$$[M_{\mu\nu}, M_{\rho\sigma}] = -i(g_{\mu\rho}M_{\nu\sigma} - g_{\nu\rho}M_{\mu\sigma} + g_{\mu\sigma}M_{\rho\nu} - g_{\nu\sigma}M_{\rho\mu})$$

$$[M_{\mu\nu}, P_{\rho}] = i(g_{\nu\rho}P_{\mu} - g_{\mu\rho}P_{\nu}) \tag{A.3}$$

$$[P_{\mu}, P_{\nu}] = 0$$

Lorentz behavior of D (dilatation generator):

$$[M_{\mu\nu}, D] = 0 \qquad \text{(i.e., } D \text{ is Lorentz scalar)} \tag{A.4}$$

$$[P_{\mu}, D] = iP_{\mu} \qquad (P_{\mu} \text{ acts as a step-up operator with respect to } D) \tag{A.5}$$

Lorentz behavior of K_{μ} (special conformal generator):

$$[M_{\mu\nu}, K_{\rho}] = -i(g_{\rho\mu}K_{\nu} - g_{\rho\nu}K_{\mu}) \qquad (K_{\mu} \text{ is a four-vector}) \tag{A.6}$$

$$[P_{\mu}, K_{\nu}] = -2i(g_{\mu\nu}D - M_{\mu\nu}) \tag{A.7}$$

K_{μ}, D commutators:

$$[K_{\mu}, K_{\nu}] = 0 \tag{A.8}$$

$$[D, K_\mu] = iK_\mu \qquad (K_\mu \text{ acts as a step-down operator with respect to } D)$$

$$(A.9)$$

Linear realizations of the group of conformal transformations can be obtained in six dimensions. The transformations are those which leave invariant a bilinear form with metric $(+ - - -, - +)$. In four dimensions (Minkowski space) the realization is nonlinear. One has:

$$x'_\mu = a_\mu + \Lambda_\mu{}^\nu x_\nu \qquad \text{(infinitesimal transformations: generators } P_\mu, M_{\mu\nu})$$

$$(A.10)$$

$$x'_\mu = e^\lambda x_\mu, \quad \lambda \text{ real} \qquad \text{(dilatations: generator} D) \qquad (A.11)$$

$$x'_\mu = \frac{x_\mu + c_\mu x^2}{1 + 2c_\nu x^\nu + c^2 x^2} \qquad c_\mu \text{ real} \qquad \text{(special conformal transformations:}$$
$$\text{generators } K_\mu) \qquad (A.12)$$

The independent parameters are $4(a_\mu) + 6(\Lambda_\mu{}^\nu) + 1(\lambda) + 4(c_\mu) = 15$. Special conformal transformations can be thought of as products of (inversion) $\times$ (translation) $\times$ (inversion):

$$x_\mu \rightarrow \frac{x_\mu}{x^2} \rightarrow \frac{x_\mu}{x^2} + c_\mu \rightarrow \frac{x_\mu/x^2 + c_\mu}{\left(x_\mu/x^2 + c_\mu\right)^2} = \frac{x_\mu + c_\mu x^2}{1 + 2cx + c^2 x^2}$$

The group has two Abelian subgroups: one generated by P_μ, the other by K_μ. It also has two Poincaré subalgebras:

$$(M_{\mu\nu}, P_\mu) \qquad \text{and} \qquad (M_{\mu\nu}, K_\mu) \qquad (A.13)$$

From $[P_\mu, D] = iP_\mu$ one has

$$[P^2, D] = P^\mu[P_\mu, D] + [P^\mu, D]P_\mu = 2iP^2 \qquad (A.14)$$

Suppose that there is a discrete state of mass m whose normalized vector is $|p\rangle$, where $p^2 = m^2$. From Eq. A.14

$$\langle p|[P^2, D]|p\rangle = 2i\langle p|P^2|p\rangle = 2im^2$$

$$\langle p|[P^2, D]|p\rangle = \langle p|m^2 D - Dm^2|p\rangle = 0$$

Thus $m^2 = 0$. Discrete massive states are impossible, unless the symmetry is broken. Continuum massive states can, however, exist.

The argument here is similar to that of ordinary quantum mechanics, showing that the spectrum of p is a continuum from $[q,p] = i$. Again $\langle p'|[q, p]|p'\rangle = 0 = i\langle p'|p'\rangle$; however, $\langle p'|qp - pq|p''\rangle = (p'' - p')\langle p'|q|p''\rangle = i\langle p'|p''\rangle = i\delta(p' - p'')$, showing that $q = i(\partial/\partial p)$. Indeed

$$(p'' - p')i\frac{\partial}{\partial p''}\langle p'|p''\rangle = i(p'' - p')\frac{\partial}{\partial p''}\delta(p' - p'') = i\delta(p' - p'')$$

In order to study the representations we resort to the method of induced representations.[30] Let us call G any one of the generators of the stability subgroup at $x_\mu = 0$:

$$G \equiv (M_{\mu\nu}, D, K_\mu)$$

The remaining generator is P_μ, which acts like

$$[P_\mu, \varphi(x)] = -i\partial_\mu \varphi(x) \tag{A.15}$$

To evaluate $[\varphi(x), G]$ we use Eq. A.15:

$$[\varphi(x), G] = e^{iPx}\left[\varphi(0), \tilde{G}\right]e^{-iPx}$$

$$\tilde{G} = e^{-iPx}Ge^{iPx} \tag{A.16}$$

For $\tilde{G}$ we have

$$\tilde{G} = \sum_n \frac{(-i)^n}{n!}x_{\mu_1}\cdots x_{\mu_n}[P^{\mu_1}, [P^{\mu_2}\cdots[P^{\mu_n}, G],]\cdots]$$

If $G = M_{\mu\nu}$,

$$\tilde{M}_{\mu\nu} = M_{\mu\nu} - ix_{\mu_1}[P^{\mu_1}, M_{\mu\nu}] - \tfrac{1}{2}x_{\mu_1}x_{\mu_2}[P^{\mu_1}, [P^{\mu_2}, M_{\mu\nu}],] + \cdots$$

$$= M_{\mu\nu} - x_{\mu_1}(g_\nu{}^{\mu_1}P_\mu - g_\mu{}^{\mu_1}P_\nu) = M_{\mu\nu} - (x_\nu P_\mu - x_\mu P_\nu) \tag{A.17}$$

If $G = D$,

$$\tilde{D} = D - ix_{\mu_1}[P^{\mu_1}, D] - \tfrac{1}{2}x_{\mu_1}x_{\mu_2}[P^{\mu_1}[P^{\mu_2}, D],] + \cdots = D + x_\lambda P^\lambda \tag{A.18}$$

If $G = K_\mu$,

$$\tilde{K}_\mu = K_\mu - ix_{\mu_1}[P^{\mu_1}, K_\mu] - \tfrac{1}{2}x_{\mu_1}x_{\mu_2}[P^{\mu_1}, [P^{\mu_2}, K_\mu],] + \cdots$$

$$= K_\mu - ix_{\mu_1}2i(g_\mu{}^{\mu_1}D - M_\mu{}^{\mu_1}) - \tfrac{1}{2}x_{\mu_1}x_{\mu_2}[P^{\mu_1}, 2i(g_\mu{}^{\mu_2}D - M_\mu{}^{\mu_2})]$$

$$= K_\mu + 2x^\nu(g_{\mu\nu}D + M_{\nu\mu}) + 2x_\mu x^\nu P_\nu - x^2 P_\mu \tag{A.19}$$

Thus G is always a finite linear combination of generators.[31]

Let us now examine the representations of the stability subgroup. Within a representation that behaves irreducibly under $M_{\mu\nu}$, clearly D is a multiple of 1 (from Eq. A.4). Then Eq. A.9 tells that K_μ vanishes within the representation. We thus have

$$[\varphi(0), M_{\mu\nu}] = \Sigma_{\mu\nu}\varphi(0) \tag{A.20}$$

$$[\varphi(0), D] = i\Delta\varphi(0) \qquad \text{(where Δ is a c-number to be called}$$
$$\text{the scale dimension)} \tag{A.21}$$

$$[\varphi(0), K_\mu] = 0 \tag{A.22}$$

From Eqs. A.16–A.18 and A.20–A.22

$$[\varphi(x), M_{\mu\nu}] = e^{iPx}[\varphi(0), M_{\mu\nu} - (x_\nu P_\mu - x_\mu P_\nu)]e^{-iPx}$$

$$= \Sigma_{\mu\nu}\varphi(x) - i(x_\nu\partial_\mu - x_\mu\partial_\nu)\varphi(x)$$

$$[\varphi(x), D] = e^{iPx}[\varphi(0), D + x_\lambda P^\lambda]e^{-iPx}$$

$$= i\Delta\varphi(x) + ix_\lambda\partial^\lambda\varphi(x)$$

$$[\varphi(x), K_\mu] = e^{iPx}[\varphi(0), K_\mu + 2x^\nu(g_{\mu\nu}D + M_{\mu\nu}) + 2x_\mu x^\nu P_\nu - x^2 P_\mu]e^{-iPx}$$

$$= [2x^\nu(g_{\mu\nu}i\Delta + \Sigma_{\mu\nu}) + 2x_\mu x^\nu i\partial_\nu - ix^2\partial_\mu]\varphi(x)$$

In conclusion

$$[\varphi(x), M_{\mu\nu}] = i[(x_\mu\partial_\nu - x_\nu\partial_\mu) - i\Sigma_{\mu\nu}]\varphi(x) \tag{A.23}$$

$$[\varphi(x), D] = i(\Delta + x^\rho\partial_\rho)\varphi(x) \tag{A.24}$$

$$[\varphi(x), K_\mu] = i[(2\Delta x_\mu + 2x_\mu x^\rho\partial_\rho - x^2\partial_\mu) + 2ix^\rho\Sigma_{\mu\rho}]\varphi(x) \tag{A.25}$$

and of course

$$[\varphi(x), P_\mu] = i\partial_\mu\varphi(x) \tag{A.26}$$

Representations with nonvanishing K_μ are of two types: with K_μ represented by a nilpotent matrix, or infinite dimensional.

Finite-dimensional representations that behave reducibly under $M_{\mu\nu}$ can be analyzed as before. The $M_{\mu\nu}$ can be taken as block diagonal, in a suitable basis. The D is correspondingly block diagonal by the same argument used before, and again K_μ vanishes in each block. Since

$$[D, K_\mu^{\,p}] = ip K_\mu^{\,p} \qquad\qquad (A.27)$$

where p is any power, also $K_\mu^{\,p}$ vanishes in each block. Equation A.27 follows by iterating Eq. A.9. Then K_μ must be nilpotent. Such a result is also intuitive, since K_μ lowers the dimension and the representation is finite dimensional. Finite-dimensional representations of the stability subgroup can therefore always be brought into block diagonal form for $M_{\mu\nu}$ and D with K_μ represented by a lower-diagonal matrix. Then Eq. A.25 is modified by the addition within the square bracket of the nilpotent matrix K_μ. One can always assume that the eigenvalues of D have been partially ordered into increasing dimensions $\Delta_1, \Delta_2, \ldots$. It is then apparent that the representation contains a finite number of invariant subspaces, each obtained by keeping all states with dimension lower than some Δ_i. However, the representation is not reducible within such invariant subspaces, as K_λ does not correspondingly assume a diagonal form. At the same time one has the existence of an ordered set of invariant subspaces but lacks full reducibility of the representation. Therefore such representations are called indecomposible, and they clearly can be extended to infinite dimensions.

The foregoing discussion does not exhaust the study of the possible representations. For instance, for the dilatation group there exist finite-dimensional (in particular) representations for any integer dimension m in terms of lower diagonal matrices, corresponding to the finite-dimension representations of the multiplicative group for real numbers.[30, 32] For a set of linearly independent fields $\varphi_i(x)$, the transformed set (under dilatation) $\tilde{\varphi}_i(x)$ is given by $\tilde{\varphi}_i(x) = D_{ij}(\lambda)\varphi_j(\lambda^{-1}x)$ where $D_{ij}(\lambda)$ is a representation of the dilatation group and can be written as a direct sum of $m \times m$ representations of the following type:

$$D(\lambda, m) = \lambda^d \begin{bmatrix} 1 & \log\lambda & \cdots & \dfrac{1}{(m-1)!}[\log\lambda]^{m-1} \\ & 1 & & \\ & & & \log\lambda \\ 0 & & & 1 \end{bmatrix} \qquad (A.28)$$

Such representations have some physical interest, as they allow for possible logarithms in dilatational covariant operator product expansions and can have relationships to spontaneous symmetry breaking.[33]

As is well known, the conformal algebra on space-time is isomorphic to the orthogonal $O(4,2)$ algebra. The $O(4,2)$ is a rank -3 algebra, with Casimir operators

$$C_{\mathrm{I}} = J^{AB}J_{AB}$$

$$C_{\mathrm{II}} = \epsilon_{ABCDEF}J^{AB}J^{CD}J^{EF} \qquad (\mathrm{A.29})$$

$$C_{\mathrm{III}} = J_A{}^B J_B{}^C J_C{}^D J_D{}^A$$

It is a simple task to prove that the action of the conformal group on the Minkowski space is equivalent to the action of $O(4,2)$ on the homogeneous space $[O(4,2)/IO(3,1)]\otimes D$. Let us consider an arbitrary point P in the six-dimensional pseudo-orthogonal space $O(4,2), P\equiv(\eta_A = g_A{}^B\eta_B)$, and choose as independent variables

$$x_\mu = \frac{1}{k}\eta_\mu, \qquad k = \eta_5 + \eta_6, \quad \text{and} \quad \eta^2 \quad (\eta^2 = \eta^A\eta_A) \quad (\mathrm{A.30})$$

A transformation $\Lambda \in O(4,2)$, acting as $\eta'^A = \Lambda_B^A \eta^B$, induces on the new variables the following transformations:

$$x'_\mu = L_\mu{}^\nu x_\nu + a_\mu \qquad \text{(Poincaré transformations)}$$

$$k' = k \qquad (\mathrm{A.31})$$

$$x'_\mu = e^\lambda x_\mu \qquad \text{(dilatations)}$$

$$k' = e^{-\lambda}k \qquad (\mathrm{A.32})$$

$$x'_\mu = \frac{x_\mu + c_\mu(x^2 - \eta^2/k^2)}{1 + 2c\cdot x + c^2(x^2 - \eta^2/k^2)} \qquad \text{(special conformal transformations)}$$

$$k' = k[1 + 2c\cdot x + c^2(x^2 - \eta^2/k^2)] \qquad (\mathrm{A.33})$$

We then see that, in order to recover the conformal transformations laws in space-time, the point $x \in M_4$ ($M_4 =$ Minkowski space) has to be identified with the set $x_\mu = \{\rho\eta_\mu, \rho k\}$, on the cone $\eta^2 = 0$.

Let us now consider operator-valued spinor functions defined on the cone $\eta^2 = 0$. They transform according to

$$\delta\psi_{\{\alpha\}}(\eta) = -i\epsilon^{AB}J_{AB}{}^{\{\beta\}}_{\{\alpha\}}\psi_{\{\beta\}}(\eta)$$

$$= -i\epsilon^{AB}(L_{AB}\delta^{\{\beta\}}_{\{\alpha\}} + S^{\{\beta\}}_{\{\alpha\}})\psi_{\{\beta\}}(\eta), \quad L_{AB} = i(\eta_B\partial_A - \eta_A\partial_B) \quad (\mathrm{A.34})$$

where $S_{\{\alpha\}}^{\{\beta\}}$ is the matrix of an irreducible representation of the spinor group SU(2,2), locally isomorphic to $O(4,2)$. We assume that these functions are homogeneous of degree λ, that is,

$$\eta^A \partial_A \psi_{\{\alpha\}}(\eta) = \lambda \psi_{\{\alpha\}}(\eta), \qquad \eta^A \partial_A = k\frac{\partial}{\partial k} \qquad (A.35)$$

Note that in general, for $\eta^2 \neq 0, \eta^A \partial_A = k(\partial/\partial k) + 2\eta^2(\partial/\partial \eta^2)$, so that Eq. A.35 holds only for $\eta^2 = 0$. This is due to the fact that only the hypersurface $\eta^2 = 0$ is variant under dilatations on the six-dimensional space:

$$\eta_A \rightarrow \lambda \eta_A$$

The function

$$\psi'_{\{\alpha\}}(x) = k^{-\lambda} \psi_{\{\alpha\}}(\eta) \qquad (A.36)$$

is then defined on space-time. However, the operator $\psi'_{\{\alpha\}}(x)$ is nonlocal in the sense that

$$[\psi'_{\{\alpha\}}(x), P_\mu] = \left(i\frac{\partial}{\partial x_\mu} + \pi_\mu\right)\psi'_{\{\alpha\}}(x) \qquad (A.37)$$

where $\pi_\mu = S_{6\mu} + S_{5\mu}$. From Eq. A.37 one easily sees that the new operator-valued function

$$O_{\{\alpha\}}(x) = (e^{-ix\cdot\pi}\psi')_{\{\alpha\}}(x) = k^{-\lambda}(e^{-ix\cdot\pi})_{\{\alpha\}}^{\{\beta\}}\psi_{\{\beta\}}(\eta) \qquad (A.38)$$

transforms according to a representation of the conformal algebra on space-time induced from a representation of the stability algebra at $x = 0$ with matrices $\Sigma_{\mu\nu}, \Delta, K_\mu$:

$$\Sigma_{\mu\nu} = S_{\mu\nu}, \qquad \Delta = S_{65} - i\lambda I, \qquad K_\mu = S_{6\mu} - S_{5\mu} \qquad (A.39)$$

In discussing irreducible representations in space-time we shall limit ourselves to a particular family of representations which are relevant in operator product expansions. We shall consider tensor representations which contain SL(2,C) tensors of the type $[n/2, n/2]$.

Classification of the relevant irreducible representations is achieved by making use of the following two basic lemmas:

Lemma 1. Every irreducible (infinite-dimensional) representation of conformal algebra which contains a ladder of Lorentz tensors of order $n+k, k = 0, 1, 2, \ldots$ (i.e., irreducible SL(2,C) representations of the type $[(n+k)/2, (n+k)/2]$) is uniquely specified by an irreducible Lorentz tensor $(n/2, n/2)$ of given dimension l_n, annihilated by K_λ, that is, by an irreducible representation of $SL(2, C) \otimes D$. The last assertion follows from the structure of the stability algebra.

The proof of Lemma 1 follows from the fact that the Casimir operators (A.29) are given in such representations by

$$C_I = 2l_n(l_n - 4) + 2n(n + 2)$$

$$C_{II} = 0$$

$$C_{III} = n(n + 2)[3 + l_n(l_n - 4)] \qquad (A.40)$$

as can be obtained by evaluating their eigenvalues on the lowest-order tensor $(n/2, n/2)$ annihilated by K_λ. Therefore these representations are specified by two numbers, n and l_n, where n is a nonnegative integer and l_n assumes any value (with the exception $l_n = 2 + n$).

Lemma 2. Every irreducible representation of the conformal algebra, which according to Lemma 1 is uniquely specified by a Lorentz tensor of order n (annihilated by K_λ) and its dimension l_n, can be uniquely enlarged $(l_n \neq 2 + n)$ to a tensor representation of $O(4, 2)$ acting on $O(4, 2)/IO(3, 1) \otimes D$.

The tensors $\psi_{A_1 \cdots A_n}(\eta)$ are specified by the following properties:

(a) They are homogeneous of degree $-l_n$.
(b) They are irreducible, that is, symmetric and traceless.
(c) They satisfy two sets of supplementary conditions: $\eta^{A_1} \psi_{A_1 \cdots A_n}(\eta) = 0$ and $\partial^{A_1} \psi_{A_1 \cdots A_n}(\eta) = 0$ (generalized Lorentz condition).

It is possible to prove that these properties for the tensors $\psi_{A_1 \cdots A_n}$ are equivalent to the following ones:

(a') The tensors are irreducible with respect to the orbital part of the algebra $O(4, 2)$.

(b') They are irreducible with respect to the spin part of the algebra $O(4, 2)$.

(c') They are irreducible with respect to the whole algebra, that is, LS is a constant on these representations.

In addition to Eq. A.38 one finds for the "redundant" components

$$O(x)_{\alpha_1 \cdots \alpha_{n-k}, 6 \cdots 6} = 2^{-k} \frac{\Gamma(l_n - 2 - n)}{\Gamma(l_n - 2 - n + k)} \partial_{\mu_1} \cdots \partial_{\mu_k} O^{\mu_1 \cdots \mu_k}_{\alpha_1 \cdots \alpha_{n-k}}(x) \qquad (A.41)$$

and that indices 5 and 6 are interchangeable.

REFERENCES

1. R. Wilson, *Phys. Rev.*, **179**, 1499 (1969).

2. S. Ciccariello, R. Gatto, G. Sartori, and M. Tonin, *Ann. Phys.*, **65**, 265 (1971).

3. S. Ferrara, R. Gatto, and A. F. Grillo, *Nucl. Phys.*, **B34**, 349 (1971).

4. R. A. Brandt and G. Preparata, *Nucl. Phys.*, **B27**, 541 (1971); Y. Frishman, *Phys. Rev. Letters*, **25**, 960 (1970).

5. *Bateman Project*, McGraw-Hill, New York, Vol. 1, Chapter VI.

6. H. Fritsch and M. Gell-Mann, *Proceedings of the International Conference on Duality and Symmetry in Hadron Physics*, ed. by E. Gotsman, Weizmann Science Press of Israel, Jerusalem, 1971.

7. A. A. Migdal, *Phys. Letters*, **37B**, 98 (1971); S. Ferrara, A. F. Grillo, and G. Parisi, Frascati Report LNF 72/38 (1972).

8. A. M. Polyakov, *Sov. Phys. JETP*, **28**, 533 (1969).

9. A. A. Migdal, *Phys. Letters*, **37B**, 98 (1971).

10. E. J. Schreier, *Phys. Rev. D*, **3**, 980 (1971).

11. S. Ferrara, R. Gatto, and A. F. Grillo, *Springer Tracts in Modern Physics*, Vol. 67 (1973) Springer-Verlag, Berlin.

12. M. D'Eramo, G. Parisi, and L. Peliti, *Lettere Nuovo Cimento*, **2**, 878 (1971); S. Ferrara and G. Parisi, *Nucl. Phys.*, **B42**, 281 (1972).

13. S. Ferrara, R. Gatto, A. F. Grillo, and G. Parisi, *Lettere Nuovo Cimento*, **4**, 115 (1972).

14. D. G. Boulware, L. S. Brown, and R. D. Peccei, *Phys. Rev. D*, **2**, 293 (1970).

15. S. Ferrara, R. Gatto, and A. F. Grillo, *Lettere Nuovo Cimento*, **2**, 1363 (1971).

16. *Bateman Project*, McGraw-Hill, New York, Vol. 2, p. 186.

17. S. Ferrara, R. Gatto, A. F. Grillo, and G. Parisi, *Nucl. Phys.*, **B49**, 77 (1972).

18. S. Ferrara, R. Gatto, A. F. Grillo, and G. Parisi, *Phys. Letters*, **38B**, 333 (1972).

19. L. O'Raifertaigh, *Phys. Rev.*, **139B**, 1052 (1965).

20. G. Parisi, Rome Preprint 391 (1972).

21. G. Mack and K. Symanzik, *Commun. Math. Phys.*, **27**, 247 (1972).

22. K. Symanzik, *Commun. Math. Phys.*, **6**, 228 (1967).

23. C. G. Callan, Jr., S. Coleman, and R. Jackiw, *Ann. Phys.*, **59**, 42 (1970).

24. S. Ferrara, R. Gatto, and A. F. Grillo, *Nuovo Cimento*, **12A**, 959 (1972).

25. E. Del Giudice, P. Di Vecchia, S. Fubini, and R. Musto, Chapter 8 in this volume.

26. H. Leutwyler, article to be published.

27. W. Thirring, *Ann. Phys.*, **3**, 91 (1958); K. Johnson, *Nuovo Cimento*, **20**, 773 (1961).

28. G. F. Dell'Antonio, Y. Frishman, and D. Zwanziger, *Phys. Rev. D*, **6**, 988 (1972).

29. P. A. M. Dirac, *Ann. Math.*, **37**, 429 (1936); F. Gursey, *Nuovo Cimento*, **3**, 988 (1956). For recent reviews see G. Mack and A. Salam, *Ann. Phys.*, **53**, 174 (1969), and S. Ferrara, R. Gatto, and A. F. Grillo, ref. 11.

30. G. W. Mackey, *Bull. Am. Math. Soc.*, **69**, 628 (1963); R. Herman, *Lie Groups for Physicists*, Benjamin, New York, 1966; M. Jacobson, *Lie Algebras*, Interscience, New York, 1967.

31. L. O'Raifertaigh, *Phys. Rev. Letters*, **14**, 575 (1965).

32. P. Otterson and W. Zimmermann, *Commun. Math. Phys.*, **24**, 107 (1972); G. F. Dell'Antonio, New York University Report 12/72 (1972).

33. S. Ferrara and A. F. Grillo, *Lettere Nuovo Cimento*, **2**, 177 (1971); S. Ferrara, R. Gatto, and A. F. Grillo, *Phys. Letters*, **42B**, 264 (1972); R. Brandt and W. Ng, article to be published.

34. R. J. Crewther, *Phys. Rev. Letters*, **28**, 1421 (1972).

CHAPTER 5

Conformal Covariant
Quantum Field Theory

G. Mack

1. SURVEY

Considerable progress has been made in the last 2 or 3 years in the understanding of short-distance behavior in quantum field theory (QFT). This problem is of much interest both from a theoretical and from a phenomenological point of view. The theorist knows that it is intimately connected with the problem of ultraviolet divergences that occurs in canonical perturbation theory and has been considered as one of the main stumbling blocks in constructive QFT. Experimentally, the short-distance behavior of the theory can be probed with the help of weak and electromagnetic interactions, as is done, for example, in the celebrated SLAC experiments.[1]

The analysis of the short-distance behavior of perturbation theoretically renormalizable Lagrangian field theories proceeds from the Callan-Symanzik equation[2] for its n-point vertex functions (=full-propagator amputated, one-particle irreducible Green functions), or from the equivalent renormalization group.[3] One assumes that the Callan-Symanzik function $\beta(\bar{g})$ possesses a (first) nontrivial zero at a value $\bar{g} = g_\infty$ of the physical coupling constant; this then leads to definite conclusions. These conclusions are, however, not quite the same for Yukawa-type theories, that is, theories with interactions mediated by scalar or pseudoscalar fields, and gauge field theories like quantum electrodynamics (QED). The difference comes from gauge invariance, which prohibits the gauge fields from acquiring an anomalous dimension, and also enforces[4] a slope $\beta'(g_\infty) = 0$. We shall limit this discussion to Yukawa-type theories, which we regard as models of strong interactions.* It is then consistent to assume for the rest of this report a nonvanishing slope $\beta'(g_\infty) < 0$.

By integrating the Callan-Symanzik partial differential equations one finds then, under certain continuity assumptions,[6] that the short-distance (or large-momentum) behavior of the vertex functions $\Gamma(p_1 \cdots p_n; m^2, \bar{g})$ of the (realistic) finite mass theory is described by a dilatation-invariant asymptote, the so-called Gell-Mann/Low limit theory,[2] with vertex functions $\Gamma_{GML}(p_1 \cdots p_n)$:

$$\Gamma(\lambda p_1 \cdots \lambda p_n; m^2, \bar{g}) = r(\bar{g})^{-n} \Gamma_{GML}(\lambda p_1 \cdots \lambda p_n) + \text{negligible as } \lambda \to \infty \quad (1)$$

The asymptotic behavior is independent both of coupling constant $\bar{g}$ and mass m, apart from overall normalization factors.

The important point is that Γ_{GML} are vertex functions of a bona fide local QFT. This theory is not only exactly dilatation invariant but, as Schroer has shown by studying the stress tensor,[7] also exactly conformal invariant. The problem of short-distance behavior in the sense of the limit of Eq. 1 is thereby reduced to that of studying the properties and possible construction of an exactly conformal invariant QFT. This is the motivation for the following considerations.

The Green functions of Lagrangian field theory satisfy a set of coupled integral equations[8] shown in Figures 3 and 4 (Section 2) and 9 (Section 3). In the case of the dressed propagator (and three-point functions[8]) they are actually integrodifferential equations when written in finite, properly renormalized form. All of these integral equations are exactly the same for arbitrary values of physical masses and coupling constants, since these parameters do not explicitly enter anywhere into them. In canonical perturbation theory masses and coupling constants enter only through the boundary conditions (the usual renormalization conditions fixing the zero of the inverse propagator on the mass shell, etc.) which have to be supplied in addition to the equations in order to guarantee a unique solution. It is clear, then, that exactly the same integral equations should hold for the Gell-Mann/Low limit theory. The demand of exact conformal invariance will play the role of boundary condition.

---

*Quantum electrodynamics has been studied by Baker and Johnson, by Adler, and by others.[4,5]

One must therefore look for conformal invariant solutions of these integral equations.

In the next section we briefly review the Migdal-Polyakov bootstrap approach to conformal invariant QFT.[9-14] This approach uses the (formal) iterative solution of those integral equations for the $n \geqslant 4$ point functions (Figure 9). This iterative solution is known under the name of "skeleton graph expansions." They give the four-point function $\langle T(\varphi(x_1) \cdots \varphi(x_4)) \rangle$ and higher ones in the form of infinite series. The general term in these series is to be constructed out of the dressed propagators and three-point vertices according to well-known rules.[15] One has to write down all possible skeleton graphs, that is, graphs without self-energy and vertex correction subgraphs. With every line in such a graph one associates a dressed propagator, and with every vertex a dressed vertex function. In the end one has to integrate over internal coordinates or momenta.

The great power of conformal symmetry becomes apparent in the construction of the dressed propagators and three-point vertices to be used in the skeleton graph expansions. In principle these have to be determined as solutions of the remaining two integral equations, Figures 3 and 4—the Schwinger-Dyson equations for propagator and three-point vertex. Usually this is a complicated affair. In canonical perturbation theory it involves summing infinite series of Feynman diagrams. Exact conformal symmetry, however, determines uniquely the dressed propagator and the dressed three-point vertices up to some constants—coupling constant g and dynamical field dimension(s) d. This was found by Polyakov.[10] Thus, by using our knowledge that the Gell-Mann/Low limit theory should be conformal invariant, we are in effect *able to perform a partial summation of the usual perturbation series,* modulo the appearance of parameters g and d, which have still to be determined.

Now these unique conformal invariant expressions also solve the Schwinger-Dyson equations for propagator and three-point vertex, and in this way one obtains a system of algebraic equations for coupling constant g and field dimension(s) d. They are customarily called the "vertex bootstrap" and "propagator bootstrap" and were first written down by Migdal[9] and by Parisi and Peliti,[11] respectively. Since there are always as many equations as unknown parameters, one expects that in general* the resulting theory will have no continuous free parameter, in agreement with the previously mentioned result of the Callan-Symanzik or renormalization group analysis (g is related to g_∞). The bootstrap equations still involve

---

*It is a priori conceivable that degeneracies appear for theories with special symmetries, so that not all parameters are uniquely determined in these cases. [This requires special properties of $\beta(g)$, which could be checked by canonical perturbation theory.] Examples are the Baxter model in statistical mechanics and the Thirring model, which has $\beta(g) \equiv 0$.

infinite power series in g; they come from inserting the skeleton graph expansions for the Bethe-Salpeter kernel, which is a special four-point amplitude (see above).

The Migdal-Polyakov bootstrap theory has recently been examined in some detail. It has been shown by Todorov and the present author that the theory is free from ultraviolet and infrared divergences, that is, the Green functions are well defined.[12] An S-matrix does not exist though, since one is dealing with an infraparticle theory.[16,17] A crucial ingredient of the theory is the anomalous, that is, dynamically determined, dimensions d of the fields.[16] Anomalous dimensions lead to better ultraviolet convergence properties than those of canonical perturbation theory; in particular, the right-hand side of the vertex bootstrap (Eq. 8) is not overall divergent in momentum space. Absence of a logarithmic divergence here is essential for the self-consistency of the whole scheme.

It is also implicit in a result of Symanzik[18] that the theory satisfies locality and spectrum condition. This is in fact true, skeleton graph by skeleton graph. We shall come back to this point later. Furthermore, it has been shown by Symanzik and the present author[14] that the theory satisfies generalized unitarity, for values of g and d such that the vertex and propagator bootstrap equations are satisfied. It is interesting to contrast this with canonical perturbation theory, where unitarity holds in a sense identically in the coupling constant. It is instructive to see the role played, for example, by the vertex bootstrap in the proof of unitarity; we shall therefore give a sketch of the argument later on.

Currents and their properties have also been examined.[14] Amplitudes involving currents are constructed in essentially the same way as all others. Their three-point functions are determined by conformal invariance up to some constants, as discussed by Migdal,[9] Schreier,[19] Gatto et al.,[20] and others. The constants have to be determined from algebraic equations obtained by inserting the conformal invariant ansatz into a Bethe-Salpeter equation analog to the vertex bootstrap mentioned before. The higher n-point functions, as well as some amplitudes involving only currents, have to be determined again by skeleton graph expansions. Symanzik and the present author have shown that this construction guarantees the validity of correct Ward identities which imply current conservation and correct current commutation relations.[14] Peculiarities can occur, however, in an integer number D of space-time dimensions for amplitudes involving only currents, that is, fields of canonical dimensionality, and no other fields. Their Wightman functions are conformal invariant, conserved, and all that, in the presence of only strong interactions. However, for the two- and three-point functions, for example, it is not possible to define the T^+-product so that the time-ordered Green functions are dilatation-invariant distributions, and in some cases there even appear "anomalous" contact terms in the Ward identities. This is the origin of the well-known triangle anomalies, which have been discussed so often that we shall not dwell further on the matter.[21]

Of particular interest is the question of Bjorken scaling.[22] As has been shown by the present author,[23] and more recently also discussed by Christ, Hasslacher, and Mueller,[24] the existence of a dilatation symmetric Gell-Mann/Low limit theory implies that the moments of the structure functions, describing deep inelastic electron-nucleon scattering, scale as

$$\int_0^2 d\omega \, \omega^{s-2} \nu W_2(q^2, \omega) \sim \text{const.} \, (-q^2)^{-\sigma_s/2}, \qquad (2)$$

$$s = 2, 4, 6, \ldots \quad \text{as} \quad q^2 \to -\infty$$

in Bjorken's notation. Here σ_s is the anomalous part of the dimension d_s of a symmetric s-rank tensor field occurring in the Wilson's operator product expansion[16] of $J_\mu^{em}(x) J_\nu^{em}(0)$ around the tip of the light cone, $x = 0$, namely,

$$\sigma_s = d_s - s - 2 \qquad (3)$$

Canonical Bjorken scaling in the strong form implied, for example, by the validity of a light-cone algebra would thus demand that $\sigma_s = 0$ for all $s = 2, 4, 6, \ldots$, that is, there is an infinite tower of tensor fields of canonical dimension $d_s = s + 2$. However, there is a theorem of Ferrara, Gatto, Grillo, and Parisi which says that then all these tensors would have to be conserved.[25] It assumes that the two-point Wightman functions of the tensor fields are exactly conformal invariant. Parisi has used this theorem to argue that exactly canonical Bjorken scaling can be true only if the Gell-Mann/Low limit theory is free and therefore also satisfies a light-cone algebra.[26] It is not clear at present, however, whether a free Gell-Mann/Low limit theory is in fact a consistent possibility.

The author has examined φ^3 theory in $6 + \epsilon$ space-time dimensions as a model[27] and found that it possesses a nontrivial conformal invariant QFT as a Gell-Mann/Low limit. The bootstrap equations can be solved, and the field dimensions computed as power series in ϵ. In general, the anomalous parts σ_s come out nonzero, except that $\sigma_2 = 0$ because the stress tensor must have canonical dimension. But all σ_s for $s > 2$ come out very small:

$$\tfrac{1}{2} \sigma_s = \left[\frac{1}{18} - \frac{2}{3(s+2)(s+1)} \right] \epsilon + \cdots$$

We feel, therefore, that a noncanonical law (Eq. 2) with small values of $\frac{1}{2}\sigma_s$ of the order 0.1 or so should be considered as a real possibility. Earlier hopes that this might be avoided have so far not materialized since we have been unable to verify the technical assumptions necessary to guarantee a canonical Bjorken scaling.

The Migdal-Polyakov bootstrap approach achieves a partial summation of perturbation theory (as we explained) and is thus a notable step forward toward a theory of strong interactions. However, its reliance on skeleton graph expansions is an old-fashioned feature smacking of perturbation theory, and attempts are currently being made to find something better. It is still too early to say or even guess what progress will be possible. However, some powerful tools are available.

As a first tool, there is an integral representation due to Symanzik for a general conformal invariant n-point Green function which exhibits manifest locality and spectrum condition.[18] The great simplification thereby brought about in the implementation of locality and spectrum condition is considered by this author as one of the sweetest fruits of conformal symmetry.

The second tool consists of Wilson's operator product expansions[16] around the tip (!) of the light cone. They embody some of the information contained in the coupled set of integral equations for Green functions mentioned above; see, for example, Appendix A of ref. 6. An extensive study of conformal invariant operator product expansions has been carried out by Ferrara, Gatto, Grillo, and Parisi,[28] culminating in the shadow-operator formalism[29] about which more can be found in Professor Tonin's contribution.[30] These authors have, in particular, also been able to build into the operator expansions manifest support properties in x-space which are implied by locality, thus fixing the coefficients of all derivatives of fields which occur on the right-hand side of the Wilson expansion.

In Symanzik's integral representation the n-point Green function is expressed in terms of a kernel depending on a number of complex variables, of which $\frac{1}{2}n(n-3)$ are linearly independent. We feel that it may be easier to approximate these kernels, since their singularity structure is very much constrained by the presumed validity of conformal invariant operator product expansions. We conjecture that they are meromorphic functions with simple poles as a rule. Certain integrals over the residues of these poles would then again have to be meromorphic functions with simple poles in the remaining variables, and so on. At this point one starts to encounter mathematical structures somewhat reminiscent of those familiar from dual-resonance models. One may wonder, therefore, whether it may not be possible to put to use also some of the tools employed there. The coupled integral equations for Green functions can be rewritten as integral equations for the kernels. Unfortunately, though, the complexity of the resulting formulas increases rapidly with n.

2. SKELETON THEORY

As is well known, a conformal covariant field transformation law suitable for the fundamental fields in Lagrangian QFT can be written as[31, 32]

$$\delta\varphi(x) = \epsilon(d + x_\nu \partial^\nu)\varphi(x) \tag{4a}$$

for infinitesimal dilatations, and as

$$\delta\varphi(x) = \epsilon^\mu\left(2dx_\mu + 2x_\mu x_\nu \partial^\nu - x^2\partial_\mu - 2ix^\nu \Sigma_{\mu\nu}\right)\varphi(x) \tag{4b}$$

for infinitesimal special conformal transformations. Here $\Sigma_{\mu\nu}$ are the spin matrices in the Lorentz transformation law of the field $\varphi(x)$, and d is a new quantum number called the dimension of mass of the field $\varphi(x)$. Equations 4 are not the most general ones compatible with conformal covariance. There is an extra term[32] on the right-hand side of Eq. 4b in the transformation law of derivatives of fields like $\nabla\varphi(x)$. Even Eq. 4a is not the most general. As Dell'Antonio has emphasized,[33] there is a possibility that d may be a triangular matrix which cannot be diagonalized. This requires, however, a multiplet of fields with the same Lorentz transformation law and can therefore not apply to the fundamental fields in the Lagrangian models normally considered. (For other fields see ref. 34.)

We shall require that our theory be exactly conformal invariant in the sense that the time-ordered Green functions, considered as analytic functions of their arguments,[40, 41] are unchanged under the infinitesimal change $\delta\varphi$ of the fields—Eq. 4 above.

The construction of the conformal invariant skeleton theory starts from the observation that the integral equations for dressed propagator and three-point vertices allow for conformal invariant solutions.[9, 11] More specifically one proceeds as follows.[12, 14]

Conformal invariance fixes uniquely the dressed propagator and three-point vertex, up to some constants (coupling constant g and field dimension d). For example, in scalar φ^3 theory in D space-time dimensions

$$G(x,0) = 2^d\Gamma(d)(-x^2 + i0)^{-d} \tag{5}$$

$$\Gamma(x_1 x_2 x_3) = \frac{-ig\Gamma(\delta_1)x_{23}^{-2\delta_1}\Gamma(\delta_2)x_{13}^{-2\delta_2}\Gamma(\delta_3)x_{12}^{-2\delta_3}2^{\Sigma\delta_i + 1}}{\Gamma(D - \Sigma\delta_i)} \tag{6}$$

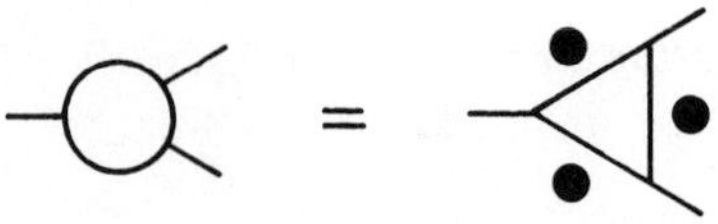

Figure 1. The dressed vertex, Eq. 6. Every line represents a generalized Feynman propagator (Eq. 10).

with $x_{ij}{}^{\alpha} = [-(x_i - x_j)^2 + i0]^{\alpha/2}$, $\delta_1 = \delta_2 = \delta_3 = \frac{1}{2}(D - d)$ if there is only one field φ, with dynamical dimension d. Equation 6 for the vertex can be graphically represented as in Figure 1.

Using these propagators and vertices, the $n \geqslant 4$ point functions may be constructed by skeleton graph expansions. In particular, the Bethe-Salpeter kernel may be expanded as shown in Figure 2. In formulas one has

$$B(x_1 x_2; x_3 x_4) = \int d^D y_1 d^D y_2 \{\Gamma(x_1 x_3 y_1) G(y_1 y_2) \Gamma(y_2 x_2 x_4) + (x_3 \leftrightarrow x_4)\}$$

$$+ \cdots \qquad (7)$$

The renormalized Schwinger-Dyson equations (henceforth called boot-straps) for three-point vertices and propagators are solved by the conformal invariant ansatz, and one obtains a system of algebraic equations for coupling constants g and field dimensions d. There are as many equations as unknowns, so that one may expect a unique or discrete set of solutions (see Section 1).

The vertex bootstrap is shown in Figure 3. In formulas one has

$$\Gamma(x_1 x_2 x_3) = \frac{1}{2} \int d^D y_1 \cdots d^D y_4 \Gamma(x_1 y_1 y_2) G(y_1 y_3) G(y_2 y_4) B(y_3 y_4; x_3 x_4)$$

$$(8)$$

with the Bethe-Salpeter kernel from Eq. 7.

For propagator one can use, for instance, Figure 4. The cross stands for the operation $-i(x_i - x_f)^{\nu} \nabla_i{}^{\mu}$, $\mu \neq \nu$. In formulas,

$$+ i(x_1{}^{\nu} - x_2{}^{\nu}) \nabla_{x_1}{}^{\mu} G^{-1}(x_1 x_2) = \frac{1}{2} \int d^D y_1 d^D y_2 B(x_1 x_2; y_1 y_2)$$

$$\times (-i)(y_1{}^{\nu} - y_2{}^{\nu}) \nabla_{y_1}{}^{\mu} G(y_1 y_2) \qquad (9)$$

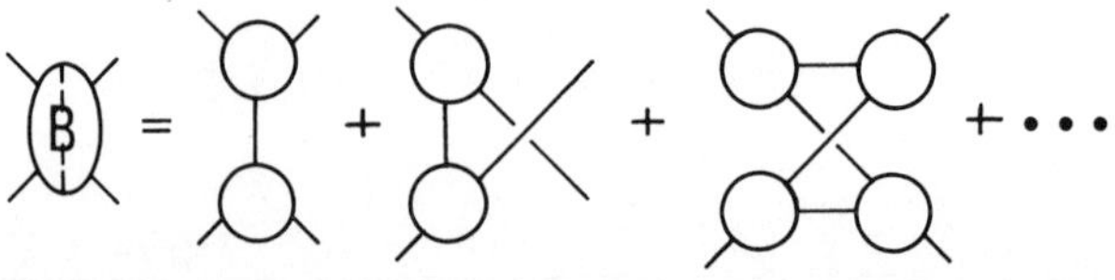

Figure 2. Skeleton graph expansion of the Bethe-Salpeter kernel.

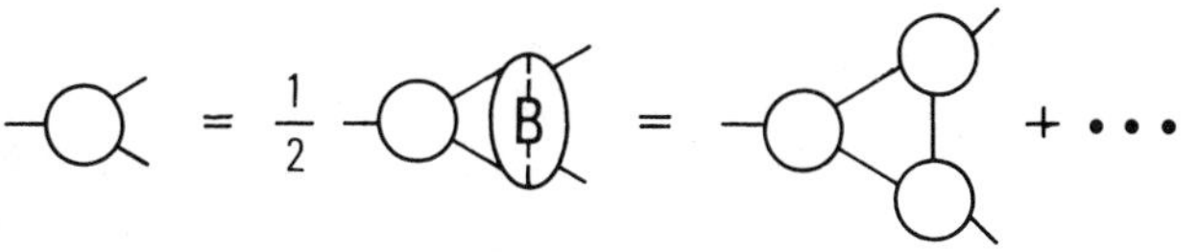

Figure 3. The vertex bootstrap, Eq. 8.

with G^{-1} the inverse propagator in the convolution sense.

Instead of Eq. 9 one can use generalized two-point unitarity, as was done in the original paper of Parisi and Peliti.[11] This leads to equivalent results,[14] but is less convenient for calculations.

A bare vertex is absent in Eq. 8 since it would not be conformal invariant. This is in agreement with the compositeness condition, $Z_1 = Z_3 = 0$.

In order for the construction just explained to make sense one must show that the expressions so obtained are well defined, that is, free from divergences, and conformal invariant. This has been verified to be true for the individual terms in the skeleton graph expansions by Todorov and the present author.[12]

To prove absence of divergences one starts from the observation that every skeleton graph in the theory is represented by a generalized Feynman integral in the sense of Speer, that is, it is an integral over a product of generalized Feynman propagators

$$2^\delta \Gamma(\delta)(-x^2+i0)^{-\delta} = -i(2\pi)^{-D/2}\int d^D p\, e^{-ipx} 2^\lambda \Gamma(\lambda)(-p^2-i0)^{-\lambda}$$

$$\lambda = \tfrac{1}{2}D - \delta$$

(10)

where $D =$ number of space-time dimensions. (For spinor lines there is a factor $i\not{\partial}$ in front.) Such a representation holds, in particular, for the dressed three-point vertex and propagator, as is evident from Eqs. 5 and 6. In general there is one generalized Feynman propagator for every line in the Migdal graph G_M, which is obtained by substituting Figure 1 for the dressed vertex into a skeleton graph G.

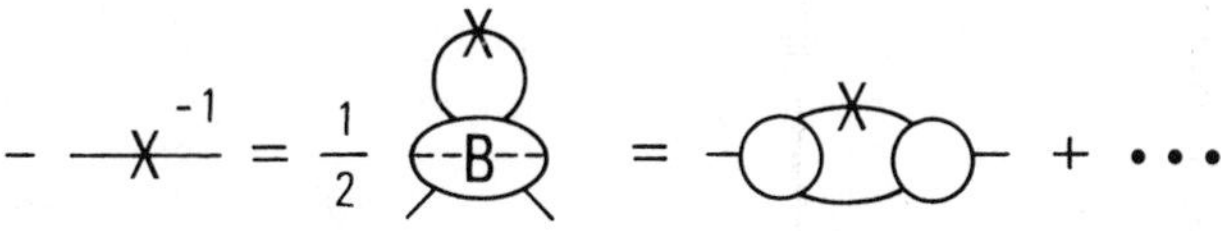

Figure 4. The propagator bootstrap. The cross stands for the operation $-i(x_i - x_j)^\nu \nabla_i{}^\mu$, $\mu \neq \nu$; cf. Eq. 9.

To explain the argument for ultraviolet convergence, let us first recall the situation for ordinary Feynman integrals encountered in the perturbation theoretic treatment of renormalizable theories like QED in four space-time dimensions.[15] Convergence of a Feynman integral holds if all one-particle irreducible subgraphs H are overall convergent. This in turn requires that their superficial degree of divergence $\mu_H < 0$. The essential point is then that μ_H can be computed, and therefore the question of overall divergence be decided, by merely looking at the configuration of external lines of H. For example, in QED one has the well-known formula $\mu_H = 4 - \frac{3}{2}F - B$, with F and B the numbers of external fermion and boson lines, respectively, of H.

A similar statement holds for the conformal invariant skeleton theory. Again it is necessary and sufficient that all one-particle irreducible subgraphs H of a Migdal graph G_M be overall convergent, and this last question can also here be decided by merely looking at the configuration of external lines of the subgraph H. This is a consequence of "conservation of dimension" at every vertex of the Migdal graph, which follows from conformal symmetry (see below).

One knows from the work of Speer or from Dyson's power-counting theorem that a generalized Feynman integral will be ultraviolet convergent if for every one-particle irreducible subgraph H of G_M the following inequality is satisfied:

$$\sum_{l \in L(H)} (\lambda_l - 1) > \tfrac{1}{2}\mu_H \tag{11}$$

Equivalently,

$$-\sum_{l \in L(H)} \delta_l > \tfrac{1}{2}D(n_H - 1) \tag{12}$$

with $\lambda_l = \frac{1}{2}D - \delta_l$. Summation is over all lines l of the subgraph H, and μ_H is the canonical superficial degree of divergence of the subgraph H. We consider φ^3 theory in D space-time dimensions. Then

$$\mu_H = (D-2)L_H - D(n_H - 1) \tag{13}$$

where L_H is the number of lines in H, and n_H the number of vertices.

By Eqs. 5 and 6, exponents δ_l in the generalized propagators (Eq. 10) are $\delta_l = d$ and $\frac{1}{2}(D-d)$ for undotted and dotted lines, respectively. As a consequence one has "conservation of dimension" at every vertex v of a Migdal graph:

$$\sum_{S(v)} \delta_l = D \tag{14}$$

Summation is over the three lines (one dotted + two undotted) incident at vertex v. Equation 14 makes it possible to express the left-hand side of Eq. 11 or 12 in terms of the configuration of external lines only, for instance,

$$\sum_{l \in L(H)} (\lambda_l - 1) = \tfrac{1}{2}\mu_H - \tfrac{1}{2}D + \tfrac{1}{2}\sum_{\text{ext}} \delta_l \qquad (15)$$

where summation on the right-hand side is over the external lines of H. The ultraviolet convergence condition (Eq. 11) becomes then

$$\tfrac{1}{2}\sum_{\text{ext}} \delta_l > \tfrac{1}{2}D \qquad (16)$$

Thus the problem is reduced to one of classification of all possible configurations of external lines. For this purpose one uses the fact that dotted external lines of H can be created only by cutting into a dressed vertex of the skeleton graph G. The final result is that condition 11 for ultraviolet convergence is satisfied for some range of values of the field dimensions. For pseudoscalar Yukawa theory in four space-time dimensions one finds the restrictions[12]

$$1 < d_M < 3; \qquad \tfrac{3}{2} < d_B < \tfrac{5}{2} \qquad (< \text{ is } \lesssim \text{ throughout}) \qquad (17)$$

for pseudoscalar and Dirac fields, respectively.

Conditions for infrared convergence may be formulated in a similar way.[36] One can show that the generalized Feynman integrals are infrared convergent at nonexceptional external momenta if

$$\sum_{l \in L(R)} (\lambda_l - 1) < \tfrac{1}{2}\mu_R \qquad (18)$$

Here summation is over all lines of a reduced graph R. A reduced graph is obtained from the original (Migdal) graph by contracting each line to a point. Inequality 18 must be satisfied for all reduced graphs R for which all external vertices are fused into one as a consequence of the contractions. Absence of infrared singularities holds for nonexceptional momenta, in the terminology of Symanzik.[6] This includes all Euclidean external momenta except when a partial sum of them vanishes.

In the construction of models like φ^3 theory in $6 + \epsilon$ dimensions it is useful to know that generalized Feynman integrals can be analytically continued[35] in all λ_l beyond the domains of Eqs. 11 and 18. They are meromorphic functions of all λ_l with poles on hypersurfaces, given by (scalar case)

1. Ultraviolet type:

$$\sum_{l \in L(H)} (\lambda_l - 1) = \tfrac{1}{2}\mu_H - m, \quad m = 0, 1, 2, \ldots$$

2. Infrared type:

$$\sum_{l \in L(R)} (\lambda_l - 1) = \tfrac{1}{2}\mu_R + m, \quad m = 0, 1, 2, \ldots \tag{19}$$

Here H and R are, respectively, subgraphs and reduced graphs, as described above. It turns out that infrared singularities do not in fact occur in conformal invariant theory, that is, when Eq. 14 is fulfilled. A simple explanation for this fact has been given by Adler.[37]

Although it is very useful to know these analyticity properties, we should emphasize one point. While Green functions can be defined by analytic continuation for field dimensions outside the range of Eq. 17, there is no reason to believe that this would still provide a physically acceptable theory. The objection is essentially that positivity properties (=unitarity) are not invariant under analytic continuation in general. More specifically, such analytic continuation is guaranteed to be physically correct only when it is equivalent to subtracting local counterterms. Thus "overall" ultraviolet divergences are harmless (they only stem from the difficulty of defining a T-product), but continuation beyond ultraviolet singularity surfaces coming from subgraphs H with some dotted external lines would be dangerous. With this remark we conclude our discussion of convergence properties.

In the proof[14] of *generalized unitarity* one makes use of an algebraic identity which is known as Veltman's cutting formula.[38] It supplies an expression for absorptive parts of Feynman integrals and generalized Feynman integrals in the sense of Speer.[35]

Let us consider a generalized Feynman propagator:

$$i\Delta_F(x) = \Gamma(\delta)(-x^2 + i\epsilon)^{-\delta} \quad (\delta \text{ real}) \tag{20}$$

It may be split into a positive frequency part Δ^+ and a negative frequency part Δ^- as follows:

$$i\Delta_F(x) = \theta(x^0)\Delta^+(x) + \theta(-x^0)\Delta^-(x) \tag{21}$$

with

$$\Delta^+(x) = \Gamma(\delta)(-x^2 + i\epsilon x^0)^{-\delta} \propto \int_{p^2 > 0} d^D p\, \theta(p^0) e^{-ipx}(p^2)_+^{\delta - 1/2D} \tag{22}$$

and $\Delta^-(x) = \Delta^+(-x)$.

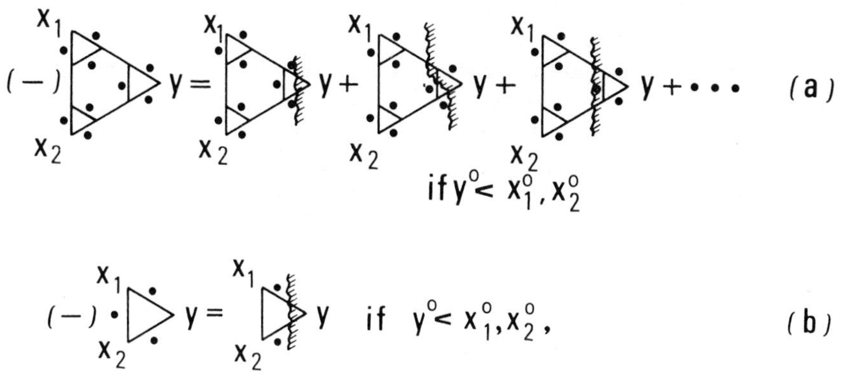

Figure 5. Veltman's cutting rule applied to vertex graphs. On the left-hand side we have omitted the cut, which is to the right of the entire graphs in both (a) and (b). This is possible by the rules given in the text. There are corresponding formulas with the cut shaded on the other side.

Let us consider (Feynman) graphs with cuts through them. Examples are shown on the right-hand side of Figure 5a. There may be several types of lines in the graph; in particular, in the conformal invariant theory one must distinguish between dotted and undotted lines. It will be understood that some value is assigned to the exponent δ in Eq. 20 for every type of line. For ordinary Feynman integrals $\delta \equiv 1$. For spinor lines, Δ_F and $\Delta^{\pm}$ should be replaced by $S_F = i\not{\partial}\Delta_F$ and $S^{\pm} = i\not{\partial}\Delta^{\pm}$, respectively.

To every graph with specified position of the cut one assigns an integral according to the following rules.

Write down for every line:

a factor $i\Delta_F(x_i - x_f)$ if its end points x_i, x_f are both on the unshaded side of the cut;

a factor $\overline{i\Delta_F}(x_i - x_f)$ if both end points x_i, x_f are on the shaded side of the cut;

a factor $\Delta^+(x_i - x_f)$ if x_i is on the unshaded side and x_f on the shaded side of the cut;

a factor $\Delta^-(x_i - x_f)$ if x_i is on the shaded side and x_f on the unshaded side of the cut.

Similarly, for every vertex write down:

a factor $-ig$ if the vertex is on the unshaded side of the cut;

a factor $+ig$ if the vertex is on the shaded side of the cut.

Let us call "internal" these vertices over whose arguments we wish to integrate. As a consequence of the rules, only positive energy can flow from the unshaded to the shaded side of the cut.

Veltman's cutting formula may now be stated as follows. Consider some given (Feynman) graph, and let its vertices be separated into two groups, one group called "marked" or x-type vertices, and the other group "unmarked" or y-type vertices. For every marked vertex we specify once and for all whether it is to be on the shaded or on the unshaded side of the cut. There is one formula for every graph and for every way of selecting marked vertices and assigning them to either side of the cut. The cutting formula reads

$$\sum_{\text{cuts}} (\text{graph with cut}) = 0 \qquad (23)$$

provided the conditions stated below are fulfilled.

Summation is over all possibilities of drawing a cut through the given (Feynman) graph in such a way that each of the marked vertices always stays on its preassigned side of the cut. This may include terms where the graph is entirely on either the shaded or the unshaded side of the cut, so that no line is cut.

In Eq. 23 "(graph with cut)" means, of course, the integral assigned to the graph with specified position of the cut according to the above rules. The formula is valid provided all internal vertices (integration variables) are unmarked (y type), and also the earliest external vertex is y type. In other words, there must be a y-type vertex such that $y^0 < x_i^0$ for all arguments x_i of the marked vertices. An important special case occurs when there are no marked vertices at all.

The cutting formula is actually an algebraic identity for the integrand and remains valid after integration over internal vertices is carried out. The formula remains valid and meaningful also for Feynman integrals, which are overall divergent in momentum space. Divergent proper subgraphs, however, are ruled out.

To illustrate the formula we give two examples in Figure 5. Integration over internal vertices is understood in (a).

Let us now turn to the generalized unitarity relation for the three-point vertex. Since we know this vertex explicitly by Eq. 6, we can also write down immediately its absorptive part in any channel. The result is shown in Figure 6. Its right-hand side can be written in formulas by the rules given above, with an appropriate overall factor supplied.

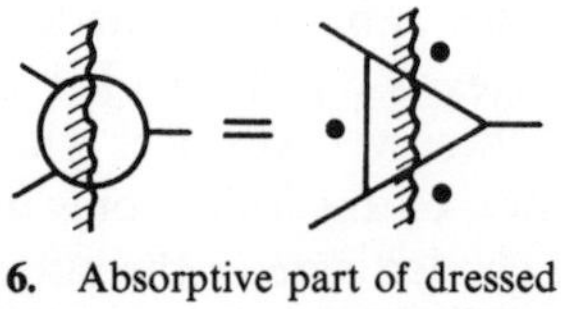

Figure 6. Absorptive part of dressed vertex.

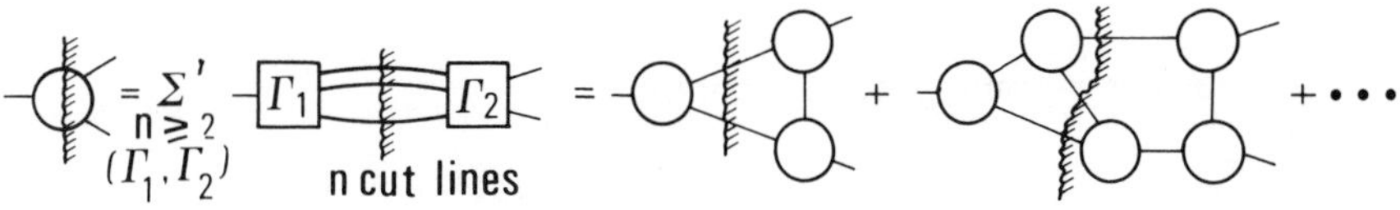

Figure 7. The generalized unitarity relation for the three-point vertex. A cut line stands for the positive frequency absorptive part of a dressed propagator. Complex conjugation is understood for the part of the graph on the shaded side of the cut. For explanation of boxes see text.

The generalized unitarity relation for the three-point vertex is shown in Figure 7. If we consider all amplitudes expressed in terms of their skeleton graph expansion, then the summation is over pairs (Γ_1,Γ_2) of skeleton graphs inside the boxes so that the whole graph (with the cut imagined absent) does not contain any self-energy subgraph. Note that this form of the unitarity relation involves absorptive parts of dressed propagators rather than free ones ($=$ phase space).

Let us now apply Veltman's cutting formula to the skeleton graphs occurring on the right-hand side of the vertex bootstrap Eq. 8. We insert the triangular representation Figure 1 of the dressed vertex and choose two of the external vertices as marked. The result for the simplest graph is shown in Figure 5a. Similarly we obtain the equation shown in Figure 5b from the graphical representation (Figure 1) of the dressed vertex. Inserting into the vertex bootstrap (Eq. 8), we obtain the equation shown in Figure 8, which is valid for restricted arguments $y^0 < x^{10}, x_2{}^0$. However, both sides of the equation are holomorphic functions in the lower y^0 halfplane, because only positive energy can flow through the cut.[41] Thus they agree everywhere by uniqueness of analytic continuation. Figure 8 is an integral equation for the absorptive part of the vertex. Assuming that it can be solved by iteration, we obtain from it the unitarity relation. For instance, iterating once, we recover the two explicit terms on the right-hand side of the unitarity relation of Figure 7, and so on.

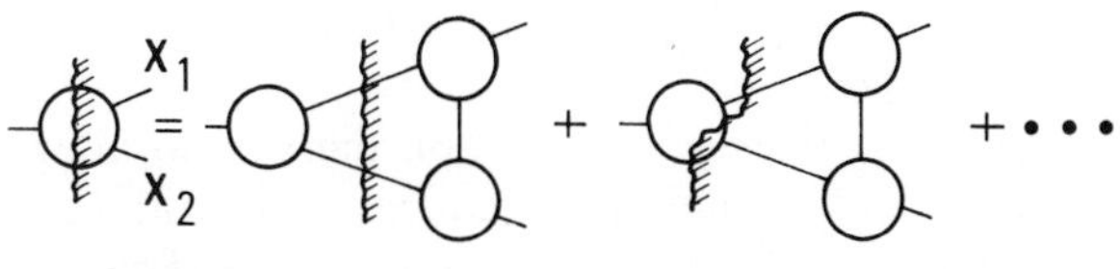

Figure 8. Integral equation for absorptive part of the three-point vertex.

3. GENERAL DEVELOPMENTS

Let us consider n-point Green functions:

$$G(x_1 \cdots x_n) = \langle T(\varphi_1(x_1) \cdots \varphi_n(x_n)) \rangle \qquad (24)$$

For simplicity we shall consider only scalar fields $\varphi_i(x_i)$, with dimensions d_i. Extension of the following considerations to fields of arbitrary spin is straightforward. To preserve the symmetrical shape of the formulas it is advisable, however, to use the manifestly conformal covariant formalism, into which we shall not go here.[12, 32]

First we would like to explain the integral representation due to Symanzik, which exhibits locality and spectrum condition satisfied by conformal invariant Green functions in a manifest form.[18] It reads as follows:

$$G(x_1 \cdots x_n) = (2\pi i)^{-n(n-3)/2} \int_\Gamma \omega K_n(\delta_{ij}) \prod_{i<j} \left\{ \Gamma(\delta_{ij}) x_{ij}^{-2\delta_{ij}} \right\}$$

$$x_{ij}^{-2\alpha} = \left[-(x_i - x_j)^2 + i0 \right]^{-\alpha} \qquad (25)$$

The δ_{ij} are complex variables with $\delta_{ij} = \delta_{ji}$ and $\delta_{ij} = 0$ for $i = j$. They are constrained to the hypersurface Γ, defined by

$$\sum_j \delta_{ij} = d_i, \qquad i = 1, \ldots, n \qquad (26)$$

where $d_i = $ dimension of $\varphi_i(x_i)$. Thus there are $\frac{1}{2}n(n-3)$ independent ones among the δ_{ij}. Integration is over the imaginary part of exponents δ_{ij} subject to restriction 26. The precise choice of the paths of integration must be specified, together with the kernel K_n; ω is the differential form of hypersurface Γ defined by Eq. 26. For example, for the four-point function one may parametrize

$$\left. \begin{array}{l} \delta_{12} = \delta_{34} = u \\ \delta_{13} = \delta_{24} = v \\ \delta_{14} = \delta_{23} = d - u - v \end{array} \right\}, \qquad \omega = du\, dv \qquad (27)$$

if all $d_i = d$. For the three-point function there is no integration left in Eq. 25, that is, $\omega \equiv 1$. The formula then reduces to the unique expression for the conformal invariant three-point function. In the skeleton theory, formula 25 holds, skeleton graph by skeleton graph, with kernels K_n that come out as integrals over a product of B functions and depend, of course, on the graph. This is proved with the help of the "n-star formula," which says that[18]

$$-i\pi^{-D/2}\int d^D u \prod_{j=1}^{n} \left\{ \Gamma(d_j)[-(x_j-u)^2+i0]^{-d_j} \right\} = \text{right-hand side of Eq. 25}$$

$$\text{with } K(\delta)\equiv 1 \qquad (28)$$

provided $\sum_j d_j = D$, and $D = $ number of space-time dimensions. For $n=3$, Eq. 28 reduces to the "vertex graph identity" of d'Eramo, Parisi, and Peliti.[39] Equation 28 makes it possible to carry out all internal integrations of any Migdal graph in x-space until one arrives at a formula having form 25.

In Eq. 25 it is easy to go over to the Wightman functions.[41] All one has to do is change the $i\epsilon$ prescription to

$$x_{ij}^{-2\delta} = \left[-(x_i-x_j)^2 + i\epsilon\left(x_i^0-x_j^0\right) \right]^{-\delta}$$

If the integrals over δ_{ij} are sufficiently well convergent, localityh is then manifest: Wightman functions corresponding to different orderings of fields are known to be boundary values of the same analytic function.[41] They are seen to agree for the interchange of fields with relatively spacelike arguments, since

$$\left[-x^2+i\epsilon x^0 \right]^{-\delta} = \left[-x^2-i\epsilon x^0 \right]^{-\delta} \qquad \text{for } x^2<0$$

The spectrum condition is also manifest since

$$\left[-x^2+i\epsilon x^0 \right]^{-\delta} \propto \int_{p^2>0} d^D p\, e^{-ipx}\theta(p^0)(p^2)_+^{-D/2+\delta}$$

An integral representation of form 25 holds also for vertex functions ($=$ one-particle irreducible, full-propagator amputated Green functions) and so on.

It is this author's feeling that it may be easier to approximate the kernels $K_n(\delta_{ij})$ rather than to deal with the Green functions themselves.

The Green functions in Lagrangian QFT satisfy a set of coupled integral equations. They have been written down by Symanzik for φ^3 theory in six dimensions (or so),[8] and by Taylor, by Wu, and by Johnson for φ^4 theory in four dimensions.[42] We reproduce in Figure 9 the result of ref. 8 for φ^3 theory. These equations are valid for $n \geqslant 3$. For the three-point vertex and the propagator one has instead the Schwinger-Dyson equations

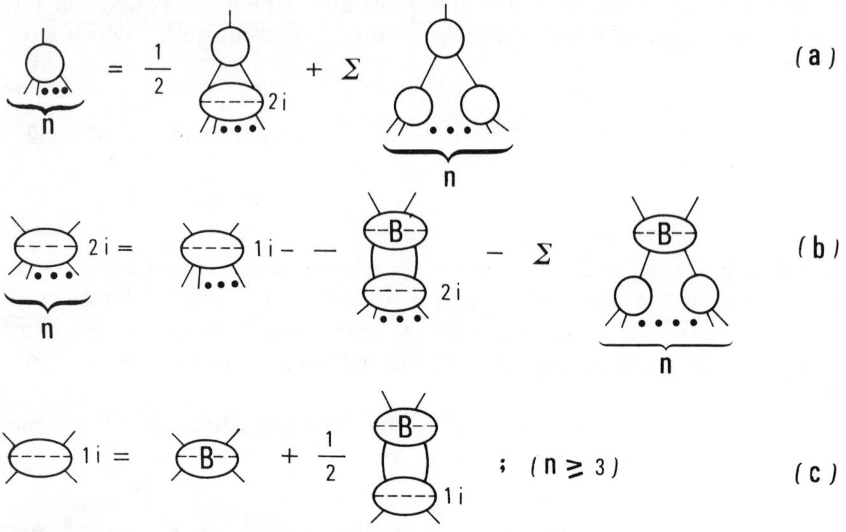

Figure 9. Coupled set of integral equations for Green functions in Lagrangian QFT (φ^3 theory), $n \geqslant 3$. In addition, one has the equations of Figures 3 and 4 for propagator and three-point vertex. Part (*c*) is the Bethe-Salpeter equation. For explanation of graphical notation see text.

(Figures 3 and 4). The round symbols with short legs stand for the full, amputated Green functions. Lines stand for dressed propagators throughout. The one-particle irreducibility prescription "1*i*" is explained in Figure 10. Essentially the same equations can be used for any (conformal invariant) Yukawa-type theory, even where in perturbation theory the Bethe-Salpeter kernel is logarithmically divergent. This divergence is cured by the anomalous dimensions.

In a skeleton graph theory, the two-particle irreducibility prescription "2*i*" means that one should sum over all skeleton graphs inside the ovals which are such that the graph cannot be cut into two pieces along the dashed line without cutting more than two lines. The Bethe-Salpeter kernel is also two-particle irreducible in this sense along the dashed line (cf.

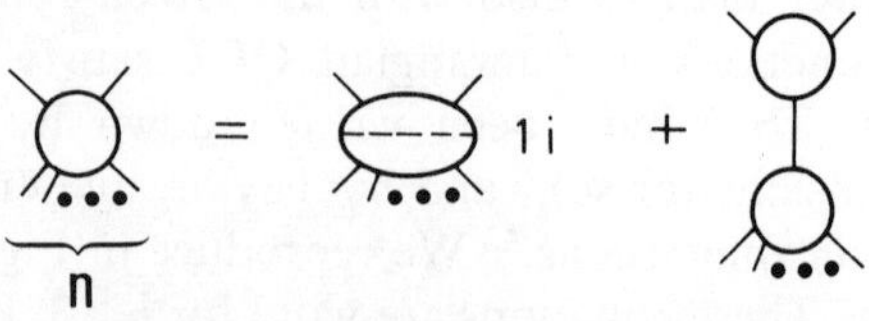

Figure 10. Definition of one-particle irreducibility prescription.

Figure 2). In general, that is, without reference to skeleton graphs, all the various amplitudes distinguished by symbols "B," "$2i$," "$1i$," and so on must be considered defined as solutions of the coupled integral equations (Figures 3, 4, and 9).

These integral equations for Green functions can be rewritten as integral equations for the kernels in Eq. 25. To this end one inserts the integral representation 25 and analogs for all Green functions, the Bethe-Salpeter kernel, and so on. The integrations over internal coordinates x_j may then be performed with the help of the n-star formula (Eq. 28). From the result one can read off the equations for the kernels.

For instance, let $K(u,v)$ be the kernel for the amputated four-point Green function, one-particle irreducible in one channel, in parametrization 27. (For d read D-d everywhere because of the amputation.) Let, furthermore, $H(u',v')$ be the kernel for representation 25 of the Bethe-Salpeter kernel, in the same parametrization. The Bethe-Salpeter equation (Figure 9c) then takes the form

$$K(u,v) = H(u,v) + \int\limits_{-i\infty}^{+i\infty} \int du'\, dv'\, du''\, dv''\, r(uv; u'v'u''v'')\, H(u',v')\, K(u'',v'')$$

$$(29)$$

Unfortunately the explicit expression for the "phase space factor" $r(\cdots)$ is quite complicated.

The kernels K_n are functions of complex variables δ_{ij}. They seem convenient objects to study because their singularity structure is strongly constrained by the validity of conformal invariant operator product expansions. We conjecture that they are meromorphic functions on the hypersurface (Eq. 26) with simple poles as a rule.

Let us now recall the concept of operator product expansions around the tip of the light cone. For instance,

$$\varphi(x)\varphi(0) = \sum_n C_n(x)O_n(0) \qquad \text{as} \quad x \to 0 \qquad (30)$$

where O_n are local fields, and C_n are singular c-number functions. According to Wilson's hypothesis, $C_n(x)$ are homogeneous functions of x of degree $-2d + d_n$, with d_n and d the dimensions of fields O_n and φ, respectively.[16] Because of Lorentz invariance they will thus be of the form (without loss of generality one may take O_n as traceless tensor fields)

$$C_n(x) = \text{const.} x_{\mu_1} \cdots x_{\mu_s} (-x^2 + i\epsilon x^0)^{-d + d_n/2 - s/2} \qquad (31)$$

In conformal invariant φ^3 theory, the fields involved in the most singular terms in Eq. 30 are the unit operator I, the fields $\varphi(0)$, $\nabla_\mu \varphi(0)$, $\nabla_\mu \nabla_\nu \varphi(0)$, and $:\varphi^2(0):$. The conformal invariant field $:\varphi^2:$ has dimension[43] $D-d$ and is not related to $\Box \varphi(!)$.

Expansions like Eq. 30 are also valid inside time-ordered products. They can be rewritten in terms of vertex functions.[44] For instance, in φ^3 theory

$$\Gamma(0xyz) = \text{const.}(-x^2+i0)^{-\alpha}\langle T(:\varphi^2(0):\varphi(y)\varphi(z))\rangle^{\text{prop}}$$

$$+ \text{less singular as } x\to 0 \tag{32}$$

The previously mentioned result on the dimension of φ^2 implies that $\alpha = \frac{1}{2}(D-d)$. The superscript "prop" means that one should amputate on arguments y,z and take the completely one-particle irreducible part.

Let us now see how we can reproduce Eq. 32 by postulating a particular singularity of the kernel $\overline{K}$ for the four-point vertex function. Let us write

$$\Gamma(x_1 x_2 x_3 x_4) = (2\pi i)^{-2} \int_{\eta-i\infty}^{\eta+i\infty} du\, dv\, \overline{K}(u,v)\Gamma(u)x_{12}^{-2u}$$

$$\times \left[\Gamma(u)x_{34}^{-2u}\Gamma(v)^2(x_{13}x_{24})^{-2v}\Gamma(w)^2(x_{14}x_{23})^{-2w} \right]$$

$$\tag{33}$$

with $w = -u-v+D-d$ and $\eta > \alpha$. Suppose now that $\overline{K}(u,v)$ has as its first singularity in u to the left of the path of the u integration a simple pole at $u = \alpha$. Since the expression in brackets has a limit when $x_1 \to x_2$, for $x_2 \neq x_3 \neq x_4$, we obtain by shifting the path of the u integration past the pole

$$\Gamma(x_1 x_2 x_3 x_4) = \text{const.} x_{12}^{-2\alpha} \left[\Gamma(\alpha)x_{34}^{-2\alpha}\Gamma(-\alpha+D-d) \right.$$

$$\left. \times (x_{24}x_{23})^{-2(-\alpha+D-d)} \right]$$

$$+ \text{less singular as } x_1 \to x_2 \qquad (x_3 \neq x_4) \tag{34}$$

This agrees with Eq. 32. The expression in brackets on the right-hand side of Eq. 34 is the unique conformal invariant expression for the three-point vertex on the right-hand side of Eq. 32.

It is also easy to see that this vertex must satisfy an eigenvalue equation analogous to Figure 3. This follows from the Bethe-Salpeter equation (Figure 9c) for the four-point function by using Weinberg's power-counting theorem[45] to discard the contribution coming from the inhomogeneous first term when $x_1 \to x_2$, $x_3 \neq x_4$. The eigenvalue equation determines α; it is fulfilled for $\alpha = \frac{1}{2}(D - d)$ because then the expression in brackets in Eq. 34 becomes identical to the ordinary three-point vertex, Eq. 6, which satisfies the vertex bootstrap (Figure 3) by hypothesis.

REFERENCES AND NOTES

1. E. Bloom et al., *Phys. Rev. Letters*, **23**, 930 (1969).

2. C. G. Callan, *Phys. Rev. D*, **2**, 1451 (1970); K. Symanzik, *Commun. Math. Phys.*, **18**, 227 (1970).

3. M. Gell-Mann and F. E. Low, *Phys. Rev.*, **95**, 1300 (1954); N. N. Bogolubov and D. V. Shirkov, *Introduction to the Theory of Quantized Fields*, Interscience, New York, 1959, Chapter 17.5; K. Wilson, *Phys. Rev. D*, **3**, 1818 (1971).

4. S. L. Adler, *Phys. Rev. D*, **5**, 3021 (1972).

5. M. Baker and K. Johnson, *Phys. Rev.*, **183**, 1292 (1969) and *Phys. Rev. D*, **3**, 2516 (1971); S. L. Adler and W. A. Bardeen, *ibid.*, **4**, 3045 (1971).

6. K. Symanzik, *Commun. Math. Phys.*, **23**, 49 (1971).

7. B. Schroer, *Lettere Nuovo Cimento*, **2**, 867 (1971), Chapter 3 in this volume.

8. K. Symanzik, in *Lectures on High Energy Physics*, ed. by B. Jaksic, Gordon and Breach, New York, 1965.

9. A. A. Migdal, *Phys. Letters*, **37B**, 98, 386 (1971).

10. A. M. Polyakov, *JETP Letters*, **12**, 381 (1970).

11. G. Parisi and L. Peliti, *Lettere Nuovo Cimento*, **2**, 627 (1971).

12. G. Mack and I. Todorov, Trieste Preprint IC/71/139 (October 1971), submitted to *Phys. Rev. D*.

13. A. M. Polyakov, *JETP Letters*, **32**, 296 (1971).

14. G. Mack and K. Symanzik, *Commun. Math. Phys.*, **27**, 247 (1972).

15. J. D. Bjorken and D. Drell, *Relativistic Quantum Fields*, McGraw-Hill, New York, 1965.

16. K. Wilson, *Phys. Rev.*, **179**, 1499 (1969).

17. B. Schroer, *Fortschr. Physik*, **11**, 1 (1963).

18. K. Symanzik, *Lettere Nuovo Cimento*, **3**, 734 (1972).

19. E. Schreier, *Phys. Rev. D*, **3**, 980 (1971).

20. S. Ferrara, R. Gatto, and A. F. Grillo, *Springer Tracts in Modern Physics*, Vol. 67, Springer-Verlag, Berlin, 1973.

21. S. L. Adler, Vol. 67, in *Lectures on Elementary Particles and Quantum Field Theory*, by S. Deser, M. Grisaru, and H. Pendleton, MIT Press, Cambridge, Mass., 1970; R. Jackiw, in *Lectures on Current Algebra and Its Applications*, ed. by S. Treiman, R. Jackiw, and D. Gross, Princeton University Press, Princeton, N. J. (1972); R. Crewther, *Phys. Rev. Letters*, **28**, 1421 (1972).

22. J. D. Bjorken, *Phys. Rev.*, **179**, 1547 (1969).

23. G. Mack, *Phys. Rev. Letters*, **25**, 400 (1970); *Nucl. Phys.*, **B35**, 592 (1971), Section 3.

24. N. Christ, B. Hasslacher, and A. Mueller, Columbia University Preprint CO-3067(2)-9 (1972).

25. S. Ferrara, R. Gatto, A. F. Grillo, and G. Parisi, *Phys. Letters*, **38B**, 333 (1972); Chapter 4 in this volume.

26. G. Parisi, article to appear in *Phys. Letters*.

27. G. Mack, Lectures at the 1972 Kaiserslautern Summer School, to appear in *Springer Tracts in Modern Physics*, Springer-Verlag, Berlin; See also K. Wilson, *Phys. Rev. Letters*, **28**, 548 (1972); K. Wilson and M. E. Fisher, *ibid.*, **28**, 240 (1972).

28. S. Ferrara, R. Gatto, and A. F. Grillo, *Phys. Letters*, **36B**, 124 (1971); *Nucl. Phys.*, **B34**, 349 (1971); *Lettere Nuovo Cimento*, **2**, 1335 (1971); and ref. 20.

29. S. Ferrara and G. Parisi, *Nucl. Phys.*, **B42**, 281 (1972); Chapter 4 in this volume; S. Ferrara, R. Gatto, A. F. Grillo, and G. Parisi, *Lettere Nuovo Cimento*, **4**, 115 (1972); S. Ferrara, A. F. Grillo, and G. Parisi, Frascati Preprint LNF 72/38 (1972).

30. M. Tonin, Chapter 6 in this volume (p. 131); L. Bonora, L. Sartori, and M. Tonin, *Nuovo Cimento*, **10A**, 667 (1972).

31. H. A. Kastrup, *Nucl. Phys.*, **58**, 561 (1964); J. E. Wess, *Nuovo Cimento*, **18**, 1086 (1960); G. Mack, *Nucl. Phys.*, **B5**, 499 (1969).

32. G. Mack and Abdus Salam, *Ann. Phys. (N.Y.)*, **53**, 174 (1969).

33. G. E. Dell'Antonio, New York University Technical Report 12/72 (1972).

34. S. Ferrara, R. Gatto, and A. F. Grillo, *Physics Letters*, **42B**, 264 (1972).

35. E. R. Speer, *Generalized Feynman Amplitudes*, Princeton University Press, Princeton, N. J., 1969.

36. G. Mack, unpublished results.

37. S. L. Adler, *Massless Euclidean QED on the 5-Dimensional Unit Hypersphere*, NAL Preprint NAL-THY-58 (1972).

38. M. Veltman, *Physica*, **29**, 186 (1963).

39. M. d'Eramo, G. Parisi, and L. Peliti, *Lettere Nuovo Cimento*, **2**, 878 (1971).

40. M. Hortascu, R. Seiler, and B. Schroer, *Phys. Rev. D*, **5**, 2518 (1972).

41. R. F. Streater and A. S. Wightman, *PCT, Spin and Statistics and All That*, Benjamin, New York, 1964.

42. J. G. Taylor, *Nuovo Cimento Suppl.*, **1**, 859 (1963); T. T. Wu, *Phys. Rev.*, **125**, 1436 (1962); R. W. Johnson, *J. Math. Phys.*, **11**, 2161 (1970).

43. This is implicit in the result of ref. 14, Appendix C.

44. W. Zimmermann, in *Lectures on Elementary Particles and Fields* (1970 Brandeis University Summer Institute), Vol. 2, ed. by S. Deser, M. Grisaru, and H. Pendleton, MIT Press, Cambridge, Mass., 1971.

45. S. Weinberg, *Phys. Rev.*, **118**, 838 (1960).

CHAPTER 6

Conformal Symmetry in Wilson Operator Product Expansions

L. Bonora
S. Ciccariello
G. Sartori
M. Tonin

In this chapter we discuss a conformal covariant Wilson operator product expansion (OPE) of two general tensor local operators.[1] This representation can be considered as a generalization of a previous one obtained by Ferrara, Gatto, and Grillo on the light cone.[2]

A conformal covariant representation for scalar operators[3] equivalent to ours[4] was recently obtained by these same authors, using the six-dimensional formalism. The content of the representation is strongly connected with recent results obtained by many authors on two- and three-point conformal covariant Green functions.[5-13] In fact the results of refs. 5–13 can be readily reobtained from our representation if the vacuum is assumed to be invariant under conformal transformations.

The advantage of working with OPE rather than with Green functions lies in the fact that OPE, in opposition to Green, functions, presumably remain conformal covariant also when conformal symmetry is spontaneously broken.

Our representation is the following:

$$A^{\alpha_1\cdots\alpha_r}(x)B^{\beta_1\cdots\beta_s}(y) = P_{\gamma_1}^{\ \alpha_1}(x-y)\cdots P_{\gamma_r}^{\ \alpha_r}(x-y)$$

$$\times \sum_N \int d^4t \frac{R_{\nu_1\cdots\nu_n}^{\gamma_1\cdots\gamma_r;\beta_1\cdots\beta_s}[\Lambda_\rho(x,t;y)]P^{\nu_1\mu_1}(t-y)\cdots P^{\nu_n\mu_n}(t-y)}{\left[(x-y)^2\right]^{\lambda_1}\left[(t-x)^2\right]^{\lambda_2}\left[(t-y)^2\right]^{\lambda_3}}\cdot O_{\mu_1\cdots\mu_n}(t)$$

$$(1)$$

where $\{O_{\nu_1\cdots\nu_n}^N\}$ is a complete set of local operators, $A^{\alpha_1\cdots\alpha_r}, B^{\beta_1\cdots\beta_s}$ being two operators of this set.

Notice that, contrary to usual Wilson expansions, the derivatives of the operators $O_{\nu_1\cdots\nu_n}^N$, for example, $\partial_{\mu_1}\cdots\partial_{\mu_m}O_{\nu_1\cdots\nu_n}^N$ do not appear explicitly in this expansion.

In Eq. 1, $\lambda_1, \lambda_2, \lambda_3$ are real numbers completely specified in terms of the dimensions l_A, l_B, l_N of the operators involved:

$$\lambda_1 = \frac{l_B + l_A + l_N}{2} - 2$$

$$\lambda_2 = \frac{l_A - l_B - l_N}{2} + 2 \qquad (2)$$

$$\lambda_3 = \frac{l_B - l_A - l_N}{2} + 2$$

The reflection operator $P^{\rho\sigma}(x)$ can be written as follows:

$$P^{\rho\sigma}(x) = g^{\rho\sigma} - \frac{2x^\rho x^\sigma}{x^2} \qquad (3)$$

with $P^{\rho\tau}(x)P_{\tau\sigma}(x) = g_\sigma^{\ \rho}$.

It can be conveniently used to express the transformation law of the fields under finite special conformal transformations in the following way:

$$e^{iKc}O_{\nu_1\cdots\nu_n}^N(x)e^{-iKc} = \left(\frac{x_c^2}{x^2}\right)^{l_N} P_{\nu_1\lambda_1}(x)P^{\lambda_1\mu_1}(x_c)\cdots P_{\nu_n\lambda_n}(x)P^{\lambda_n\mu_n}(x_c)O_{\mu_1\cdots\mu_n}^N(x_c)$$

$$(4)$$

where K_μ are the generators of special conformal transformations, c_μ are real numbers, and $x_c^\mu = (x^\mu - x^2c^\mu)/(1 - 2cx + x^2c^2)$.

$R^{\alpha_1\cdots\alpha_s;\beta_1\cdots\beta_t}_{\nu_1\cdots\nu_n}[\Lambda_\rho(xt;y)]$ is the most general tensor which can be constructed with the vector

$$\Lambda_\rho(xt;y) = \left[\frac{(x-y)^2(t-y)^2}{(x-t)^2}\right]^{1/2}\left[\frac{(x-y)_\rho}{(x-y)^2} - \frac{(t-y)_\rho}{(t-y)^2}\right] \qquad (5)$$

The following identities hold:

$$P_{\mu\nu}(t-y)\Lambda^\nu(xt;y) = \Lambda_\mu(xy;t)$$

$$P_{\mu\nu}(y)\Lambda^\nu(xt;y) = -\Lambda_\mu\left(\frac{-x}{x^2}, \frac{-t}{t^2}; \frac{-y}{y^2}\right) \qquad (6)$$

$$P_{\mu\rho}(x)P^{\rho\sigma}(x-y)P_{\sigma\nu}(y) = P_{\mu\nu}\left(\frac{x}{x^2} - \frac{y}{y^2}\right)$$

The conformal covariance of Eq. 1 can be easily verified using the transformation law of Eq. 4. More simply, one can prove that Eq. 1 is conformal covariant by showing that it is covariant under inversion, $x_\mu \to -x_\mu/x^2$. The transformation laws of the fields under inversion I were obtained recently by Nobili[9] in the form

$$IO^N_{\nu_1\cdots\nu_n}(x)I^{-1} = (x^2)^{-l_N}P_{\nu_1}{}^{\mu_1}(x)\cdots P_{\nu_n}{}^{\mu_n}(x)O^N_{\mu_1\cdots\mu_n}\left(\frac{x}{x^2}\right) \qquad (7)$$

The covariance of Eq. 1 is immediate, using Eq. 7 and the identities of Eqs. 6.

To give a precise meaning to the integral in Eq. 1 we shall work out the calculations in the Euclidean space and go back to the Minkowski space only in the final formulas.

In order to put Eq. 1 into the usual Wilson form it is necessary to expand $O^N_{\nu_1\cdots\nu_n}(t)$ around the point $t_\mu = y_\mu$, make a Feynman parametrization, and finally integrate over t and over the Feynman parameter. In this way one obtains the proper coefficients of the operators O^N and of their derivatives in Wilson's OPE, and realizes explicitly that conformal covariance fixes the coefficients of the derivatives of the operators themselves.

If one stops before performing the last integration over the Feynman parameter and retains only the most singular terms on the light cone, the expansion of ref. 2 is recovered. The representation given by Eq. 1 holds only if all the operators involved transform according to Eq. 4. In this case, they belong to representations of the stability subgroup at $x=0$ which remain irreducible when they are restricted to the Lorentz group. They are characterized by the following condition:

$$[K_\rho, O^N(0)] = 0 \tag{8}$$

More general representations exist too. Let us define, for instance:

$$Q \equiv \begin{pmatrix} Q^0 \\ Q^1 \\ \cdot \\ \cdot \\ \cdot \\ Q^m \end{pmatrix} \tag{9}$$

where Q^r $(r=1,\ldots,n)$ is a Lorentz tensor of dimension $l_Q - r$, that is,

$$Q^r \equiv \left\{ Q^{(r)}_{\alpha_1 \cdots \alpha_{n_r}} ; \quad \alpha_i = 0,\ldots,3; \quad i = 1,\ldots,n_r \right\}$$

The following commutation relations:

$$[D, Q(0)] = i\Delta Q(0)$$

$$[M_{\mu\nu}, Q(0)] = i\Sigma_{\mu\nu} Q(0) \tag{10}$$

$$[K_\rho, Q(0)] = i\kappa_\rho Q(0)$$

characterize a representation [13] provided that Δ is a diagonal $m \times m$ matrix and $\Delta_{rr} = l_q - r$ $(r=0,\ldots,m)$; $\Sigma_{\mu\nu}$ is also a diagonal $m \times m$ matrix whose diagonal elements $\Sigma_{\mu\nu}^{(r)}$ are spin operators which specify the Lorentz properties of the tensors Q^r; and, finally, κ_ρ is a triangular matrix connecting Q^r only to Q^{r+1} and satisfying the relations

$$[\kappa_\rho, \kappa_\sigma] = 0$$

$$[\Sigma_{\mu\nu}, \kappa_\rho] = g_{\mu\rho} \kappa_\nu - g_{\nu\rho} \kappa_\mu$$

In general it is possible to redefine the operators in the tower Q by adding to them linear combinations of derivatives of lower-dimensional operators of the same tower in such a way that the new operators satisfy Eq. 8. Exceptions occur only for particular values of the dimensions, as will be shown in a simple example. Let A_μ be a vector field with dim l and B a scalar field with dim $l+1$ and suppose that

$$[K_\rho, B(0)] = iA_\rho$$

$$[K_\rho, A_\mu(0)] = 0 \tag{11}$$

One has also

$$[K_\rho, \partial_\mu A_\mu(0)] = i(l-3)A_\rho$$

so that

$$\overline{B} = B - \frac{\partial_\mu A_\mu}{l-3}$$

satisfies

$$\left[K_\rho, \overline{B}(0)\right] = 0 \tag{12}$$

Obviously, $l=3$ is an exceptional case.

More generally, exceptional cases occur when operators $Q^{(4)}_{\mu_1 \cdots \mu_n}$ of twist $\tau = 4$ exist which are connected by K_ρ to other operators $O^{(2)}_{\mu_1 \cdots \mu_{n+1}}$ of twist $\tau = 2$ as follows:

$$\left[K_\rho, O^{(4)}_{\mu_1 \cdots \mu_n}(0)\right] = ic O^{(2)}_{\rho\mu_1 \cdots \mu_n}(0) \tag{13}$$

Such operators as $O^{(4)}$ do not appear in simple field theoretical models. However, we suspect that their existence is required in models where conformal invariance is spontaneously broken. In fact, in any spontaneously broken conformal invariant theory, a preferred field σ exists which obeys the following anomalous commutation relations:

$$[D, \sigma(0)] = \lambda$$

$$[K_\rho, \partial_\mu \sigma(0)] = g_{\mu\rho}\lambda$$

λ being a real number.

If one believes in naive manipulations, it is easy to check that the operators

$$O^{(4)}_{\mu_1 \cdots \mu_n} = \, : \partial^\rho \sigma O^{(2)}_{\rho\mu_1 \cdots \mu_n} :$$

where $O^{(2)}_{\mu_0 \mu_1 \cdots \mu_n}$ have twist $\tau = 2$, satisfy the commutation relations of Eq. 13.

It is possible to generalize Eq. 1 when some of the operators involved belong to these more general representations. To this aim the transformation laws of the operators Q under finite special conformal transformations are required. They can be obtained in the form:

$$\exp(iKc)Q' \exp(-iKc)$$

$$= \left[\exp\left(\kappa_\rho \frac{c^\rho - x^\rho c^2}{1 - 2cx + c^2 x^2} \right) \right]_{rs} \left[\left(\frac{x_c^2}{x^2} \right)^L \right]_{s,t} \left\{ [P(x)P(x_c)]^N \right\}_{t,u} \cdot Q^u(x_c)$$

$$(14)$$

Here the following shortened notations are used:

$$\left[(x^2)^L \right]_{rs} Q^s \equiv \delta_{rs} (x^2)^{l-r} Q^r$$

$$\left\{ [P(x)]^N \right\}_{rs} Q^s \equiv \delta_{rs} P^{\beta_1 \alpha_1}(x) \cdots P^{\beta_{nr} \alpha_{nr}}(x) Q^{(s)}_{\alpha_1 \cdots \alpha_{ns}}$$

and so on.

With the same notations, a conformal covariant OPE can be written as follows when the involved operators transform according to Eq. 14:

$$A^a(x)B^b(0) = \sum_R \int \frac{d^4c}{(c^2)^2} \left[\exp\left(-\kappa_\rho^A \frac{x_\rho}{x^2} \right)(c^2)^{-(L_A/2)} \left(\frac{1}{x^2} \right)^{L_A} [P(x)]^{N_A} \right]_{a,\bar{a}}$$

$$\cdot \left\{ \exp\left(\kappa_\sigma^B \frac{x_\sigma}{x^2} \right)(c^2)^{(L_B/2)} \right\}_{b,\bar{b}} \cdot f^{\bar{a},\bar{b},\bar{r}}(c) \cdot$$

$$\cdot \left[\left(\frac{1}{x^2} \right)^{-L_R} (c^2)^{L_R/2} [P(x)]^{N_R} \exp\left(\kappa_\tau^R \frac{x_\tau}{x^2} \right) \right]_{\bar{r},r} \cdot \exp(iKc)Q_R^r(c)\exp(-iKc)$$

$$(15)$$

where $f^{\bar{a},\bar{b},\bar{r}}(c)$ is the most general tensor involving c_μ of homogeneity degree zero in c_μ.

The representation in Eq. 15 can be easily obtained using the same method as in ref. 1.

REFERENCES

1. L. Bonora, G. Sartori, and M. Tonin, *Nuovo Cimento*, **10A**, 667, 1972.
2. S. Ferrara, R. Gatto, and A. F. Grillo, *Phys. Letters*, **36B**, 124 (1971).
3. S. Ferrara, R. Gatto, and A. F. Grillo, *Lettere Nuovo Cimento*, **2**, 1363 (1971); *Springer Tracts in Modern Physics*, Vol. 67, Springer Verlag, Berlin, and LNF 71/83 (1971).
4. L. Bonora, *Lettere Nuovo Cimento*, **3**, 548 (1972).
5. A. M. Polyakov, *Soviet Phys. JETP*, **28**, 533 (1969), and *JETP Letters*, **12**, 538 (1971).
6. M. D'Eramo, G. Parisi, and L. Peliti, *Lettere Nuovo Cimento*, **2**, 878 (1971); G. Parisi, LNF 72/13.
7. A. A. Migdal, *Phys. Letters*, **37B**, 98, 386 (1971).
8. G. Mack and I. T. Todorov, Trieste Preprint IC/71/139 (1971); see Chapter 5 of this volume.
9. R. Nobili, Padova Preprint IFPTH 1/72.
10. E. J. Schreier, *Phys. Rev. D*, **3**, 980 (1972).
11. S. Ferrara, R. Gatto, A. F. Grillo, and G. Parisi, *Phys. Letters*, **38B**, 333 (1972).
12. S. Ferrara, R. Gatto, A. F. Grillo, and G. Parisi, *Nucl. Phys.*, **B49**, 77 (1972).
13. G. Mack and K. Symanzik, Desy Preprint 72/20 (1972); see Chapter 5 of this volume.
14. G. Mack and A. Salam, *Ann. Phys.*, **53**, 174 (1969).

Light-Cone Current Algebra, π° Decay, and e^+e^- Annihilation

W. A. Bardeen
H. Fritzsch
M. Gell-Mann

1. INTRODUCTION

The indication from deep inelastic electron scattering experiments at SLAC that Bjorken scaling may really hold has motivated an extension of the hypotheses of current algebra to what may be called light-cone current algebra.[1] As before, one starts from a field theoretical quark model (say one with neutral vector "gluons") and abstracts exact algebraic results, postulating their validity for the real world of hadrons. In light-cone algebra, we abstract the most singular term near the light cone in the commutator of two-vector or axial vector currents, which turns out to be given in terms of bilocal current operators that reduce to local currents when the two space-time points coincide. The algebraic properties of these bilocal operators, as abstracted from the model, give a number of predictions for the Bjorken functions in deep inelastic electron and neutrino experiments. None is in disagreement with experiment. These algebraic properties, by the way, are the same as in the free quark model.

From the mathematical point of view, the new abstractions differ from the older ones of current algebra (commutators of "good components" of current densities at equal times or on a light plane) in being true only formally in a model with interactions, while failing to each order of renormalized perturbation theory, like the scaling itself. Obviously it is hoped that, if the scaling works in the real world, so do the relations of light-cone current algebra, in spite of the lack of cooperation from renormalized perturbation theory in the model.

The applications to deep inelastic scattering involve assumptions only about the connected part of each current commutator. We may ask whether the disconnected part—for example, the vacuum expected value of the commutator of currents—also behaves in the light-cone limit as it does formally in the quark-gluon model, namely, the same as for a free quark model. Does the commutator of two currents, sandwiched between the hadron vacuum state and itself, act at high momenta exactly as it would for free quark theory? If so, then we can predict immediately and trivially the high-energy limit of the ratio

$$\sigma(e^+ + e^- \to \text{hadrons})/\sigma(e^+ + e^- \to \mu^+ + \mu^-)$$

for one-photon annihilation.

In contrast to the situation for the connected part and deep inelastic scattering, the annihilation results depend on the statistics of the quarks in the model. For three Fermi-Dirac quarks, the ratio would be $(\frac{2}{3})^2 + (-\frac{1}{3})^2 + (-\frac{1}{3})^2 = \frac{2}{3}$, but do we want Fermi-Dirac quarks? The relativistic "current quarks" in the model, which are essentially square roots of currents, are of course not identical with "constituent quarks" of the naive, approximate quark picture of baryon and meson spectra. Nevertheless, there should be a transformation, perhaps even a unitary transformation, linking constituent quarks and current quarks (in a more abstract language, a transformation connecting the symmetry group $[\text{SU}(3) \times \text{SU}(3)]_{W, \infty, \text{strong}}$ of the constituent quark picture of baryons and mesons, a subgroup of $[\text{SU}(6)]_{W, \infty, \text{strong}}$,[2] with the symmetry group $[\text{SU}(3) \times \text{SU}(3)]_{W, \infty, \text{currents}}$,[3] generated by the vector and axial vector charges). This transformation should certainly preserve quark statistics. Therefore the indications from the constituent quark picture that quarks obey peculiar statistics should suggest the same behavior for the current quarks in the underlying relativistic model from which we abstract the vacuum behavior of the light-cone current commutator.[4]

In the constituent quark picture of baryons,[5] the ground-state wave function is described by $(56, 1), L = 0^+$ with respect to $[SU(6) \times SU(6) \times SU(3)]$ or $(56, L_z = 0)$ with respect to $[SU(6) \times O(2)]_W$. It is totally symmetric in spin and SU(3). In accordance with the simplicity of the picture, one might expect the space wave function of the ground state to be totally symmetric. The entire wave function is then symmetrical. Yet baryons are to be antisymmetrized with respect to one another, since they do obey the Pauli principle. Thus the peculiar statistics suggested for quarks has then symmetrized in sets of three and otherwise antisymmetrized. This can be described in various equivalent ways. One is to consider "para-Fermi statistics of rank 3"[6] and then to impose the restriction that all physical particles be fermions or bosons; the quarks are then fictitious (i.e., always bound) and all physical three-quark systems are totally symmetric overall. An equivalent description, easier to follow, involves introducing nine types of quarks, that is, the usual three types in each of three "colors," say red, white, and blue. The restriction is then imposed that all physical states and all observable quantities like the currents be singlets with respect to the SU(3) of color (i.e., the symmetry that manipulates the color index). Again, the quarks are fictitious. Let us refer to this type of statistics as "quark statistics."

If we take the quark statistics seriously and apply it to current quarks as well as constituent quarks, then the closed-loop processes in the models are multiplied by a factor of 3, and the asymptotic ratio $\sigma(e^+e^- \rightarrow \text{hadrons})$ $/\sigma(e^+e^- \rightarrow \mu^+\mu^-)$ becomes $3 \cdot \frac{2}{3} = 2$.

Experiments at present are too low in energy and not accurate enough to test this prediction, but in the next year or two the situation should change. Meanwhile, is there any supporting evidence? Assuming that the connected light-cone algebra is right, we should like to know whether we can abstract the disconnected part as well, and whether the statistics are right. In fact, there is evidence from the decay of the π^0 into 2γ. It is well known that in the partially conserved axial current (PCAC) limit, with $m_\pi^2 \rightarrow 0$, Adler and others[7] have given an exact formula for the decay amplitude $\pi^0 \rightarrow 2\gamma$ in a "quark-gluon" model theory. The amplitude is a known constant times $(\sum Q_{1/2}^2 - \sum Q_{-1/2}^2)$, where the sum is over the types of quarks and the charges $Q_{1/2}$ are those of $I_z = \frac{1}{2}$ quarks, while the charges $Q_{-1/2}$ are those of $I_z = -\frac{1}{2}$ quarks. The amplitude agrees with experiment, within the errors, in both sign and magnitude if $\sum Q_{1/2}^2 - \sum Q_{-1/2}^2 = 1$.[8] If we had three Fermi-Dirac quarks, we would have $(\frac{2}{3})^2 - (-\frac{1}{3})^2 = \frac{1}{3}$, and the decay rate would be wrong by a factor of $\frac{1}{9}$. With "quark statistics," we get $\frac{1}{3} \cdot 3 = 1$ and everything is all right, assuming that PCAC is applicable.

There is, however, the problem of the derivation of the Adler formula. In the original derivation a renormalized perturbation expansion is applied to the "quark-gluon" model theory, and it is shown that only the lowest-order closed-loop diagram survives in the PCAC limit,[9] so that an exact expression can be given for the decay amplitude. Clearly this derivation does not directly suit our purposes, since our light-cone algebra is not obtainable by renormalized perturbation theory term by term. Of course, the situation might change if all orders are summed.

Recently it has become clear that the formula can be derived without direct reference to renormalized perturbation theory, from considerations of light-cone current algebra. Crewther has contributed greatly to clarifying this point,[10] using earlier work of Wilson[11] and Schreier.[12] Our objectives in this chapter are to call attention to Crewther's work, to sketch a derivation that is somewhat simpler than his, and to clarify the question of statistics.

We assume the connected light-cone algebra, and we make the further abstraction, from free quark theory or formal "quark-gluon" theory, of the principle that not only commutators but also products and physically ordered products of current operators obey scale invariance near the light cone, so that, apart from possible subtraction terms involving four-dimensional δ functions, current products near the light cone are given by the same formula as current commutators, with the singular functions changed from $\epsilon(z_0)\delta[(z^2)]$ to $(z^2 - i\epsilon z_0)^{-1}$ for ordinary products or $(z^2 - i\epsilon)^{-1}$ for ordered products.

Then it can be shown from consistency arguments that the only possible form for the disconnected parts (two-, three-, and four-point functions) is that given by free quark theory or formal "quark-gluon" theory, with only the coefficient needing to be determined by abstraction from a model. (In general, of course, the coefficient could be zero, thus changing the physics completely.) Then, from the light-cone behavior of current products, including connected and disconnected parts, the Adler formula for $\pi^0 \to 2\gamma$ in the PCAC limit can be derived in terms of that coefficient.

If we take the coefficient from the model with "quark statistics," predicting the asymptotic ratio of $\sigma(e^+e^- \to \text{hadrons})/\sigma(e^+e^- \to \mu^+\mu^-)$ to be 2 for one-photon annihilation, we obtain the correct value of the $\pi^0 \to 2\gamma$ decay amplitude, agreeing with experiment in magnitude and sign. Conversely, if for any reason we do not like to appeal to the model, we can take the coefficient from the observed $\pi^0 \to 2\gamma$ amplitude and predict in that way that the asymptotic value of $\sigma(e^+e^- \to \text{hadrons})/\sigma(e^+e^- \to \mu^+\mu^-)$ should be about 2.

Some more complicated and less attractive models that agree with the observed $\pi^0 \to 2\gamma$ amplitude are discussed in Section 3.

2. LIGHT-CONE ALGEBRA

The ideas of current algebra stem essentially from the attempt to abstract, from field theoretic quark models with interactions, certain algebraic relations obeyed by weak and electromagnetic currents to all orders in the strong interaction, and to postulate these relations for the system of real hadrons, while suggesting possible experimental tests of their validity. In four dimensions, with spinor fields involved, the only renormalizable models are ones that are barely renormalizable, such as a model of spinors coupled to a neutral vector "gluon" field. Until recently, the relations abstracted, such as the equal-time commutation relations of vector and axial charges or charge densities, were true in each order of renormalized perturbation theory in such a model. Now, however, one is considering the abstraction of results that are true only formally, with canonical manipulation of operators, and that fail, by powers of logarithmic factors, in each order of renormalized perturbation theory, in all barely renormalizable models (although they might be all right in a super-renormalizable model, if there were one).

The reason for the recent trend is, of course, the tendency of the deep inelastic electron scattering experiments at SLAC to encourage belief in Bjorken scaling, which fails to every order of renormalized perturbation theory in barely renormalizable models. There is also the availability of beautiful algebraic results, with Bjorken scaling as one of their predictions, if formal abstractions are accepted. The simplest such abstraction is that of the formula giving the leading singularity on the light cone of the connected part of the commutator of the vector or axial vector currents,[1] for example:

$$[F_{i\mu}(x), F_{j\nu}(y)] \doteq [F_{i\mu}{}^5(x), F_{j\nu}{}^5(y)]$$

$$\doteq \frac{1}{4\pi} \partial_\rho \{ \epsilon(x_0 - y_0) \delta[(x-y)^2] \}$$

$$\times \{ (if_{ijk} - d_{ijk}) [s_{\mu\nu\rho\sigma} F_{k\sigma}(y,x) + i\epsilon_{\mu\nu\rho\sigma} F_{k\sigma}{}^5(y,x)]$$

$$+ (if_{ijk} + d_{ijk}) [s_{\mu\nu\rho\sigma} F_{k\sigma}(x,y) - i\epsilon_{\mu\nu\rho\sigma} F_{k\sigma}{}^5(x,y)] \} \quad (1)$$

On the right-hand side we have the connected parts of bilocal operators $F_{i\mu}(x,y)$ and $F_{i\mu}{}^5(x,y)$, which reduce to the local currents $F_{i\mu}(x)$ and $F_{i\mu}{}^5(x)$ as $x \to y$. The bilocal operators are defined as observable quantities only in the vicinity of the light-cone, $(x-y)^2 = 0$. Here

$$s_{\mu\nu\rho\sigma} = \delta_{\mu\rho}\delta_{\nu\sigma} + \delta_{\nu\rho}\delta_{\mu\sigma} - \delta_{\mu\nu}\delta_{\rho\sigma}.$$

Formula 1 gives Bjorken scaling by virtue of the finite matrix elements assumed for $F_{i\mu}(x,y)$ and $F_{i\mu}{}^5(x,y)$; in fact, the Fourier transform of the matrix element of $F_{i\mu}(x,y)$ is just the Bjorken scaling function. The fact that all charged fields in the model have spin $\frac{1}{2}$ determines the algebraic structure of the formula and gives the prediction $(\sigma_L/\sigma_T)_{Bj}\to 0$ for deep inelastic electron scattering, not in contradiction with experiment. The electrical and weak charges of the quarks in the model determine the coefficients in the formula, and give rise to numerous sum rules and inequalities for the SLAC-MIT experiments in the Bjorken limit, again none in contradiction with experiment.

The formula for the leading light-cone singularity in the commutator contains, of course, the physical information that near the light cone we have full symmetry with respect to $SU(3)\times SU(3)$ and with respect to scale transformations in coordinate space. Thus there is conservation of dimension in the formula, with each current having $l=-3$ and the singular function $x-y$ also having $l=-3$.

A simple generalization of the abstraction that we have considered turns into a closed system, called the basic light-cone algebra. Here we commute the bilocal operators as well, for instance, $F_{i\mu}(x,u)$ with $F_{j\nu}(y,v)$, as all of the six intervals among the four space-time points approach 0, so that all four points tend to lie on a lightlike straight line in Minkowski space. Abstraction from the model gives us, on the right-hand side, a singular function of one coordinate difference, say $x-v$, times a bilocal current $F_{i\alpha}$ or $F_{i\alpha}{}^5$ at the other two points, say y and u, plus an expression with (x,v) and (y,u) interchanged, and the system closes algebraically. The formulas are just like Eq. 1. We shall assume here the validity of the basic light-cone algebraic system, and discuss the possible generalization to products and to disconnected parts. In Section 4, we conclude from the generalization to products that the form of an expression like $\langle\mathrm{vac}|F_{i\alpha}(x)$ $F_{j\beta}(y,z)|\mathrm{vac}\rangle$ for disconnected parts is uniquely determined from the consistency of the connected light-cone algebra to be a number N times the corresponding expression for three free Fermi-Dirac quarks, when x,y, and z tend to lie on a straight lightlike line. The $\pi^0\to 2\gamma$ amplitude in the PCAC approximation is then calculated in terms of N and is proportional to it. Thus we do not want N to be zero.

The asymptotic ratio $\sigma(e^+e^-\to\mathrm{hadrons})/\sigma(e^+e^-\to\mu^+\mu^-)$ from one-photon annihilation is also proportional to N. We may either determine N from the observed $\pi^0\to 2\gamma$ amplitude and then compute this asymptotic ratio approximately, or else appeal to a model and abstract the exact value of N, from which we calculate the amplitude of $\pi^0\to 2\gamma$. In a model, N depends on the statistics of the quarks, which we discuss in the next section.

3. STATISTICS AND ALTERNATIVE SCHEMES

As we remarked in Section 1, the presumably unwanted Fermi-Dirac statistics for the quarks, with $N = 1$, would give $\sigma(e^+e^- \to \text{hadrons})$ $/\sigma(e^+e^- \to \mu^+\mu^-) \to 2/3$. (Such quarks could be real particles, if necessary.) Now let us consider the case of "quark statistics," equivalent to para-Fermi statistics of rank 3 with the restriction that all physical particles be bosons or fermions. (Quarks are then fictitious, permanently bound. Even if we applied the restriction only to baryons and mesons, quarks would still be fictitious, as we can see by applying the principle of cluster decomposition of the S-matrix.)

The quark field theory model or the "quark-gluon" model is set up with three fields, q_R, q_B, and q_W, each with three ordinary SU(3) components, making nine in all. Without loss of generality, they may be taken to anticommute with one another as well as with themselves. The currents all have the form $\bar{q}_R q_R + \bar{q}_B q_B + \bar{q}_W q_W$, and are singlets with respect to the SU(3) of color. The physical states too are restricted to be singlets under the color SU(3). For example, the $q\bar{q}$ configuration for mesons is only $\bar{q}_R q_R + \bar{q}_B q_B + \bar{q}_W q_W$, and the qqq configuration for baryons is only $q_R q_B q_W - q_B q_R q_W + q_W q_R q_B - q_R q_W q_B + q_B q_W q_R - q_W q_B q_R$. Likewise all the higher configurations for baryons and mesons are required to be color singlets.

We do not know how to incorporate such restrictions on physical states into the formalism of the "quark-gluon" field theory model. We assume without proof that the asymptotic light-cone results for current commutators and multiple commutators are not altered. Since the currents are all color singlets, there is no obvious contradiction.

The use of quark statistics then gives $N = 3$ and $\sigma(e^+e^- \to \text{hadrons})$ $/\sigma(e^+e^- \to \mu^+\mu^-) \to 2$. This is the value that we predict.

We should, however, examine other possible schemes. First, we might treat actual para-Fermi statistics of rank 3 for the quarks without any further restriction on the physical states. In that case, there are excited baryons that are not fermions and are not totally symmetric in the $3q$ configuration; there are also excited mesons that are not bosons. Whether the quarks can be real in this case without violating the principle of "cluster decomposition" (factorizing of the S-matrix when a physical system is split into very distant subsystems) is a matter of controversy; probably they cannot. In this situation, N is presumably still 3.

Another situation with $N = 3$ is that of a physical color SU(3) that can really be excited by the strong interaction. Excited baryons now exist that are in octets, decimets, and so on with respect to color, and mesons in octets and higher configurations. Many conserved quantum numbers exist, and new interactions may have to be introduced to violate them. This is a wildly speculative scheme. Here the nine quarks can be real if necessary, that is, capable of being produced singly or doubly at finite energies and identified in the laboratory.

We may consider a still more complicated situation in which the relationship of the physical currents to the current nonet in the connected algebra is somewhat modified, namely, the Han-Nambu scheme.[13] Here there are nine quarks, capable of being real, but they do not have the regular quark charges. Instead, the u quarks have charges $1, 1, 0$, averaging to $\frac{2}{3}$; the d quarks have charges $0, 0, -1$, averaging to $-\frac{1}{3}$; and the s quarks also have charges $0, 0, -1$, averaging to $-\frac{1}{3}$. In this scheme, not only can the analog of the color variable really be excited, but also it is excited even by the electromagnetic current, which is no longer a "color" singlet. Since the expressions for the electromagnetic current in terms of the current operators in the connected algebra are modified, this situation cannot be described by a value of N. It is clear, however, from the quark charges, that the asymptotic behavior of the disconnected part gives, in the Han-Nambu scheme, $\sigma(e^+e^- \rightarrow \text{hadrons})/\sigma(e^+e^- \rightarrow \mu^+\mu^-) \rightarrow 4$. Because the formulas for the physical currents are changed, numerical predictions for deep inelastic scattering are altered too. For example, instead of the inequality $\frac{1}{4} \leqslant [F^{en}(\xi)/F^{ep}(\xi)] \leqslant 4$ for deep inelastic scattering of electrons from neutrons and protons, we would have $\frac{1}{2} \leqslant [F^{en}(\xi)/F^{ep}(\xi)] \leqslant 2$. However, comparison of asymptotic values with experiment in this case may not be realistic at the energies now being explored. The electromagnetic current is not a color singlet; it directly excites the new quantum numbers, and presumably the asymptotic formulas do not become applicable until above the thresholds for the new kinds of particles. Thus, unless and until entirely new phenomena are detected, the Han-Nambu scheme really has little predictive power.

A final case to be mentioned is one in which we have ordinary "quark statistics" but the usual group SU(3) is enlarged to SU(4) to accomodate a "charmed" quark u' with charge $\frac{2}{3}$ which has no isotopic spin or ordinary strangeness but does have a nonzero value of a new conserved quantum number, charm, which would be violated by weak interactions (in such a way as to remove the strangeness-changing part from the commutator of the hadronic weak charge operator with its Hermitian conjugate). Again the expression for the physical currents in terms of our connected algebra is altered, and again the asymptotic value of $\sigma(e^+e^- \rightarrow \text{hadrons})$ $/ \sigma(e^+e^- \rightarrow \mu^+\mu^-)$ is changed, this time to $[(\frac{2}{3})^2 + (-\frac{1}{3})^2 + (-\frac{1}{3})^2 + (\frac{2}{3})^2] \cdot 3 = \frac{10}{3}$. Just as in the Han-Nambu scheme, the predictive power is very low here until the energy is above the threshold for making "charmed" particles.

We pointed out in Section 1 that for three Fermi-Dirac quarks the Adler amplitude is too small by a factor of 3. For all the other schemes quoted above, however, it comes out just right and the decay amplitude of $\pi^0 \to 2\gamma$ in the PCAC limit agrees with experiment. One may verify that for all of these schemes $\sum Q_{1/2}^2 - \sum Q_{-1/2}^2 = 1$. The various schemes are summarized in the following table.

Scheme	$\dfrac{(e^+e^- \to \text{hadrons})}{(e^+e^- \to \mu^+\mu^-)}$	Can quarks be real?
"Quark statistics"	2	No
Para-Fermi statistics rank 3	2	Probably not
Nine Fermi-Dirac quarks	2	Yes
Han-Nambu, Fermi-Dirac	4	Yes
Quark statistics + charm	10/3	No
Para-Fermi, rank 3 + charm	10/3	Probably not
Twelve Fermi-Dirac + charm	10/3	Yes

In what follows, we shall confine ourselves to the first scheme, as requiring the least change in the present experimental situation.

4. DERIVATION OF THE $\pi^0 \to 2\gamma$ AMPLITUDE IN THE PCAC APPROXIMATION

In the derivation sketched here, we follow the general idea of Wilson's and Crewther's method. We lean more heavily on the connected light-cone current algebra, however, and we do not need to assume full conformal invariance of matrix elements for small values of the coordinate differences.

To discuss the $\pi^0 \to 2\gamma$ decay in the PCAC approximation, we shall need an expression for

$$\langle \text{vac} | \mathsf{F}_{e\alpha}(x) \mathsf{F}_{e\beta}(y) \mathsf{F}_{3\gamma}^5(x) | \text{vac} \rangle$$

when $x \approx y \approx z$. (Here e is the direction in SU(3) space of the electric charge.) In fact, we shall consider general products of the form

$$\langle \text{vac} | \mathsf{F}(x_1) \mathsf{F}(x_2) \cdots \mathsf{F}(x_n) | \text{vac} \rangle$$

where F's stand for components of any of our currents, and we shall examine the leading singularity when $x_1, x_2, \ldots, x_n$ tend to lie among a single lightlike line. (The case when they tend to coincide is then a specialization.)

We assume not only the validity of the connected light-cone algebra, which implies scale invariance for commutators near the light cone, but also scale invariance for products near the lightcone, with leading dimension $l = -3$ for all currents. There may be subtraction terms in the products, or at least in physical ordered products, for example, subtractions corresponding to four-dimensional δ functions in coordinate space; these are often determined by current consrvation. But apart from the subtraction terms the current products near the light cone have no choice, because of causality and their consequent analytic properties in coordinate space, but to obey the same formulas as the commutators, with $i\pi\epsilon(z_0)\delta(z^2)$ replaced by $\frac{1}{2}(z^2 - iz_0\epsilon)^{-1}$ for products and $\frac{1}{2}(z^2 - i\epsilon)^{-1}$ for physical ordered products.

Our general quantity $\langle \text{vac} | \mathsf{F}(x_1)\mathsf{F}(x_2) \cdots \mathsf{F}(x_n) | \text{vac} \rangle$ may now be reduced, using successive applications of the product formulas near the light cone and ignoring possible subtraction terms, since all the intervals $(x_i - x_j)^2$ tend to zero, as they do when all the points x_i tend to lie on the same lightlike line.

A contraction between two currents $\mathsf{F}(x_i), \mathsf{F}(x_j)$ gives a singular function $S(x_i - x_j)$ times a bilocal $\mathsf{F}(x_i x_j)$. If we now contract another local current with the bilocal, we obtain $S(x_i - x_j)S(x_k - x_j)\mathsf{F}(x_i, x_k)$ and so on.

As long as we do not exhaust the currents, our intermediate states have particles in them and we are using the connected algebra generalized to products. Finally, we reach the stage where we have a string of singular functions multiplied by $\langle \text{vac} | \mathsf{F}(x_i, x_j)\mathsf{F}(x_k) | \text{vac} \rangle$, and the last contraction amounts to knowing the disconnected matrix element of a current product. However, the leading singularity structure of this matrix element ca. also be determined from the light-cone algebra by requiring consistent reductions of the three current amplitudes.

We can algebraically reduce a three-current amplitude in two possible ways. For each reduction, the algebra implies the existence of a known light-cone singularity. The reductions may also be carried out for an amplitude with a different ordering of the currents. One reduction of this amplitude yields the same two-point function as before, whereas the other reduction implies the existence of a second singularity in the two-point function. Hence we may conclude that the leading singularity of the two-point function when all points tend to a light line is given by the product of the two singularities identified by these reductions. Similarly, the leading singularity of the three-current amplitude is given by the product of the three singularities indicated by the different reductions. Since the connected light-cone algebra can be abstracted from the free quark model, the result of this analysis implies that the leading singularities of the two- and three-point functions are also given by the free quark model (say, with Fermi-Dirac quarks) and the only undetermined parameter is an overall factor, N, by which all vacuum amplitudes must be multiplied.

Since the singularity structure of the two-point function is determined, we can identify at least a part of the leading light line singularity of the n current amplitudes. Each different reduction of the n current amplitudes implies free quark singularities associated with this reduction. For two, three, and four current amplitudes, all of the singularities can be directly determined from the different reductions. For the five and higher-point functions not all of the singularities can be directly determined, but it is plausible that these others also have the free quark structure.

For the asymptotic value of $\sigma(e^+e^- \rightarrow \text{hadrons})/\sigma(e^+e^- \rightarrow \mu^+\mu^-)$, we are interested in the vacuum expected value of the commutator of two electromagnetic currents, and it comes out equal to N times a known quantity. Similarly, more complicated experiments testing products of four currents, for example, e^+e^- annihilation into hadrons and a massive muon pair or "γ" – "γ" annihilation into hadrons, might be considered. Also these processes are, in the corresponding deep inelastic limit, completely determined by the number N.

Returning to $\pi^0 \rightarrow 2\gamma$ in the PCAC approximation, we have $\langle \text{vac} | \mathsf{F}_{e\alpha}(x) \mathsf{F}_{e\beta}(y) \mathsf{F}_{3\gamma}{}^5(z) | \text{vac} \rangle$ as the three space-time points approach a lightlike line, apart from subtraction terms, in terms of N times a known quantity. We now need only appeal to Wilson's argument (as elaborated by Crewther). The vacuum expected value of the physically ordered product $T(\mathsf{F}_{e\alpha}(x), \mathsf{F}_{e\beta}(y), \partial_\gamma \mathsf{F}_{3\gamma}{}^5(z))$, taken at low frequencies, is what we need for the $\pi^0 \rightarrow 2\gamma$ decay with PCAC, and the Wilson-Crewther argument shows that it is determined from the small-distance behavior of $\langle \text{vac} | \mathsf{F}_{e\alpha}(x) \mathsf{F}_{e\beta}(y) \mathsf{F}_{3\gamma}{}^5(z) | \text{vac} \rangle$, with the subtraction terms (which are calculable from current conservation in this case) playing no rôle. This remarkable superconvergence result, that the low-frequency matrix element can be calculated from a surface integral around the leading short-distance singularity (which is the same as the singularity if all three points tend to a lightlike line), makes possible the derivation of $\pi^0 \rightarrow 2\gamma$ in the PCAC approximation from the light-cone current algebra. We come out with the Adler result (i.e., the result for three Fermi-Dirac quarks) multiplied by N.

Thus the connected light-cone algebra provides a link between the $\pi^0 \to 2\gamma$ decay and the asymptotic ratio $\sigma(e^+e^- \to \text{hadrons})/\sigma(e^+e^- \to \mu^+\mu^-)$. Of course, one might doubt the applicability of PCAC to π^0 decay, or to any process in which other currents are present in addition to the axial vector current connected to the pion by PCAC. If the connected algebra is right, including products, then failure of the asymptotic ratio of the e^+e^- cross sections to approach the value 2 would be attributed either to such a failure of PCAC when other currents are present or else to the need for an alternative model such as we discussed in Section 3.

As a final remark, let us mention the "finite theory approach," as discussed in ref. 4 in connection with the light-cone current algebra. Here the idea is to abstract results not from the formal "quark-gluon" field theory model, but rather from the sum of all orders of perturbation theory (insofar as that can be studied) under two special assumptions. The assumptions are that the equation for the renormalized coupling constant that allows for a finite coupling constant renormalization has a root and that the value of the renormalized coupling constant is that root. Under these conditions, the vacuum expected values of at least some current products are less singular than in the free theory. Since the Adler result still holds in the "finite theory case," the connected light-cone algebra would have to break down. In particular, the axial vector current appearing in the commutator of certain vector currents is multiplied by an infinite constant. There are at present two alternative possibilities for such a "finite theory":

1. Only vacuum expected values of products of singlet currents are less singular than in the free theory;[14] only the parts of the algebra that involve singlet currents are wrong (e.g., the bilocal singlet axial vector current is infinite); the e^+e^- annihilation cross section would still behave scale invariantly.

2. All vacuum expected values of current products are less singular than in the free theory; the number N is zero; all bilocal axial vector currents are infinite; the e^+e^- annhilation cross section would decrease more sharply at high energies than in the case of scale invariance.

1. ACKNOWLEDGMENTS

For discussions, we are indebted to D. Maison, B. Zumino, and other members of the staff of the Theoretical Study Division of CERN. We are pleased to acknowledge also the hospitality of the Theoretical Study Division.

REFERENCES

1. H. Fritzsch and M. Gell-Mann, "Proceedings of the Coral Gables Conference on Fundamental Interactions at High Energies, January 1971," in *Scale Invariance and the Light Cone,* Gordon and Breach, New York, (1971).

2. H.J. Lipkin and S. Meshkov, *Phys. Rev. Letters,* **14**, 670 (1965).

3. R. Dashen and M. Gell-Mann, *Phys. Letters,* **17**, 142 (1965).

4. H. Fritzsch and M. Gell-Mann, *Proceedings of the International Conference on Duality and Symmetry in Hadron Physics,* Weizmann Science Press of Israel, Jerusalem, 1971.

5. G. Zweig, CERN Preprints TH. 401 and 412 (1964).

6. See, for example, O. W. Greenberg, *Phys. Rev. Letters,* **13**, 598 (1964).

7. S. L. Adler, *Phys. Rev.,* **177**, 2426 (1969); J. S. Bell and R. Jackiw, *Nuovo Cimento,* **60A**, 47 (1969).

8. S. L. Adler, in *Lectures on Elementary Particles and Fields* (1970 Brandeis University Summer Institute), MIT Press, Cambridge, Mass., 1971, and references quoted therein.

9. S. L. Adler and W. A. Bardeen, *Phys. Rev.,* **182**, 1517 (1969).

10. R. J. Crewther, Cornell preprint (1972).

11. K. G. Wilson, *Phys. Rev.,* **179**, 1499 (1969).

12. E. J. Schreier, *Phys. Rev. D,* **3**, 982 (1971).

13. M. Han and Y. Nambu, *Phys. Rev.,* **139**, 1006 (1965).

14. See also B. Schroer, Chapter 3 in this volume (p. 42).

CHAPTER 8

Light-Cone Physics
and Duality

E. Del Giudice
P. Di Vecchia
S. Fubini
R. Musto

1. INTRODUCTION

In recent years important contributions to our understanding of hadron physics have been obtained by following two rather different approaches.

In the framework of a pure theory of strong interactions considerable attention has been devoted to study of the properties of dual-resonance models (DRM). The interest in these models is based on the fact that they incorporate some general requirements of S-matrix theory, such as analyticity of the first and second kinds and crossing, and they also exhibit very attractive physical features (e.g., a large degeneracy of the spectrum and linear Regge trajectories with a universal slope).[1]

On the other hand, study of the electromagnetic and weak interactions of hadrons was instrumental in obtaining important new physical insights.

In this volume the properties of the products of currents for lightlike distances, especially of current commutators, and their consequences for the asymptotic behavior (Bjorken limit) of scattering processes are extensively discussed.

At first sight these two lines of investigation appear quite unrelated to each other. We can mention, for example, the difficulties encountered by the program of building dual amplitudes for currents. Nevertheless, a belief that a possible relationship may exist between these two different types of approaches is now developing. Let us consider, for example, the extremely large degeneracy of the spectrum, exponentially increasing with the energy, that is perhaps the most striking feature of the DRM. This degeneracy, when seen from the point of view of the statistical models of the hadrons, suggests an underlying picture of the hadrons as made up of an infinite number of constituents moving almost freely. This picture, then, is not remote from the one advocated by the parton model, in which the electromagnetic current interacts directly with the almost free constituents of the nucleon.

Furthermore, recent developments in the analysis of the properties of the DRM are leading to an extremely simple and attractive physical picture for a specific critical dimension D of space-time. In fact, it has been shown that for $D \leqslant 26$ the ordinary $\alpha(0) = 1$ model ($D \leqslant 10$ for the Neveu-Schwarz model) is free from negative norm states (ghosts).[2] In addition, at the critical dimension, the physical picture given by the model is extremely similar to the infinite-momentum frame picture. In fact, any physical state can be obtained by applying to the "vacuum" (corresponding to the lower energy level, the tachyon with squared mass equal to -1) an arbitrary number of purely transverse "photon" operators with collinear momenta.[3]

The purpose of this chapter is to further investigate these analogies, starting from the light-cone point of view and recovering some interesting properties of the DRM. We shall follow essentially the line of an earlier paper[4] that we published, but more emphasis is given here to a discussion of the deep inelastic structure functions that can be explicitly obtained as an output of our approach.

2. BASIC ASSUMPTIONS

We start with the assumption that elementary particles are, in some way, composite systems made up of quarks which, at least in the present deep inelastic experiments, appear as pointlike objects.

The experimental validity of the Bjorken scaling suggests that, for what concerns the light-cone properties of hadrons, the "true" quark field can be approximated by an "asymptotic" field which obeys the free massless equation:

$$\Box \phi(x) = 0 \tag{1}$$

For simplicity we will start with spinless quarks. We recall that Eq. 1 is invariant not only under the Poincaré group, but also under the larger conformal group.

Another fundamental property of Eq. 1 is that its general integral can be written in the form

$$\phi(\vec{x}, t) = \int f(t - \vec{x} \cdot \vec{u}; \vec{u}) \, d\Omega_{\vec{u}}$$

$$= \int d\rho \int d\Omega_{\vec{u}} \, f\left(\rho, \vec{u}\right) \delta\left(t - \vec{x} \cdot \vec{u} - \rho\right) \tag{2}$$

where the integral in $d\Omega_{\vec{u}}$ is evaluated over all the directions of a unit vector $\vec{u}$:

$$\vec{u}^2 = 1 \tag{3}$$

In order to avoid the appearance of unpleasant divergent quantities, which are present any time we consider matrix elements of a product of operators $f(\rho, \vec{u})$ belonging to the same direction $\vec{u}$, we define the averaged operator:

$$P_i(\rho) = \frac{1}{\sqrt{\Delta \Omega_i}} \int_{\Delta \Omega_i} d\Omega f(\rho, \vec{u}) \tag{4}$$

so that Eq. 2 can be expressed as

$$\phi(\vec{x}, t) = \sqrt{\Delta \Omega} \sum_i P_i(t - \vec{x} \cdot \vec{u}_i) \tag{5}$$

The commutation relations and the vacuum expectation value of the field $P_i(\rho)$ are given by

$$\left[P_i(\rho_1), P_j(\rho_2)\right] = \delta_{ij} \frac{i}{8\pi^2} \delta'(\rho_1 - \rho_2) \tag{6}$$

$$\langle 0|P_i(\rho_1) P_j(\rho_2)|0\rangle = -\frac{1}{16\pi^3} \delta_{ij} \frac{1}{(\rho_1 - \rho_2 - i\epsilon)^2} \tag{7}$$

Equation 6 shows that each direction gives rise to orthogonal subspaces.

Up to now we have only discussed, very briefly, the kinematical properties of the parton field. We now introduce our main dynamical assumptions. We assume that not only the quark field but also the compound field obeys, near the light cone, the d'Alembert equation

$$\Box A(x) = 0 \tag{8}$$

In analogy with what we did in the case of the quark field, we can make the following decomposition:

$$A(\vec{x}, t) = \Delta\Omega \sum_i \chi_i(\rho) \tag{9}$$

The field $\chi_i(\rho)$ is then constructed as a function of the quark field $P_i(\rho)$:

$$\chi_i(\rho) = F[P_i(\rho)] \tag{10}$$

As a consequence of assumptions 8 and 10 we see that among all possible multiquark states the single-particle states are those obtained by the product of an arbitrary number of collinear quark fields. This shows the analogy of our model both with the parton model in the infinite-momentum frame and with the DRM, where for a critical value of the space-time dimension the physical states are obtained as a product of an arbitrary number of "photon" operators all aligned along a certain common lightlike direction.[2] We must notice, however, that our model is unable to give a correct description of the "wee" partons, that is, partons of very low momentum that it is impossible to assign to any precise direction. Therefore, we expect that our model will fail to describe correctly features, such as the behavior of the structure functions for $\omega \to 0$, strictly related, in the parton model, to the distribution of the "wee" partons.

On the other hand, we notice that the DRM gives rise to masses of the physical particles which are nonvanishing. This is a consequence of the fact that, even if the "photon" operators carry a lightlike four-momentum, as in the case of Eqs. 1 and 8, they are applied to a vacuum state (which, in the DRM, is associated with the ground state with a definite momentum) whose momentum, combined with the momentum of the "photons," gives rise to a nonvanishing mass for the excited particles.

It is clear that the "collinearity assumption" in our present form is too crude and probably requires modification for future development.

3. COMPOUND STATES AND THEIR DEEP INELASTIC STRUCTURE FUNCTIONS

We can now discuss the transformation properties of our parton field under the conformal group. As stated previously, we will be interested only in the case of partons all moving along the same direction (say, the z direction). Then we will be interested only in the subgroup of the full conformal group leaving the z direction invariant.

The generators of such a subgroup are, in the usual notations,

$$J_3 = M_{12}, \qquad \Lambda = \frac{D - M_{03}}{2} \qquad (11)$$

$$L_+ = \frac{i}{2}(P_0 + P_3), \qquad L_0 = \frac{i}{2}(M_{03} + D), \qquad L_- = \frac{i}{2}(K_0 - K_3) \quad (12)$$

The algebraic properties of the five operators defined in Eqs. 11 and 12 are most interesting. First of all, J_3 and Λ commute with all other operators.

The three fundamental operators L_i obey the $O(2,1)$ algebra given by:

$$[L_0, L_\pm] = \pm L_\pm$$
$$[L_+, L_-] = -2L_0 \qquad (13)$$

Finally the commutation relations of L_i with $P(\rho)$ are as follows:

$$[L_+, P(\rho)] = \frac{dP}{d\rho}$$

$$[L_0, P(\rho)] = \left(\rho \frac{d}{d\rho} + 1 \right) P(\rho) \qquad (14)$$

$$[L_-, P(\rho)] = \left(\rho^2 \frac{d}{d\rho} + 2\rho \right) P(\rho)$$

The operators Λ and J_3 commute with $P(\rho)$. The fact that Λ commutes with $P(\rho)$ is quite general. On the other hand, the zero commutator of J_3 with $P(\rho)$ is a consequence of the fact that $\phi(x)$ is a spinless field. In the case of quarks endowed with spin, J_3 will have nonvanishing commutators with the relevant operators.

We notice at this point that, since we are considering the case of massless quarks oriented along the same direction, the value of the total angular momentum will coincide with that of its component along the direction of motion. This means that the spin of the composite particles will have no orbital component and will originate only from the spin of the quarks. Therefore, in the present unrealistic case of spinless quarks, we shall deal with spinless composite particles.

We wish to define now a new quantum number which will allow us to classify the different states that can be obtained in terms of collinear quarks. The operator W associated with such a quantum number should be diagonalizable at the same time as the momentum and should have the same eigenvalue independently from the Lorentz frame we are using.

In other terms,

$$[W, L_0] = 0$$
$$[W, L_+] = 0$$
(15)

Such an operator is provided by the Casimir operator of the $O(2, 1)$ group:

$$W = L_0^2 - \tfrac{1}{2}(L_+ L_- + L_- L_+)$$
(16)

Then we can classify the single-particle compound states by means of the eigenvalues of the Casimir operator.

In other words, we require that the compound field belong to an irreducible representation of $O(2, 1)$:

$$[L_+, \chi(\rho)] = \frac{d\chi}{d\rho}$$

$$[L_0, \chi(\rho)] = \left(\rho \frac{d}{d\rho} + \lambda\right)\chi(\rho)$$
(17)

$$[L_-, \chi(\rho)] = \left(\rho^2 \frac{d}{d\rho} + 2\lambda\rho\right)\chi(\rho)$$

We can now obtain the general expression for the operator $\chi(\rho)$ associated with a compound state.

The most general operator constructed out of the quark field whose dimensionality is equal to N is given by

$$[P(\rho)]^{n_1}\left[\frac{dP(\rho)}{d\rho}\right]^{n_2}\left[\frac{d^2P(\rho)}{d\rho^2}\right]^{n_3} \cdots$$
(18)

with the condition

$$n_1 + 2n_2 + 3n_3 + \cdots = N \qquad (19)$$

The number of these operators is given by the partition function of N objects; we denote it by $T(N)$. We have to take an arbitrary linear combination of them and impose the correct commutation relations (Eq. 17). The number of operators of type 18 which are covariant under $O(2,1)$ transformations with $\lambda = N$ is then given by

$$P(N) = T(N) - T(N-1) \qquad (20)$$

The action of the operator W on such states, which we denote by $|\psi, \lambda\rangle$, is given by

$$W|\psi, \lambda\rangle = \lambda(\lambda - 1)|\psi, \lambda\rangle \qquad (21)$$

The degeneracy of physical states for large values of λ is given by the asymptotic expression of the partition function:

$$d(\lambda) \sim \exp\left(\frac{2\pi}{\sqrt{6}} \sqrt{\lambda} \right) \qquad (22)$$

If we now make the formal substitution

$$\lambda \rightarrow bm^2 \qquad (23)$$

we recover the exponential degeneracy of the spectrum given by the DRM. The "correspondence principle" (Eq. 22) leads also to a quantization for integer values of the physical particles, as we would expect from a model based on linear Regge trajectories.

We see that in our extreme "collinear" model we lose track of the mass operator, which is not important for considerations valid at short distances; however, from our approach we get a new quantum number λ which seems to enjoy properties very similar to the mass of the physical states in the DRM.

To further investigate this analogy, we have to go beyond this extremely unrealistic model in which both the quarks and the compound states are spinless. To this purpose, in the next section we will discuss the case of a spin-$\frac{1}{2}$ quark field.

In order to gain some insight into the physical consequences of our model we conclude this section with a discussion of the properties of the electromagnetic structure function in our model. Let us consider the matrix element of the bilocal operator evaluated on the light cone, between states of one compound particle of momentum p, directed along the direction $\vec{u}_z$:

$$\langle p | : (\phi(x)\phi(0))_{LC} : | p \rangle \qquad (24)$$

The Fourier transform of this matrix element gives the momentum distribution of the parton inside the compound particle and, when generalized to a more realistic case, is related to the structure functions measured in deep inelastic electron scattering. The state $\langle p |$ is given in terms of the field of the compound particle $\chi_\lambda(\rho)$ by

$$\langle p, \lambda | = C(p) \int_{-\infty}^{\infty} \langle 0 | \chi_\lambda(\rho) e^{ip\rho} \, d\rho \qquad (25)$$

where the constant $C(p)$ has to be fixed through the normalization requirements. For the first few levels the field $\chi_\lambda(\rho)$ is uniquely determined by our conformal requirement, so that the matrix element 24 can be evaluated.

As an example, we can consider the most general states which are coupled to two partons. The structure of these fields is as follows:

$$\psi_n = : \sum_{h=0}^{n-2} c_h \frac{d^h P}{d\rho^h} \frac{d^{(n-2-h)} P(\rho)}{d\rho^{n-2-h}} : \qquad (26)$$

where $n = 0, 2, 4, \ldots$ and

$$c_h = (-1)^h \frac{(n-1)(n-h-1)}{h!(h+1)!} \left[\frac{\Gamma(n-1)}{\Gamma(n-h)} \right]^2 c_0 \qquad (27)$$

Following the same line as in Appendix C of ref. 4, we find that the structure function associated with the field ψ_n is given by

$$f_n(\omega) \sim (1-\omega)\omega^2 F(2-n, n+1; 2; 1-\omega) \qquad (28)$$

Recalling that

$$F(2-n, n+1; 2; 0) = F(2-n, n+1; 2; 1) = 1 \qquad (29)$$

we see that the behavior near the points $\omega \sim 0$ and $\omega \sim 1$ is universal for such states.

We can also consider the states corresponding to the compound fields

$: P^n(\rho):$. Their structure functions are the following:

$$F_n(\omega) \sim (1-\omega)^{2n-3}\omega^2 \tag{30}$$

The above examples give an idea of the validity of our model. The structure functions that we obtain are quite reasonable for $\omega \sim 1$, but they fall off too fast when $\omega \to 0$. This problem is common to all models with a finite number of partons and clearly suggests that our collinearity assumption is too strong for the "wee" partons that contribute at $\omega \sim 0$. We notice that the behavior near $\omega \sim 0$ of the structure functions 29 and 30 is the same; for a general compound state $|\psi\rangle$ the structure function behaves near $\omega \sim 0$ as

$$\omega^{2+2j}$$

where j is the smallest derivative of the quark field present in $|\psi\rangle$.

For $\omega \sim 1$ the structure function of a general compound state $|\psi\rangle$ behaves as

$$(1-\omega)^{2n-3+2i}$$

where n is the number of quarks of which $|\psi\rangle$ is made, and i is the highest derivative of the quark field present in $|\psi\rangle$.

4. SPIN-$\frac{1}{2}$ QUARKS

In this section we discuss the main results of our model, concerning the particle spectrum and the structure functions, in the more realistic case of spin-$\frac{1}{2}$ quarks.

We start with the free massless Dirac equation for the quark field:

$$\gamma_\mu \frac{\partial}{\partial x_\mu} \psi(x) = 0 \tag{31}$$

We will write for $\psi(x)$ an unspecified Poisson bracket, without committing ourselves to a Fermi or a Bose statistics:

$$\left[\psi_\alpha^+(x), \psi_\beta(x')\right]_{t=t'} = \delta^{(3)}\left(\vec{x} - \vec{x}'\right)\delta_{\alpha\beta} \tag{32}$$

As in Section 2 we perform the "velocity" decomposition (Eq. 2):

$$\psi_\pm(x) = \int d\Omega \int_{-\infty}^{\infty} d\rho\, \delta'\left(t - \vec{x}\cdot\vec{u} - \rho\right)g_\pm\left(\rho, \vec{u}\right)\xi^\pm\left(\vec{u}\right) \tag{33}$$

where

$$\psi_\pm(x) = \tfrac{1}{2}(1 \pm i\gamma_5)\psi(x) \tag{34}$$

and $\xi^\pm(\vec{u}\,)$ are normalized spinors obeying the equation

$$\xi^\pm\left(\vec{u}\,\right) = \pm\left(\vec{\sigma}\cdot\vec{u}\,\right)\xi^\pm\left(\vec{u}\,\right) \tag{35}$$

The reasons for the appearance of $\delta'(t - \vec{x}\cdot\vec{u} - \rho)$ in Eq. 33, rather than $\delta(t - \vec{x}\cdot\vec{u} - \rho)$ as in Eq. 2, are discussed thoroughly in Appendix A of ref. 4.

As in the scalar case, it is useful to average the operator $g_\pm(\rho, \vec{u}\,)$ around a given direction $\vec{u}_i$, and we define:

$$S_\pm^{(i)}(\rho) = \frac{1}{\Delta\Omega}\int_{\Delta\Omega} g_\pm\left(\rho, \vec{u}\,\right)d\Omega \tag{36}$$

Then Eq. 33 reads

$$\psi_\pm(x) = \sqrt{\Delta\Omega}\,\sum_i \frac{dS_i(\rho)}{d\rho} \tag{37}$$

Using Eqs. 32 and 37 we obtain the following Poisson brackets for the operators $S_\pm^i(\rho)$:

$$[S_\pm^{(i)}(\rho), S_\mp^{(j)}(\rho')] = 0$$

$$[S_\pm^{(i)}(\rho), S_\mp^{\dagger(j)}(\rho')] = 0 \tag{38}$$

$$[S_\pm^{(i)}(\rho), S_\pm^{(j)}(\rho')] = 0$$

$$[S_\pm^{(i)}(\rho), S_\pm^{\dagger(j)}(\rho')] = \frac{1}{4\pi^2}\delta(\rho - \rho')\delta_{ij}$$

The nonvanishing Green functions are:

$$\langle 0|S_\pm^{(i)}(\rho)S_\pm^{\dagger(j)}(\rho')|0\rangle = -\frac{i}{(2\pi)^3}\frac{1}{\rho - \rho' - i\epsilon}\delta_{ij} \tag{39}$$

The commutators of $S_\pm(\rho)$ with the fundamental operators $J_z, L_0, L_\pm$ are:

$$[J_z, S_\pm(\rho)] = \pm S_\pm(\rho)$$

$$[L_+, S_\pm(\rho)] = \frac{d}{d\rho} S_\pm(\rho)$$

$$[L_0, S_\pm(\rho)] = \left(\rho\frac{d}{d\rho} + \tfrac{1}{2}\right) S_\pm(\rho) \tag{40}$$

$$[L_-, S_\pm(\rho)] = \left(\rho^2\frac{d}{d\rho} + \rho\right) S_\pm(\rho)$$

We see that $S_\pm(\rho)$ belongs to a representation $\lambda = \frac{1}{2}$ of $O(2,1)$. In order to obtain the structure of the compound states we can now proceed as in the scalar case.

The most general compound field of conformal quantum number λ is a superposition with appropriate coefficients of terms of the type:

$$S_+{}^{n_1}\left[\frac{dS_+}{d\rho}\right]^{n_2}\cdots S_-{}^{n'_1}\left[\frac{dS_-}{d\rho}\right]^{n'_2}\cdots$$

$$\tag{41}$$

$$S_+{}^{\dagger m_1}\left[\frac{dS_+^\dagger}{d\rho}\right]^{m_2}\cdots S_-{}^{\dagger m'_1}\left[\frac{dS_-^\dagger}{d\rho}\right]^{m'_2}$$

where

$$\lambda = n_1 + 2n_2 + 3n_3 + \cdots + n'_1 + 2n'_2 + \cdots$$

$$+ m_1 + 2m_2 + 3m_3 + \cdots + m'_1 + 2m'_2 + 3m'_3 + \cdots \tag{42}$$

The coefficients of the superposition are fixed by the requirement that the compound field be covariant under the group $O(2,1)$.

Then we again obtain, for large values of λ, the Hagedorn exponential increase of levels. Since we are dealing with quarks having a spin different from zero, we can now derive some interesting properties concerning the spin of excited levels. It is easy to see, in fact, that the spin of the compound states will never exceed λ, and that the most probable value of the spin is proportional to $\sqrt{\lambda}$ for large values of λ.

In order to obtain more detailed information on the compound-particle states in terms of the quark field, we still lack two main ingredients:

1. A precise commitment to the quark statistics.
2. The introduction of internal quantum numbers.

Therefore, in order to calculate the electron-proton structure function, we introduce internal quantum numbers for the field $S_\pm(\rho)$ and define

$$S_\pm(\rho) \equiv \begin{pmatrix} U_\pm(\rho) \\ D_\pm(\rho) \end{pmatrix} \qquad (43)$$

whose $U_\pm(\rho)$ and $D_\pm(\rho)$ are, respectively, fields corresponding to the value $\pm \frac{1}{2}$ of the third component of the isotopic spin.

We also assume the validity of an SU(6) scheme and the fact that the quarks satisfy the Fermi statistics.

Then the nucleon and the $N^*_{3/2,3/2}$ resonance have the same space structure. The lowest possible value of λ allowed is then $\lambda = \frac{9}{2}$, corresponding to the $N^*_{3/2,3/2}$ field:

$$: U_+(\rho) \dot{U}_+(\rho) \ddot{U}_+(\rho) :$$

We can now build two expressions having the correct commutation relations with L_-, both corresponding to the values $J = \frac{1}{2}$ and $T_3 = \frac{1}{2}$, namely:

$$K(\rho) = : U_+(\rho) \dot{U}_+(\rho) \ddot{D}_-(\rho) + \ddot{U}_+(\rho) U_+(\rho) \dot{D}_-(\rho)$$

$$+ \dot{U}_+(\rho) \ddot{U}_+(\rho) D_-(\rho) : \qquad (44)$$

and

$$H(\rho) = : U_+ \dot{U}_- \ddot{D}_+ + \ddot{U}_+ U_- \dot{D}_+ + \dot{U}_+ \ddot{U}_- D_+$$

$$+ U_- \dot{U}_+ \ddot{D}_+ + \ddot{U}_- U_+ \dot{D}_+ + \dot{U}_- \ddot{U}_+ D_+ : \qquad (45)$$

The linear combination

$$2K(\rho) - H(\rho) \qquad (46)$$

is the desired pure isotopic spin $\frac{1}{2}$ which is identified with the proton field.

Using techniques similar to the ones discussed in Appendix C of ref. 5, we can now explicitly calculate the structure function $F_2^{ep}(\omega)$. The behavior of such a function for $\omega \sim 0$ and $\omega \sim 1$ is the following:

$$F_2^{ep}(\omega) \sim \omega^2, \qquad \omega \to 0$$

$$F_2^{ep}(\omega) \sim (1-\omega)^3, \qquad \omega \to 1 \tag{47}$$

Had we started with a Bose quark field, we would have obtained the following proton field:

$$: U_+{}^2 D_- - U_+ U_- D_+ : \tag{48}$$

and the following behavior for the structure function:

$$F_2^{ep} \sim \omega^2 \qquad \omega \to 0$$

$$F_2^{ep} \sim 1 - \omega, \qquad \omega \to 1 \tag{49}$$

5. CONCLUSIONS

To conclude we summarize the results we have obtained so far. We have introduced a conformal quantum number λ to classify our states. In terms of λ we have the following properties:

1. The conformal quantum number λ takes only integer values.
2. The states corresponding to small values of λ are nondegenerate.
3. For large values of λ the degeneracy increases exponentially:

$$N(\lambda) \approx \exp\left(\frac{2\pi}{\sqrt{6}} \sqrt{\lambda} \right) \tag{50}$$

4. The spin of the compound particle cannot be larger than

$$J \leqslant \lambda \tag{51}$$

5. The average value of the spin for large values of λ is proportional to $\sqrt{\lambda}$.

All these results are translated into well-known properties of the dual models if we introduce the "correspondence principle":

$$\lambda \sim bm^2 \tag{52}$$

The constant b present in Eq. 52 introduces a fundamental length which in the dual models is related to the universal slope of the Regge trajectories.

We see, then, that in our "asymptotic" model the mass of the compound particles can only be obtained a posteriori on the basis of the "correspondence principle" (Eq. 52). This is clearly due to the fact that the quark fields have been studied essentially from the point of view of their "light-cone" properties, so that they have been taken to be massless and collinear.

The hypothesis of extreme collinearity seems to be a very weak point in our model. As we have already discussed, this hypothesis prevents the introduction of "wee partons" in our model. As a consequence, we obtain structure functions (e.g., in the "realistic" spin-$\frac{1}{2}$ case) that, although quite good at $\omega \sim 1$, are in disagreement with any reasonable Regge model in the asymptotic limit $\omega \to 0$. This disease is common to all parton models with only optical quarks.

We can conclude by saying that both the program to recover the main features of the DRM, starting from the light-cone approach, and the one to obtain information on the "parton distribution" inside the nucleon have been only partially successful. Any further progress seems clearly to be bound to a reformulation or a weakening of the collinearity assumption.

REFERENCES

1. See, for instance, G. Veneziano, lectures given at the Erice Summer School (1970); S. Fubini, lectures given at Les Houches Summer School (1971).
2. R. Brower, MIT Preprint CTP 277 (1972); P. Goddard and C. Thorn, CERN Preprint TH.1493 (1972).
3. E. Del Giudice, P. Di Vecchia, and S. Fubini, *Ann. Phys.*, **70**, 378 (1972).
4. E. Del Giudice, P. Di Vecchia, S. Fubini, and R. Musto, *Nuovo Cimento,* **12A**, 813, 1972.

CHAPTER 9

"Crossing" in the Physics
of the Light Cone

G. PREPARATA

1. INTRODUCTION

Recent work has demonstrated that it is quite useful to apply light-cone (LC) techniques to the description of processes involving the absorption and the emission of "local currents" of very large virtual mass.[1] The prototypes of such processes are no doubt observed in the SLAC deep inelastic electron proton scattering experiments, whose striking scaling behavior, predicted by Bjorken,[2] has prompted extensive theoretical efforts to discover a possibly simple structure of such interactions.

    The LC approach stemmed from the aim of abstracting, from simple field theoretical models, behaviors of products of currents which one could postulate to be true in the real physical world. With the notion of "canonical" operator product expansions on the light cone, it has been possible to show that most results of the parton model[3] do in fact follow from a more general and possibly more flexible theoretical framework.[1, 4]

However this approach, powerful as it may be, so far can be fruitfully applied only to the limited class of processes which can be described directly in terms of matrix elements of products of currents between "physical" states, such as total e^+e^- annihilation cross section into hadrons, deep inelastic electron-proton scattering and its neutrino counterparts, and finally massive μ-pair production in high-energy pp collisions.[1]

Very interesting and experimentally accessible processes, like $e^+e^- \rightarrow \pi +$ anything and $e^+p \rightarrow e^+ + \pi(p) +$ anything, unfortunately do not belong to this class. This chapter intends to describe a possible approach to the connection between these processes and the ones which can be directly described by LC operator product expansions, that is, the "crossing" problem.

The material is organized as follows. In Section 2 we briefly review the field where a direct application of LC techniques is possible and indeed has been carried out. In Section 3 we formulate the "crossing" problem for the simple case of deep inelastic electron-positron annihilation into one hadron plus anything and describe the results of a general analysis. In Section 4 we find, from the basic ideas of LC physics, suggestions for laying down a scheme to extract the analyticity properties of LC amplitudes, which are needed to perform the continuation to crossed channels. In Section 5 we apply these ideas to the process $e^+e^- \rightarrow h +$ anything.

2. LIGHT-CONE OPERATOR PRODUCT EXPANSIONS; REVIEW OF THE DIRECT APPLICATIONS

One starts with writing down a light-cone operator product expansion for two currents (scalar, for simplicity) in the "canonical" form[1]

$$J\left(\frac{x}{2}\right)J\left(-\frac{x}{2}\right) \underset{x^2 \to 0}{\longrightarrow} \frac{k}{\left(x^2 - i\epsilon x_0\right)^2} + \frac{1}{x^2 - i\epsilon x_0} O\left(\frac{x}{2}, -\frac{x}{2}\right) \qquad (1)$$

where the bilocal operator $O(x/2, -x/2)$ is analytic on the whole light cone and is given by a Taylor expansion

$$O\left(\frac{x}{2}, -\frac{x}{2}\right) = \sum_{n \text{ even}} x^{\alpha_1} \cdots x^{\alpha_n} O^{(n)}_{\alpha_1 \cdots \alpha_n}(0) \qquad (2)$$

For the processes which can be related to the "correlation" function

$$\left\langle \alpha \left| J\left(\frac{x}{2}\right) J\left(-\frac{x}{2}\right) \right| \alpha \right\rangle \tag{3}$$

where $|\alpha\rangle$ is any hadronic on shell state, Eq. 1 will describe the behavior of the cross sections in the limit when the "mass" q^2 of the current $J(x)$ and all scalar products $q \cdot p_i$ (where p_i is a complete set of momenta describing $|\alpha\rangle$) go to infinity with their ratios fixed. In fact, it can be shown in general that in such a generalized Bjorken limit we are sensitive only to correlations for lightlike distances, that is, $x^2 \cong 0$.[1]

a. Total Annihilation into Hadrons

If the spin of the electromagnetic current is neglected, the cross section for the process

$$e^+ e^- \rightarrow \text{hadrons} \tag{4}$$

is given, apart from uninteresting kinematical factors, by

$$\sigma_{\text{tot}}(q^2) \sim \sum_n (2\pi)^4 \delta^4(q-n) |\langle 0|J(0)|n\rangle|^2$$

$$= \int dx\, e^{iqx} \langle 0| J\left(\frac{x}{2}\right) J\left(-\frac{x}{2}\right) |0\rangle \tag{5}$$

that is, by the Fourier transform of a correlation function of type 3 with $|\alpha\rangle = |0\rangle$, the physical vacuum state. For $q^2 \rightarrow \infty$ only the c-number term contributes in Eq. 1 and one immediately gets the prediction

$$\sigma_{\text{tot}}(q^2) \underset{q^2 \rightarrow \infty}{\sim} k \tag{6}$$

By taking the spin of the electromagnetic current and the photon propagators into account, one gets, rather than Eq. 6,

$$\sigma_{\text{tot}}(q^2) \rightarrow \frac{\text{const.}}{q^2} \tag{7}$$

which is the same, apart from the constant,[5] as the cross section for $e^+ e^- \rightarrow \mu^+ \mu^-$ in the lowest order in electromagnetic interactions.

b.   Deep Inelastic Electron and Neutrino Scattering off Protons

We shall work again with scalar currents and particles. The double differential cross section $d^2\sigma/dq^2 dv$ $(q{\cdot}p = v)$ for deep inelastic electron scatterings given by

$$\frac{d^2\sigma}{dq^2 dv} \sim (\text{factors}) W(q^2, v) \qquad (8)$$

with

$$W(q^2, v) = \sum_n (2\pi)^4 \delta^4(q + p - n) |\langle p | J(0) | n \rangle|^2$$

$$= \int dx\, e^{iqx} \langle p | J\left(\frac{x}{2}\right) J\left(-\frac{x}{2}\right) | p \rangle_{\text{connected}} \qquad (9)$$

Here $W(q^2, v)$ is again expressed as the Fourier transform of a "correlation" function of type 3 with $|\alpha\rangle = |p\rangle$, the physical one-proton state. Here we are interested only in the connected matrix element, so that only the second term in the right-hand side of Eq. 1 will be of interest. It is only a straightforward matter of evaluating Eq. 9 with the expansion 1, to obtain the Bjorken scaling law:[2]

$$\lim_{\substack{q^2 \to -\infty; \\ \omega = (-q^2/2v) \text{ fixed}}} W(q^2, v) = \frac{1}{2v} F(\omega) \qquad (10)$$

with

$$F(\omega) = \int_{-\infty}^{+\infty} d(px) e^{-i\omega p{\cdot}x} f(p{\cdot}x) \qquad (11)$$

and

$$f(p{\cdot}x) = \langle p | O\left(\frac{x}{2}, -\frac{x}{2}\right) | p \rangle \qquad (12)$$

By enlarging the set of currents considered to the full set of currents which build up the chiral $SU(3) \otimes SU(3)$ group, one can similarly obtain scaling laws of type 10 for the deep inelastic processes involving neutrinos.[1]

In addition, one can also take the proton spin into account and discuss the scattering off polarized proton targets,[6] as well as obtaining the contribution of the proton polarizability to the hyperfine splitting of hydrogen.[7]

This, briefly, is the range of applications devised for Eq. 1 when sandwiched between proton states.

c. Massive μ-Pair Production in pp Collisions

The process that one wants to describe is:

$$p(p_1) + p(p_2) \rightarrow \mu^+ \mu^- + \text{anything} \tag{13}$$

where the total four-momentum of the μ-pairs q is such that q^2 is very large. The triple differential cross section is $[qp_1 = \nu_1, \ qp_2 = \nu_2, \ (p_1 + p_2)^2 = s]$.

$$\frac{d^3\sigma}{dq^2 \, d\nu_1 \, d\nu_2} \sim \frac{1}{s} W(q^2, \nu_1, \nu_2; s) \tag{14}$$

with

$$W(q^2, \nu_1, \nu_2; s) = \sum_n (2\pi)^4 \delta^4(p_1 + p_2 - q - n)|_{\text{in}} \langle p_1 p_2 | J(0) | n \rangle|^2$$

$$= \int dx \, e^{-iqx} \, _{\text{in}} \langle p_1 p_2 | J\left(\frac{x}{2}\right) J\left(-\frac{x}{2}\right) | p_1 p_2 \rangle_{\text{in}} \tag{15}$$

with the current "correlation" function of type 3, where this time $|\alpha\rangle = |p_1 p_2\rangle_{\text{in}}$. There is no point now to carrying out a complicated analysis of the asymptotic form of $W(q^2, \nu_1, \nu_2; s)$ given by Eq. 1, which is presented in refs. 8. We recall only that the concepts of Regge behavior for strong interactions can be used fruitfully to constrain substantially the amplitude

$$_{\text{in}} \langle p_1 p_2 | O\left(\frac{x}{2}, -\frac{x}{2}\right) | p_1 p_2 \rangle_{\text{in}} \tag{16}$$

The main outcome of this analysis, apart from the interesting predictions for the functional dependence of $W(q^2, \nu_1, \nu_2; s)$ on the various variables, is that the light-cone expansion (Eq. 1) gives a description of the previously mentioned processes which does not coincide generally with the expectations of naive dimensional analysis. In fact we see here that dynamical mechanisms of purely hadronic nature, like Regge behavior, do play a crucial role in determining Eq. 16 and introduce into this description, either directly or indirectly, a wealth of dimensional parameters such as slopes of Regge trajectories and residue functions.

With this application we have practically exhausted the class of meaningful processes which can be described by a direct application of Eq. 1 or, equivalently, whose cross sections can be cast as Fourier transforms of the type of Eq. 3.

In order to proceed further, one needs some new idea and eventually has to supplement Eq. 1 with additional theoretical input. In the following section we shall formulate the problem of crossing and present the result of a general analysis[9] for the simplest case of deep inelastic e^+e^- annihilation into one hadron plus anything.

In ending this section we recall that "crossing" is not the only *indirect* application of LC expansion to obtain answers to a variety of interesting problems relating to the validity of vector meson dominance and PCAC in different physical situations. A description of this stage of LC physics is, however, beyond the scope of this exposition, and we refer the interested reader to the review contained in ref. 1.

3. THE CROSSING PROBLEM FOR DEEP INELASTIC ELECTRON-PROTON SCATTERING

A general analysis of the problem of crossing from deep inelastic scattering (DIS) to deep inelastic annihilation (DIA) has been given in ref. 9. In this section we shall formulate the problem and recall briefly the results of that analysis. The question we pose is the following: We know that the deep inelastic cross section obeys the Bjorken scaling law Eq.10; what can we say about the DIA cross section in the limit $q^2 \to \infty$ with fixed $\omega = -(q^2/2\nu) > 1$?

Apart from known kinematical factors the double differential cross section for DIA is given by

$$\overline{W}(q^2,\nu) = \sum_n (2\pi)^4 \delta(q-p-n)\langle 0|J(0)|n,p\rangle\langle n,p|J(0)|0\rangle \quad (17)$$

which, contrary to Eq. 9, cannot be cast as the Fourier transform of a product of currents. In order to have a representation in terms of products of currents for Eq. 17, one must first apply the reduction formalism to take the protons out of the intermediate states and then use completeness of the physical states to perform the remaining sum. What is obtained in this way, however, is an expression involving the vacuum expectation value of the products of two currents and two proton "sources." We expect these objects to be quite problematic, because of present lack of theoretical understanding of the nature of hadronic sources.[10] Hence a direct descrip-

Figure 1. The nonforward "Compton" amplitude.

tion of $\overline{W}(q^2,\nu)$ in terms of products of currents and sources involves ideas which go far beyond our present theoretical knowledge and therefore does not seem to be a particularly useful line of approach.

To get back into something which involves more familiar notions we consider the unequal mass, $t=0$, "Compton scattering amplitude" (again the fully scalar case), $T(s,q_1^2,q_2^2)$ (Figure 1). It is not difficult to show that $[\nu = \frac{1}{2}(s-q^2)]$

$$\overline{W}(q^2,\nu) = T_s(s+i\epsilon,q^2+i\epsilon,q^2-i\epsilon) - T_s(s-i\epsilon,q^2+i\epsilon,q^2-i\epsilon) \quad (18)$$

where $T_s(s,q_1^2,q_2^2)$, according to a Mandelstam decomposition, represents the part of the total amplitude which has only s-channel normal thresholds. In other words, one must continue $T_s(s,q_1^2,q_2^2)$ to s positive, keeping the "mass" of one current above and the other below its normal cut; $\overline{W}(q^2,\nu)$ will then be given by the discontinuity of $T_s(s,q^2+i\epsilon,q^2-i\epsilon)$ across the normal s-channel cut (see Figure 2).

From the LC expansion Eq. 1 one easily gets

$$T_s(s,q_1^2,q_2^2)$$

$$= -\int_0^1 d\alpha \int_{-(1-\alpha)}^{1-\alpha} d\beta \, \frac{F(\alpha,\beta)}{[(q_1^2+q_2^2)/2](1-\alpha)+s\alpha+\beta(q_1^2-q_2^2)/2+i\epsilon}$$

$$(19)$$

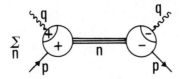

Figure 2. Diagram for $W(q^2,\nu)$.

which for the equal-mass case $(q_1^2 = q_2^2)$ takes the form

$$T_s(s, q^2) = -\int_0^1 d\alpha \frac{F(\alpha)}{q^2(1-\alpha) + s\alpha + i\epsilon} \tag{20}$$

with

$$F(\alpha) = \int_{-(1-\alpha)}^{1-\alpha} d\beta \, F(\alpha, \beta) \tag{21}$$

For $0 < \omega < 1$, $F(\omega)$ describes the deep inelastic scattering cross section via Eq. 10. In general, however, one does not have a direct connection between $W(q^2, \nu)$ given by Eq. 18 and a suitable analytic continuation of $F(\omega)$ in the region $\omega > 1$, as one realizes by performing the analytic continuation involved in Eq. 18 on the amplitude given by Eq. 19.

In fact a careful analysis of the various analytic continuations of $T_s(s, q^2)$ and $T_s(s, q_1^2, q_2^2)$ shows that $(\omega = -[q^2/(s-q^2)] > 1)$

$$\overline{W}(q^2, \nu) = \frac{1}{2\nu} \{ \operatorname{Re} F(\omega) - \tfrac{1}{2} [\Gamma(\omega + i\epsilon) - \Gamma(\omega - i\epsilon)] \} \tag{22}$$

where the function $\Gamma(\omega)$ is defined by

$$\Gamma(\omega) = \lim_{\lambda \to \infty} \int_{-\lambda}^{+\lambda} d\beta \, F(\omega, \beta + i\epsilon) \tag{23}$$

Equation 22 is a scaling law for $\overline{W}(q^2, \nu)$ similar to the one obeyed by $W(q^2, \nu)$ (Eq. 10). This is the most general conclusion we can reach from the existence of canonical LC expansion and general analyticity considerations.

As to the possible connection between $F(\omega)$ (continued for $\omega > 1$) and $\overline{W}(q^2, \nu)$, Eq. 22 shows clearly that, because of the presence of $\Gamma(\omega)$, DIS and DIA obey, in general, *separate* scaling laws. Moreover, from positivity constraints one can show that, if $F(\omega)$ has a cut for $\omega > 1$ (coming from double s, q^2 discontinuities in the DIA region) the extra piece in Eq. 22 must necessarily be different from zero.

These results are not completely satisfactory. Even though $\overline{W}(q^2, \nu)$ "scales" nontrivially, we have no way of predicting from known facts the basic features of DIA, such as multiplicities and mean energies. It may well be that this is what happens in nature, and we must be content with the already nontrivial results of scaling for $\overline{W}(q^2, \nu)$. However, we think that a lot more can be said in regard to this problem by analyzing in detail the fundamental aspects of the physics of the light cone. To this aim is directed the next section.

4. THE LIGHT-CONE PHILOSOPHY AND A POSSIBLE ANALYTICITY SCHEME

a. Mass Independence in Light-Cone Dominance

Since the introduction of the notion of scale invariance in the realm of particle physics, scaling behaviors have been intimately related to the idea that at high energies and virtual "current's" masses the appropriate physics should somewhat resemble that of a massless world with the ensuing symmetries like chiral and conformal invariance.[2] As a consequence of this idea the LC behavior of products of currents has been explicitly assumed[1] to be mass independent and chiral invariant, thus simplifying substantially the description of processes which are kinematically dominated by the light cone.

The idea of a "skeleton" hadronic theory has been advanced by K. Wilson to provide a basis for a possible field theory for hadrons in the limit when all masses and other dimensional parameters can be neglected. This "primitive" field theory would then acquire the full glory of mass spectra, Regge trajectories, and so on through a breaking mechanism which, however, should manifest itself *smoothly*. Such a smothness has been introduced into this field theoretical framework by Wilson[11] and Symanzik[12] via the notion of generalized mass terms in the breaking Hamiltonian, associated with local operators of dimensionality $d<4$.

The goal that one wants to accomplish in this way is to perturb this ideal skeleton world as little as possible, so as to obtain finally the full-fledged hadrons' theory without losing the vestiges of the primitive scale-invariant and chiral-invariant theory. As indicated above, the successful application of a mass-independent LC operator expansion is a good indication of the soundness of this approach.

As our goal will be to formulate the analyticity properties of LC amplitudes on the basis of the analytic structure of the underlying hadronic skeleton theory, we shall now attempt to understand the extent and the limitations of this possible connection.

One may start with the rather bold assumption that the physics of the LC is that of a massless world. This statement without some nontrivial qualifications is obviously untenable. In fact one can easily object that from the LC expansion (Eq. 1) the t-dependence $[t=(p'-p)^2]$ of the matrix element $\langle p'|J(x/2)J(-x/2)|p\rangle$ is tied to the t-dependence of the

Figure 3. The forward "Compton" amplitude.

matrix elements $\langle p'|O^{(n)}_{\alpha_1\cdots\alpha_n}(0)|p\rangle$, which should display the real world's (massive) singularities appropriate to a spin-n form factor, thus contradicting the assumed mass independence.

A more tenable assumption is, however, that we may consider massless those particles giving singularities in the channels which become asymptotic in the scaling limit, such as q^2 and s in the deep inelastic scattering case. Kinematically this seems quite reasonable in view of the fact that in these channels the normal thresholds are asymptotically at $s = 0$, or $q^2 = 0$, all finite masses being telescoped to zero, corresponding to the thresholds of a theory with massless particles. Much in the same way as in the Regge expansion the term $(-s)^\alpha$ corresponds to a normal cut starting at $s = 0$.

Analysis of $\lambda\phi^3$ models, which lead to LC expansions of the type in Eq. 1 and therefore have Bjorken scaling, shows, however, that one has in general anomalous (possibly complex) singularities for the forward "Compton" scattering amplitude, whose locations depend crucially on the mass ratios of the exchanged particles, thus providing examples of models which have mass-independent LC expansions but lack the analyticity of a skeleton theory.

b.   The Zero-Mass Limit for Light-Cone Amplitudes

In this and the following section we intend to lay down a possible analyticity scheme for LC amplitudes based on the ideas of the skeleton theory, conveniently adapted to meet the objections of the preceding paragraph.

For simplicity let us consider the forward scalar "Compton" amplitude $T(s, q^2)$ (Figure 3):

In the Bjorken limit we use, as in Section 2, the LC expansion (Eq. 1) to obtain

$$T(s, q^2) = -i \int dx\, e^{iqx} \langle p | T\left(J\left(\frac{x}{2}\right) J\left(-\frac{x}{2}\right)\right) | p \rangle \tag{24}$$

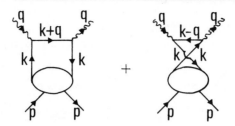

Figure 4. The quark LC diagrams associated with Eq. 24.

The LC amplitude of Eq. 24 can be diagrammatically associated with the quark-LC amplitude of Figure 4:[13]

In fact, as has been frequently observed, the $1/(x^2 - i\epsilon)$ term represents the x-space *massless* quark propagator between two *pointlike* vertices associated with respective scalar currents, while the matrix element of $O(x/2, -x/2)$, the bilocal operator, represents the sum of the s- and u-channel absorptive parts of the virtual "quark"-p scattering amplitude.

Canonical scaling in terms of the diagrams of Figure 4 is also intimately connected with the fast convergence of the "quark"-p scattering amplitude when the masses K^2 of the virtual "quark" lines increase. This leads reasonably to the conclusion that we can always assume that the mass of the quarks in quark-LC diagrams, such as those of Figure 4, can be neglected. If this were not true, one could not have a fast decrease, the rate of decrease being related to the inverse of the mean effective mass K^2 that can be carried by the "quark" lines, which scatter with the particle p. From the "precocity" of the observed SLAC scaling we can also estimate $\langle K^2 \rangle \lesssim 0.25$ GeV^2, thus obtaining a quantitative feeling about the soundness of the previous conclusion. All this suggests that in the LC regime one can recover a massless limit for the field theory (possibly free) of the constituents of the "current" (the quarks). That part of the Hamiltonian which breaks scale and chiral invariance should then constitute an insignificant perturbation at the level of the "quark" fields, while it would reveal itself strongly at the level of the particles, through the (basically unknown) dynamical mechanisms responsible for the mass spectra, particle sizes, and so on.

To sum up this discussion, we offer the following hypothesis: *In the quark-LC diagrams describing the related LC amplitudes we can neglect the masses of the quark lines..* No such hypothesis can in general be made for any of the hadron lines.

Before extracting the needed information about the analyticity of LC amplitudes from the preceding hypothesis, we would like to stress that, although quark-LC diagrams such as those of Figure 4 are a convenient way of representing in a pictorial fashion the structure of the LC amplitudes, no concrete physical meaning should at this point be attached to them.

c.   Analyticity Structure of the Light-Cone Amplitudes

We now concentrate on the quark-LC diagrams of Figure 4 to study their analytic structure according to the hypothesis that the "quark" lines can be taken as massless. From the masslessness of the quark lines the virtual quark-p scattering amplitude can have only normal thresholds in the s'- and t-channels [we carry out this analysis only for the first diagram of Figure 4, corresponding to $T_s(s, q^2)$], whose typical Landau diagrams are drawn in Figure 5.

The singularities of the full amplitude $T_s(s, q^2)$ can be assessed by considering the Landau diagrams of $T_s(s, q^2)$ corresponding to the reduced diagrams of Figure 5. Such diagrams are shown in Figure 6, where (a) and (b) give the leading Landau singularities, and (c) and (d) the normal s- and q^2-channel thresholds, respectively. From the masslessness of the quark lines, and calling M the mass of any of the normal s' thresholds and $p^2 = m^2$, the locations of the singularities of (a) and (b) in the ω-plane $(\omega = -q^2/2\nu)$ are readily determined to be as follows:

1. $\omega = 0$ normal q^2-threshold
2. $\omega = 1$ normal s-threshold
3. $\omega = (m^2 - M^2)/2m^2 \leqslant 0$ anomalous thresholds

The most important features of these results in terms of $F(\omega)$ are the following:

i.   There is an absence of complex anomalous singularities in the ω-plane.

ii.   From the stability of $p(M^2 \geqslant m^2)$ we have cuts only on the negative real axis.

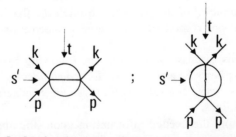

Figure 5.   Landau singularities for the quark-p scattering amplitude.

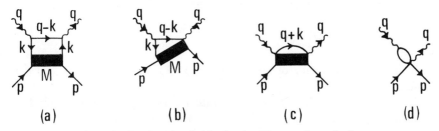

Figure 6. Landau singularities for the "Compton" amplitude.

The simplicity of this analysis suggests that without much effort it can be extended to more complicated situations like deep inelastic electroproduction of a single hadron.

5. APPLICATION TO DEEP INELASTIC ANNIHILATION AND DEEP INELASTIC SCATTERING

The general analysis of the problem of crossing from DIS to DIA outlined in Section 3 has revealed the somewhat uncomfortable situation whereby DIS and DIA are in general unrelated processes apart from their common Bjorken scaling. The analyticity of $T_s(s, q^2)$, derived in Section 4 from the hypothesis of massless quark lines, comes now to rescue us and tie these two processes together very intimately.

In fact, not only does $F(\omega)$ have only a left-hand *real* cut, but also $\Gamma(\omega + i\epsilon) - \Gamma(\omega - i\epsilon) = 0$. This can be simply verified by analyzing the Landau diagrams in Figure 6 in the unequal-mass case, and by noting that $T_s(s, q_1^2, q_2^2)$ cannot have double discontinuities in s and q_1^2, or in s and q_2^2 [which are represented by $\Gamma(\omega + i\epsilon) - \Gamma(\omega - i\epsilon)$] in the DIA, for the very simple kinematical reason that a "massless" quark cannot decay into the (massive) particle p and something else. Hence we have

$$\overline{W}(q^2, \nu) = \frac{1}{2|\nu|} \overline{F}(\omega) \tag{25}$$

$$\overline{F}(\omega) = -F(\omega) \tag{26}$$

where $F(\omega)$ is the real analytic continuation to $\omega > 1$ of the deep inelastic scattering scaling function. Equation 26 has been obtained in parton models by direct calculation by Drell and Yan;[14] this should not be at all surprising, because the diagrams they evaluate have the same structure as the quark-LC diagrams and, moreover, "partons" are stable.

From Eq. 26 immediately follows the Drell-Yan threshold theorem:[14]

$$F(\omega) \underset{\omega \to 1}{\to} c(1-\omega)^p \qquad (c>0, p \text{ odd integer}) \qquad (27)$$

which is a consequence of analyticity at $\omega = 1$, and positivity of $\overline{W}(q^2, \nu)$ and hence of $\overline{F}(\omega)$.

In addition to Eqs. 26 and 27, another very strong constraint on $F(\omega)$ follows from the analyticity discussed, which states that $F(\omega)$ is a real analytic function in the ω-plane with only a cut running from $-\infty$ to 0. One can then write a dispersion relation subtracted at the point $\omega = 1$:

$$F(\omega) = c(1-\omega)^p + \frac{(1-\omega)^{p+1}}{\pi} \int_{-\infty}^{0} \frac{d\omega'}{\omega' - \omega} \frac{\operatorname{Im} F(\omega')}{(1-\omega')^{p+1}} \qquad (28)$$

Experimentally the scaling function $F(\omega)$ shows a quite rapid decrease for $\omega \to 1$, so that one expects p to be a sufficiently big positive integer, and the dispersive integral in Eq. 28 [for suitable convergences of $\operatorname{Im} F(\omega')$ when $\omega' \to \infty$] to be dominated by the region $\omega' \cong 0$. This is very interesting because in this region $\operatorname{Im} F(\omega')$ can be conveniently parametrized à la Regge, thus making it possible to obtain, from a few-parameter fit of $F(\omega)$ in the DIS region ($0 \leqslant \omega \leqslant 1$), $F(\omega)$ for any value of $\omega > 1$. The advantage of this procedure for continuing from DIS to DIA should at this point be too obvious to need further comment. The DIA cross-section is:

$$\frac{d^3\sigma}{d^3p} = \frac{1}{2E} \frac{1}{2|\nu|} \overline{F}(\omega) \qquad (29)$$

Using for the total annihilation cross section σ_{tot} its canonical value (Eq. 6), we can write for the distribution function of the particle p as a function of its energy E and q^2

$$\frac{d^3N(q^2, E)}{d^3p} = \frac{1}{\sigma_{\text{tot}}} \frac{d^3\sigma}{d^3p} = + \frac{1}{k4E^2\sqrt{q^2}} \overline{F}(\omega) \qquad (30)$$

The multiplicity n_p of the particles p, is given by

$$n_p = \int d^3p \frac{d^3N}{d^3p} = -\frac{\pi}{2k} \int_{1}^{\sqrt{q^2}/2m} \frac{d\omega}{\omega^2} F(\omega) \qquad (31)$$

while for the energy E_p carried away by particles of type p we have

$$\sqrt{q^2} \geqslant E_p = \int d^3p \frac{d^3N}{d^3p} E = -\frac{\pi}{4k} \int_1^{\sqrt{q^2}/2m} \frac{d\omega}{\omega^3} F(\omega) \qquad (32)$$

From Eq. 32 it follows that

$$F(\omega) \underset{\omega \to \infty}{\to} \omega^{2-\epsilon} \qquad (\epsilon > 0) \qquad (33)$$

and correspondingly

$$n_p \underset{q^2 \to \infty}{\to} \left(\sqrt{\frac{q^2}{4m^2}} \right)^{1-\epsilon} \qquad (34)$$

On the other hand, Eq. 28 implies, with suitable convergence of $\operatorname{Im} F(\omega)$, that $F(\omega)$ for $\omega \to \infty$ must go like an integer power, so that Eq. 33 tells us that at most $F(\omega) \to \omega$, and that the strongest behavior of n_p is

$$n_p \underset{q^2 \to \infty}{\to} \ln\left(\frac{\sqrt{q^2}}{2m} \right) \qquad (35)$$

In the case that $p > 1$ we obtain a set of superconvergence relations which further constrains the parametrization of $\operatorname{Im} F(\omega)$. Ending this section, we would like to emphasize that in this approach even a rough knowledge of DIS data can give us almost complete information about DIA, going quite beyond the simple statement of analytic continuation.

6. CONCLUSION

In this chapter we have tried to give a solution to the problem of "crossing" in the realm of the physics of the light cone. The solution to this problem appears at this time as the only sensible way to extend the direct applications of LC techniques so far carried out to situations where a direct approach would lead to consideration of more complicated and problematic objects than the "correlation" functions (Eq. 3) of the currents.

The analysis carried out in Section 4 shows that within the context of LC physics it seems possible to find a general basis for discussing the analyticity structure of LC amplitudes, which obviously constitutes the key ingredient of "crossing." The application of the strikingly simple analyticity structure obtained in Sections 3 and 4 to the DIA cross section shows its effectiveness in constraining the DIA process in terms of DIS.

We should remark that the arguments given here to build up the appropriate analyticity scheme are, we think, quite plausible but could very well turn out to be wrong. Be that as it may, the sharpness of the predictions of Section 5 is certainly a strong point in favor of the approach presented. Experiments will soon tell us whether these predictions are right or wrong, and in either case we think that we shall learn something new.

REFERENCES

1. For an up-to-date review see R. Brandt and G. Preparata, lectures given at the Hamburg Summer School on electromagnetic interactions (1971), to be published.

2. J. D. Bjorken, *Phys. Rev.*, **179**, 1547 (1969).

3. R. P. Feynman, *Phys. Rev. Letters*, **23**, 1415 (1969); J. D. Bjorken and E. A. Paschos, *Phys. Rev.*, **185**, 1975 (1969).

4. H. Fritzsch and M. Gell-Mann, "Proceedings of the Coral Gables Conference on Fundamental Interactions at High Energy," University of Miami, 1971.

5. This constant was first shown by R. Jackiw and G. Preparata, *Phys. Rev. Letters*, **22**, 975 (1969), to be determined only by the charge structure of the constituents of the electromagnetic currents.

6. A. J. G. Hey and J. E. Mandula, CALT 68-342, to be published.

7. E. de Rafael, article to be published.

8. G. Altarelli, R. Brandt, and G. Preparata, *Phys. Rev. Letters*, **26**, 42 (1971); R. Brandt and G. Preparata, article to be published in *Phys. Rev.*

9. R. Gatto and G. Preparata, *Nucl. Phys.*, **B47**, 313 (1972).

10. For a lucid critique see K. G. Wilson, rapporteur's talk at the Cornell Conference on Electromagnetic Interactions at High Energies (1971).

11. K. G. Wilson, *Phys. Rev.*, **179**, 1499 (1969).

12. K. Symanzik, *Commun. Math. Phys.*, **18**, 227 (1970).

13. These diagrams appear in the covariant parton model of P. V. Landshoff, J. C. Polkinghorne, and R. D. Short, *Nucl. Phys.*, **B28**, 222 (1971).

14. S. D. Drell and T. M. Yan, *Phys. Rev. D*, **1**, 1617 (1970).

CHAPTER 10

Scaling Properties
of Infinite-Component Fields

H. KLEINERT

1. INTRODUCTION

A few years ago, experimentalists were producing large quantities of data on hadron resonances with higher and higher masses and spins. For the purpose of correlating all these data, infinite-component wave equations were invented.[1, 2] It was hoped that the introduction of a single local field containing at the same time many of the observed resonances would lead to a particularly economic description of electromagnetic and hadronic interactions.

To some extent, these hopes were fulfilled. For example, it was possible to describe the pionic decays of almost all observed baryon resonances by using only a very few parameters.[2, 3] An electromagnetic current was constructed for baryon resonances[4, 5] saturating the charge current algebra[6] and reproducing correctly the dipole formula for electric and magnetic form factors of the nucleons. In addition, the transition form factors to the higher resonances which were known in those days (in particular, of the Δ resonance)[7] were found to be in agreement with experiment, and it was predicted that they all show the same falloff at large q^2.[5]

The approach was inspired by the fact that the exactly soluble system of a hydrogen atom allowed for a complete description in terms of such an infinite-component wave equation. The algebraic form of this equation was then hypothesized to account also for the electromagnetic structure of hadron dynamics.

Unfortunately, from the fundamental point of view, this program turned out to have a serious defect. If one wanted all the fields and currents to be local, it was necessary to include spacelike particles, tachyons, in the Hilbert space.[6, 8] For this reason people soon became disinterested in the whole approach.

Interest was revived with the recent advent of SLAC data on deep inelastic electron-proton scattering.[9] On the one hand, these data opened up new ways of comparing the existing models with experiment; on the other hand, they made theorists ask new fundamental questions, for which these models are able to give specific answers.

The most important observation made in these experiments was certainly the phenomenon of scaling of the structure functions. This immediately raised the fundamental question of whether nature possesses some underlying scale invariance[10] which becomes visible when matter is probed by a photon of large energy and virtual mass.[11] It is an attractive idea that associated with many important local operators there is a quantum number, called dimension,[10] which is additively conserved at the strongest light-cone singularity in operator product expansions. If this idea is true, it is quite simple to explain scaling.[12]

The question of whether or not such a situation may be present in nature was first investigated in the framework of renormalizable quantum field theory. Unfortunately, such investigations have not been very successful.[13] The world described by field theory turns out to be full of anomalies unobserved in nature. The dimensions of light-cone singularities are either blurred by logarithmic factors (to any finite order in perturbation theory),[12,13] or (by summing up infinitely many Feynman graphs) these logarithmic factors pile up to give anomalous noninteger dimensions.[14] The only experimentally observed singularity, on the other hand, is a nice, clean $1/x^2$.[12] However, if one does only finite-order perturbation theory and bravely neglects the logarithmic factors, it is possible to verify in many models that the canonical dimensions of every field are, in fact, conserved at the strongest light-cone singularity.[12]

Physically, the scaling phenomena arise since highly massive and energetic photons produce an instantaneous incoherent snapshot of the virtual distribution of the particles carried by the fundamental fields of the theory.[11] One may wonder whether this picture holds also for theories in which infinitely rising trajectories of particles can be exchanged in scattering processes.[15] In such theories the mass and energy of the photon cannot grow large compared with all masses of the theory. Thus, intuitively, one would expect canonical scale invariance to break down on the light cone. We shall show that this expectation appears to be true by explicit verification in an infinite-component model.[16]

What is, then, the basic symmetry responsible for the scaling properties of the structure functions in such a theory? The answer is that there still exists a group of transformations on the fields which does *not* coincide with the canonical scale group. Observable Hermitian operators appearing in the expansion of products of currents, however, undergo standard scale transformations. Only the underlying fermion fields know the difference.

It is interesting that in a small-distance expansion introduced first by Wilson[10] both groups coincide so that there also the naive canonical dimensions of the fields are, in fact, conserved.[16]

Another interesting result of our model investigation is that conformal analyses in the presence of symmetry breaking can be carried out if one considers equal-light commutators of currents rather than light-cone expansions. Present standard analyses work in a conformal invariant limit of any theory and assume that the leading singularity structure does not change when symmetry-breaking terms are turned in (only the operators multiplying the singularity, and their matrix elements between on-shell particle states, are supposed to change).

Finally, we would like to comment on an important phenomenon, the so-called precocity[17] of scaling. Even in regions of low energy and q^2 which are strongly dominated by resonances, the scaling limit of the structure functions seems to hold if one averages only over the individual resonances. This smoothness property of nature appears to be responsible for the onset of scaling much before one would have expected it on theoretical grounds.

Also for the study of this problem, infinite-component wave equations provide a convenient theoretical laboratory. The wave equations which generalize the hydrogen atom possess a resonance spectrum up to 3.5 BeV with a continuum above. One therefore is in a position to investigate the change in the structure function when passing from the resonance to the scale-invariant deep inelastic region. This particular question will be dealt with in the future.

2. PURE RESONANCE MODELS

If an infinite-component wave equation contains only discrete states at high masses, the structure functions can be calculated in a straightforward manner from the electromagnetic transition form factors. Let W_1, W_2 be the usual invariant functions defined by†

$$W_{\mu\nu}(p,q) \equiv \left(-g_{\mu\nu} + \frac{q_\mu q_\nu}{q^2}\right)W_1 + \frac{1}{m^2}\left(p_\mu - \frac{pq}{q^2}q_\mu\right)\left(p_\nu - \frac{pq}{q^2}q_\nu\right)W_2$$

$$\equiv \frac{1}{4\pi}\int dx\, e^{iqx}\langle \mathbf{p}\tfrac{1}{2}|[\,j_\mu(x),j_\nu(0)\,]|\mathbf{p}\tfrac{1}{2}\rangle \tag{1}$$

In the physical region of $e\text{-}p$ scattering one can write

$$W_{\mu\nu}(p,q) = \tfrac{1}{2}\sum_{nj}\delta(s - m_n^2)\,W_{\mu\nu}^{nj}(p,q) \tag{2}$$

with the resonance contributions of spin j:

$$W_{\mu\nu}^{nj}(p,q) = \sum_{j_3}\langle \mathbf{p}\tfrac{1}{2}|j_\mu|\mathbf{p}+\mathbf{q}\,jj_3 n\rangle\langle \mathbf{p}+\mathbf{q}\,jj_3 n|j_\nu|\mathbf{p}\tfrac{1}{2}\rangle \tag{3}$$

Clearly, $W_{\mu\nu}^{nj}$ can be decomposed into $W_1^{nj}(q^2)$ and $W_2^{nj}(q^2)$ in just the same way as $W_{\mu\nu}$. Physical resonances usually overlap at higher energy, so that there the sum over δ functions in Eq. 2 can be replaced by

$$W_{\frac{1}{2}}(\nu,q^2) \approx \frac{1}{2}\left[\frac{dm_n^2}{dn}\right]^{-1}\sum_j W_{\frac{1}{2}}^{nj} \tag{4}$$

The electromagnetic properties of the resonances are most easily stated in terms of the following matrix elements of the currents. One goes to the rest frame of the resonance, lets the proton run in the z direction, and defines:[5]

$$\langle 0j\tfrac{1}{2}n|j^0|p\mathbf{e}_z\tfrac{1}{2}\rangle \equiv \sqrt{4m_n m}\ G_{nj}^0$$

$$\mp \frac{1}{\sqrt{2}}\langle 0j_{-1/2}^{3/2}n|j^{1\pm i2}|p\mathbf{e}_z\tfrac{1}{2}\rangle \equiv \sqrt{4m_n m}\ G_{nj}^{\pm} \tag{5}$$

Note that these matrix elements have kinematic singularities and constraints. For example, for elastic nucleon-nucleon transitions, they are

†Normalization of states: $\langle p'|p\rangle = 2p_0(2\pi)^3\delta^3(\mathbf{p}'-\mathbf{p})$.

related to the usual form factors by

$$G^0 \equiv \cosh\frac{\xi}{2} \cdot G_E(q^2) = \cosh\frac{\xi}{2} \cdot \left(F_1 + \frac{q^2}{4m^2} F_2 \right)$$

$$G^+ \equiv 0 \tag{6}$$

$$G^- \equiv \sqrt{2}\ \sinh\frac{\xi}{2} \cdot G_m(q^2) = \sqrt{2}\ \sinh\frac{\xi}{2} \cdot (F_1 + F_2)$$

where ξ is the rapidity of the nucleon ($\xi = \mathrm{arsh}|\mathbf{p}|/m$), that is,

$$\left\{ \begin{array}{c} \cosh^2 \\ \sinh^2 \end{array} \right\} \frac{\xi}{2} = \frac{1}{4m_n m} [(m_n \pm m)^2 - q^2]$$

In terms of these G-functions,† the contribution of the resonance to the structure functions becomes

$$W_1^{nj} = 4m_n m \tfrac{1}{2} \left[(G_{nj}^+)^2 + (G_{nj}^-)^2 \right]$$

$$\tag{7}$$

$$W_2^{nj} = 4m_n m \left(1 - \frac{\nu^2}{q^2} \right)^{-2} \left\{ \frac{m_n^2}{m^2} (G_{nj}^0)^2 + \left(1 - \frac{\nu^2}{q^2} \right) \tfrac{1}{2} \left[(G_{nj}^+)^2 + (G_{nj}^-)^2 \right] \right\}$$

In W_1^{nj} only the transverse form factors appear, while W_2^{nj} is of mixed type. We shall use this formula only in the scaling limit (SL), in which

$$q^2 \to \infty, \quad \nu \to \infty, \quad \xi \equiv -\frac{q^2}{2m\nu} \quad \text{fixed} \quad \in [0,1] \tag{8}$$

In this limit $(\nu/m)W_2^{nj}$ can be rewritten as

$$\frac{\nu}{m} W_2^{nj} \underset{\text{SL}}{\to} 4m_n m\xi \left\{ 8\xi(1-\xi)(G_{nj}^0)^2 + [(G_{nj}^+)^2 + (G_{nj}^-)^2] \right\} \tag{9}$$

†The G-functions are closely related to the functions $f^0_\pm$ introduced by Bjorken and Walecka, *Ann. Phys.*, **38**, 35 (1966):

$$G^0_\pm \equiv \sqrt{\frac{m_n}{m}}\ f^0_\pm .$$

Now suppose that all G-functions are rational functions of m_n^2 and q^2. Then, in the scaling limit, we can always write them in the form $f(m_n^2)h(\xi)$. This implies, in particular, that all high form factors fall off with the same power in $(-q^2)$, where a falloff like $(-q^2)^{-p}$ corresponds to a threshold behavior of $h(\xi)$ like $(1-\xi)^p$. Obviously the structure functions $[W_1(\nu,q^2),$ $(\nu/m)W_2(\nu,q^2)]$ will become functions of ξ alone if and only if the product

$$\left[\frac{dm_n^2}{dn}\right]^{-1} m_n f(m_n^2) \tag{10}$$

tends to a finite limit for $m_n^2 \to \infty$. As usual, we shall denote the scaling limits of W_1 and $(\nu/m)W_2$ by $F_1(\xi)$ and $F_2(\xi)$, respectively. Under the assumption that *all* resonances show the same falloff in q^2, the known structure functions W_1^N and $(\nu/m)W_2^N$ of the nucleons can be used to predict the threshold behavior of $F_1(\xi)$ and $F_2(\xi)$ at $\xi = 1$. Since

$$W_1^N(q^2) = -q^2 G_m^2(q^2) = -q^2(F_1+F_2)^2 \tag{11}$$

$$\frac{\nu}{m}W_2^N(q^2) = \frac{\nu}{m}\frac{4m^2}{1-(q^2/4m^2)}\left[G_E^2(q^2) - \frac{q^2}{4m^2}G_M^2(q^2)\right]$$

$$= \frac{\nu}{m}4m^2\left(F_1^2 - \frac{q^2}{4m^2}F_2^2\right) \tag{12}$$

we see that an asymptotic behavior of G_m^2 and $(4m^2/q^2)G_E^2 - G_m^2$ like $(q^2)^{-2p}$ will lead to a threshold behavior like $(1-\xi)^{2p-1}$ in $F_1(\xi)$ and $F_2(\xi)$, respectively. This connection was observed first by Drell and Yan.[18] Experimentally, the power p is equal to 2, predicting the threshold behavior of the structure as $(1-\xi)^3$. This is indeed observed for $F_2(\xi)$.

3. MAJORANA-TYPE EQUATION

As an example for a pure resonance model for the structure functions[19, 20] we discuss an infinite-component field that obeys a slight generalization of the old Majorana equation.[21, 1, 2] Let $u(jm)$ with $j^p = \frac{1}{2}^+, \frac{3}{2}^-, \frac{5}{2}^+,\ldots$ denote the states of the simplest representation space $[j_0, j_1] \equiv [\frac{1}{2}, 0]$ of the Lorentz group.† On this representation space there exists a unique vector operator

---

†If **J** and **M** are the generators of rotations and boosts, the parameters j_0 and j_1 are related to the Casimir operators of the group by[2]

$$\mathbf{J}^2 - \mathbf{M}^2 = j_0^2 + j_1^2 - 1; \qquad \mathbf{J}\cdot\mathbf{M} = ij_0 j_1$$

Γ , whose time component has the eigenvalues

$$\Gamma^0 u(jm) = (j + \tfrac{1}{2})u(jm) \tag{13}$$

Using this vector operator, we can form a Lagrangian

$$L = \partial_\mu \psi(x)^+ \partial^\mu \psi(x) - i\mu\psi(x)^+ \Gamma^\mu \overleftrightarrow{\partial}_\mu \psi(x) - \chi^2 \psi(x)^+ \psi(x) \tag{14}$$

which leads to a wave equation

$$L(p)u(\mathbf{p}) = 0 \tag{15}$$

with

$$L(p) = p^2 - 2\mu\Gamma p - \chi^2 \tag{16}$$

If p is timelike, we can transform the momentum into the rest frame and find

$$(m^2 - 2\mu\Gamma^0 m - \chi^2)u(\mathbf{0}) = 0 \tag{17}$$

which is solved by the basis states $u(jm)$ with masses

$$m_j = \mu(j + \tfrac{1}{2}) \pm [\mu^2(j + \tfrac{1}{2})^2 + \chi^2]^{1/2} \tag{18}$$

The upper branch of the spectrum goes asymptotically like

$$m_j \to 2\mu j \tag{19}$$

and is physically acceptable. The lower branch converges to zero and cannot be associated with any known particles. Unfortunately, these are not the only unphysical solutions. If p is spacelike,[22, 23] we can transform it to the form $p = (0,0,0,p^3)$, leading to a wave equation

$$[- (p^3)^2 + 2\mu\Gamma^3 p^3 - \chi^2]u((0,0,p^3)) = 0 \tag{20}$$

The matrix Γ^3 is diagonal on a basis $u(\sigma m)$ of $O(3,1)$ that diagonalizes† $J_3^2 - M_1^2 - M_2^2$ and J_3 rather than J^2 and J_3. On this basis, Γ^3 has the eigenvalue σ. As a consequence we obtain an additional spectrum of imaginary masses

$$p^3 = \mu\sigma \pm [\mu^2\sigma^2 - \chi^2]^{1/2}, \quad \sigma \in \left(\frac{\chi}{\mu}, \infty \right) \tag{21}$$

†With eigenvalue $-\sigma^2 - \tfrac{1}{4}$.

which is undesirable. In addition there are lightlike solutions.

We shall at first ignore all unphysical solutions and confine ourselves to the good particle states described by the upper branch of Eq. 18. The effect of the unphysical spectrum will be discussed later.

Electromagnetic interactions are introduced by means of the standard gauge invariant replacement

$$\partial_\mu \psi(x) \rightarrow [\partial_\mu - iA_\mu(x)]\psi(x) \tag{22}$$

This defines a current operator

$$j^\mu(x) \equiv \psi(x)^+ \left(i \overleftrightarrow{\partial}^\mu - 2\mu\Gamma^\mu\right)\psi(x) \tag{23}$$

whose matrix elements become

$$\langle 0jm|j^\mu|\mathbf{p}\tfrac{1}{2}\tfrac{1}{2}\rangle = n_j n_{1/2} u(jm) \left[(p'+p)^\mu - 2\mu\Gamma^\mu\right] e^{-i\mu\xi} u(\tfrac{1}{2}\tfrac{1}{2}) \tag{24}$$

The normalization factors

$$n_j \equiv m_j^{1/2} \left[\mu^2(j+\tfrac{1}{2})^2 + \chi^2\right]^{-1/4} \quad \left(\rightarrow \sqrt{2} \quad \text{for} \quad j \rightarrow \infty\right)$$

$$n_{1/2} = \sqrt{m/(m-\mu)} \tag{25}$$

in front are necessary in order to normalize all charges to unity. In this way we find for the G-functions of Eq. 5:[24, 20]

$$4m_j m \left(G_j^0\right)^2 = n_j^2 n_{1/2}^2 \left[(m_j + m\cosh\xi) - 2\mu(j+\tfrac{1}{2})\right]^2$$

$$\times (j+\tfrac{1}{2})(\tanh\tfrac{1}{2}\xi)^{2j-1}(\cosh\tfrac{1}{2}\xi)^{-4} \tag{26}$$

$$4m_j m \left[(G_j^-)^2 + (G_j^+)^2\right] = n_j^2 n_{1/2}^2 \mu^2 \tfrac{1}{2}(j+\tfrac{1}{2})(\tanh\tfrac{1}{2}\xi)^{2j-3}(\cosh\tfrac{1}{2}\xi)^{-8}$$

$$\times \left\{\cosh^4\tfrac{1}{2}\xi \left[j-\tfrac{1}{2} - (j+\tfrac{3}{2})\tanh^2\tfrac{1}{2}\xi\right]^2 + (j+\tfrac{3}{2})(j-\tfrac{1}{2})\right\} \tag{27}$$

Let us go to the scaling limit of large j and q^2. Then

$$\tfrac{1}{2}\cosh\xi\rightarrow\cosh^2\tfrac{1}{2}\xi\rightarrow\frac{j}{\gamma} \tag{28}$$

$$(\tanh\tfrac{1}{2}\xi)^{2j}\rightarrow e^{-\gamma} \tag{29}$$

with

$$\gamma\equiv2\frac{m}{\mu}(1-\xi) \tag{30}$$

In this limit Eqs. 26 and 27 become

$$4m_j m\left(G_j^0\right)^2\rightarrow2\frac{m}{m-\mu}\left(\frac{2m_j}{\gamma}\right)^2 je^{-\gamma}\frac{\gamma^2}{j^2} \tag{31}$$

$$4m_j m\left[\left(G_j^+\right)^2+\left(G_j^-\right)^2\right]\rightarrow2\frac{m}{m-\mu}\mu^2\frac{j}{2}e^{-\gamma}\frac{\gamma^2}{j^2}(4+\gamma^2) \tag{32}$$

Since $dm_j^2/d_j\rightarrow8\mu^2 j$, we obtain from Eq. 7:

$$W_1\underset{\text{SL}}{\rightarrow}\frac{1}{16j^2}\frac{m}{m-\mu}e^{-\gamma}\gamma^2(4+\gamma^2)\rightarrow0 \tag{33}$$

while Eq. 9 yields

$$\frac{\nu}{m}W_2\rightarrow F_2(\xi)=4\frac{m^3}{\mu^2(m-\mu)}e^{-\gamma}\xi^2(1-\xi) \tag{34}$$

We observe that the transverse structure function W_1 vanishes like $j^{-2}\alpha(q^2)^{-1}$ in the scaling limit. The mixed structure function $(\nu/m)W_2$, however, has a finite limit, which is plotted in Figure 1 (curve —·—·—·) for a parameter $\mu=m/2$.

In comparing this curve with the experimental structure functions of the proton we find the following defects.

1. The transverse structure function vanishes. Experimentally one has, on the contrary, $\sigma_L/\sigma_T\approx0.18\pm0.2$.†[9] It is known that this defect originates in the Klein-Gordon-like structure of the current.[20, 25] It will be

†Recall that the cross sections for longitudinal and transverse photons are given by

$$\sigma_L=\frac{4\pi^2\alpha}{m[\nu+(q^2/2m)]}\quad W_L\equiv\frac{4\pi^2\alpha}{m[\nu+(q^2/2m)]}\left[-W_1+\left(1-\frac{\nu^2}{q^2}\right)W_2\right],\quad \sigma_T\equiv\frac{4\pi^2\alpha}{m[\nu+(q^2/2m)]}W_1$$

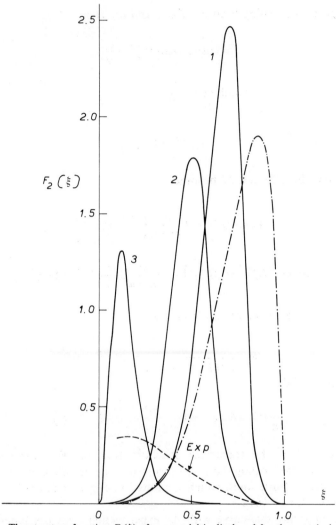

Figure 1. The structure function $F_2(\xi)$ of our model is displayed for three typical values of the mass parameters: (1) $m_1 = 0.76$, $m_2 = 0.36$, or $m_+ = 1.12$, $m_- = 0.4$; (2) $m_1 = m_2 = 0.56$, or $m_+ = 1.12$, $m_- = 0$; (3) $m_1 = 0.16$, $m_2 = 0.96$, or $m_+ = 1.12$, $m_- = -0.8$. Our curves have the threshold behavior $(1-\xi)^3$ for $\xi \approx 1$. We see that for decreasing mass m_1 of the charged constituent the peak moves left and the area decreases. In the limiting case of the hydrogen atom, $m_1/m_+ \approx 10^{-3}$, $F_2(\xi)$ shows a high and narrow peak at small $\xi \approx m_1/m_+$ [height $(8/3\pi)(1/\alpha)(m_+/m_2)$, width $\alpha m_1 m_2/m_+^2$]. The scattering of the electron on the proton leads to a similar result with m_1 and m_2 exchanged, peaking sharply for $\xi = m_2/m_+ = 1 - (m_1/m_+) \approx 1$ [height $(8/3\pi)(1/\alpha)(m_+/m_1)$, width $\alpha m_1 m_2/m_+^2$]. For comparison we show the structure function of the Majorana equation of ref. 20 (—·—·—) and the experimental $F_2(\xi)$ of the proton (—————).

necessary to couple a spinor field with an infinite-component representation to arrive at purely transverse cross sections.§

2. The threshold behavior at $\xi = 1$ is linear instead of going like $(1 - \xi)^3$. From the Drell-Yan rule (see Eq. 12)[18] we know this defect to originate in the excessively slow falloff of the model's form factors:

$$G_E(q^2) = \left(1 - \frac{q^2}{4m^2}\right)^{-3/2} \left[1 - \frac{q^2}{4m(m-\mu)}\right] \to (-q^2)^{-1/2}$$

$$(35)$$

$$G_M(q^2) = \left(1 - \frac{q^2}{4m^2}\right)^{-3/2} \frac{\mu}{2m-\mu} \to (-q^2)^{-3/2}$$

when compared with the nucleons $(-q^2)^{-2}$. A model with correct asymptotic behavior of form factors will certainly correct this defect.

3. The curve is much too high. In the parton model, the integral $\int_0^1 d\xi F_2(\xi)$ is equal to the mean-square charge per parton.† Experimentally this quantity is rather small (≈ 0.16). Somehow the constituents contained in our model have too large a charge. We shall understand this point better in the next model, which generalizes the Schrödinger equation of the hydrogen atom. In that model, the parameters occurring in the wave equation have a direct interpretation in terms of constituents.

4. The function $F_2(\xi)$ vanishes quadratically at small ξ. Experimentally $F_2(0)$ seems to approach a constant (≈ 0.35). In the parton model it is shown that a constant $F_2(0)$ means that the probability of finding N partons in the proton goes asymptotically like N^{-2}. If $P(N)$ falls off faster than that, $F_2(0)$ vanishes. Obviously the wave equation does not allow for enough constituents inside the proton. This point too will become much clearer in the next model.

Up to now we have calculated only the contribution of the good solutions to the structure functions. Fortunately, at high energies, no particles of the lower branch of Eq. 25 or spacelike solutions can be exchanged in the s-channel. However, we have omitted Z graphs with the intermediate particle being spacelike. These graphs give rise to an extra piece, which happens to be simply $F_2(-\xi)$. Numerically, this piece turns out to be rather unimportant. (Its area is 2 orders of magnitude smaller than the particle contributions.)

§See, for example, the structure functions of the Abers-Grodsky-Norton equation.[20]

†Precisely, if $P(N)$ is the probability of finding N partons, then[11]

$$\int_0^1 d\xi F_2(\xi) = \frac{\sum_N P(N) \langle \sum Q_i^2 \rangle_N}{N}$$

One may wonder whether the other unitary representations with $[j_0 j_1]_2 = [\frac{1}{2}, i\nu]$ and $\nu \neq 0$ real do not improve the situation. It is well known that the form factors in this case oscillate in q^2 with a frequency increasing with ν, indicating that they are describing particles as hollow spheres of a radius proportional to ν.† Also the corresponding structure functions show such oscillations. It is obvious that in order to obtain smooth results we have to build bulk objects by mixing many irreducible representations of different ν. For this procedure it would be necessary to know the radial functions $R(\nu)$. Rather than making ad hoc assumptions we shall simply go to a larger group that admits radial excitations right from the beginning and construct a wave function on a larger Hilbert space.

4. HYDROGEN-LIKE WAVE EQUATION

It is well known that there exists an infinite-component wave equation describing completely all dynamical features of the hydrogen atom.[2, 26, 27] Let L_{ab} $(a, b = 1, \ldots, 6)$ with the commutators

$$[L_{ab}, L_{ac}] = -ig_{aa} L_{bc} \tag{36}$$

generate the group $O(4, 2)$, that is,

$$g_{ab} = \begin{pmatrix} -1 & & & & & \\ & -1 & & & & \\ & & -1 & & & \\ & & & -1 & & \\ & & & & 1 & \\ & & & & & 1 \end{pmatrix} \tag{37}$$

The most degenerate representation of this group consists of states

$$u(nlm); \qquad n = 1, 2, 3, \ldots; \quad l = 0, 1, \ldots, n-1; \quad m = -l, \ldots, l \tag{38}$$

diagonalizing $L_{56}, \mathbf{L}^2, L_3$ (where $L_i \equiv \frac{1}{2} \epsilon_{ijk} L_{jk}$) with eigenvalues $n, l(l+1), m$, respectively. ·

The group contains a Lorentz subgroup generated by

$$J_i \equiv L_i, \qquad M_i \equiv L_{i6} \tag{39}$$

a vector

$$\Gamma^\mu \equiv (L_{56}, L_{i5}) \tag{40}$$

†The argument can be made more precise.[2]

and a scalar operator

$$S \equiv L_{46} \tag{41}$$

Therefore we can write a Lorentz invariant wave equation

$$[-(m_+ - m_-)p_\mu \Gamma^\mu + (p^2 - m_+ m_-)S + \chi]u(\mathbf{p}) = 0 \tag{42}$$

which gives rise to a conserved minimal current

$$\langle p'|j^\mu|p\rangle \equiv N'N\bar{u}(\mathbf{p}')[-(m_+ - m_-)\Gamma^\mu + (p' + p)^\mu S]u(\mathbf{p}) \tag{43}$$

where N', N are normalization factors ensuring unit charge for every particle. If $p^2 > 0$, we can bring the particle to rest and Eq. 42 becomes

$$[-(m_+ - m_-)mL_{56} + (m^2 - m_+ m_-)L_{46} + \chi]u(\mathbf{0}) = 0 \tag{44}$$

Now we have to distinguish two cases.† If

$$(m_+ - m_-)m > m^2 - m_+ m_- \tag{45}$$

we can perform a transformation

$$u(\mathbf{0}) \equiv e^{-i\theta L_{45}}\tilde{u}(\mathbf{0}) \tag{46}$$

with

$$
\begin{aligned}
\cosh\theta &= \frac{b(m^2)}{\chi}(m_+ - m_-)m \\
\sinh\theta &= \frac{b(m^2)}{\chi}(m^2 - m_+ m_-)
\end{aligned}
\tag{47}
$$

and

$$\frac{b(m^2)}{\chi} \equiv [(m^2 - m_-^2)(m_+^2 - m^2)]^{-1/2} \tag{48}$$

Then Eq. 44 goes over into

$$\tilde{L}(m^2)\tilde{u}(\mathbf{0}) \equiv -\frac{\chi}{b(m^2)}[L_{56} - b(m^2)]\tilde{u}(\mathbf{0}) = 0 \tag{49}$$

Obviously this equation is solved by

$$\tilde{u}(\mathbf{0}) = u(nlm) \tag{50}$$

†We may, in general, take $m_+ > m_-$.

with a mass spectrum given by

$$n = b(m^2), \qquad n = 1, 2, 3, \ldots \tag{51}$$

On the other hand, if

$$(m_+ - m_-)m < m^2 - m_+ m_- \tag{52}$$

we can transform again as in Eq. 44 but with an angle $\hat{\theta}$ given by

$$\cosh\hat{\theta} = \frac{\hat{b}(m^2)}{\chi}(m^2 - m_+ m_-) \tag{53}$$

$$\sinh\hat{\theta} = \frac{\hat{b}(m^2)}{\chi}(m_+ - m_-)m; \qquad \frac{\hat{b}(m^2)}{\chi} = \left[(m^2 - m_+^{\ 2})(m^2 - m_-^{\ 2})\right]^{-1/2}$$

This brings Eq. 44 to the form

$$\left(\frac{\chi}{\hat{b}(m^2)}L_{46} + \chi\right)\tilde{u}(0) = 0 \tag{54}$$

This equation is solved by a continuous set of the basis states

$$u(\hat{n}lm); \qquad \hat{n} \in [-\infty, \infty]; \quad l = 0, 1, 2, \ldots; \quad m = -l, \ldots, l \tag{55}$$

which diagonalize the operators $L_{46}, \mathbf{L}^2, L_3$. The corresponding continuum of masses is given by

$$\hat{n} = -\hat{b}(m^2) \tag{56}$$

Both mass spectra can be summarized in a single formula

$$n^2 = -\frac{\chi^2}{(m^2 - m_+^{\ 2})(m^2 - m_-^{\ 2})} \tag{57}$$

where, for $n^2 > 0$, n is integer, while for $n^2 < 0$ a continuum of values is allowed.

If we consider the case $m^2 \leqslant 0$ of spacelike solutions, they are found to follow the same formula. As in the last model, we shall discard the Z graphs in which they contribute to the structure functions. Similarly we shall here not consider lightlike solutions. The masses are discrete between

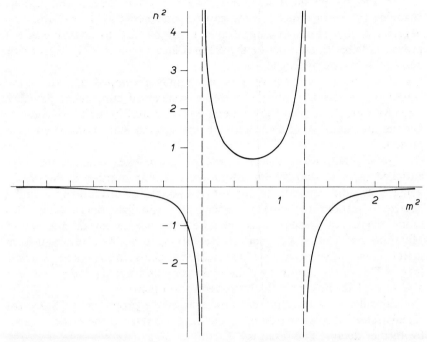

Figure 2. The mass spectrum of our wave equation is shown for the following values of the mass parameters: $m_+ = 1.12$, $m_- = 0.4$.

the values m_-^2 and m_+^2. Above and below there is a continuum (see Figure 2).

The important point about this equation is that for a particular choice of parameters it reduces exactly to the Schrödinger equation of the hydrogen atom (with some relativistic corrections). In order to see this set

$$m_+ \equiv m_1 + m_2, \qquad m_- \equiv m_1 - m_2, \qquad \chi \equiv 2\alpha m_1 m_2 \qquad (58)$$

where α is the fine structure constant. Then the upper branch of the mass spectrum becomes

$$m_n = m_+ - \frac{m_1 m_2}{m_+} \frac{\alpha^2}{2n^2} + O(\alpha^4) \qquad (59)$$

with $n = 1, 2, 3, \ldots$ denoting the bound states, and $n^2 \leqslant 0$ the continuum. This coincides with the mass spectrum of the hydrogen atom if one sets $m_1 = m_e$, $m_2 = m_p$.

It can be shown also that all electromagnetic form factors of these states are the same as those given by Schrödinger theory.[28]

In addition to these solutions, there is a lower branch obtained by changing $m_e \to -m_e$. Such a state can be interpreted as an electron in a negative energy state orbiting around a proton. Up to now, it has not proved possible to incorporate these states into a consistent field theoretic description of the hydrogen atom.

If m_1, m_2 are not equal to m_e, m_p it may be hoped that this wave equation can describe other interesting systems of constituent particles. Therefore the solutions of the general equation may be tentatively identified as an equation of hadrons with the ground state considered as a proton.

Notice that, with respect to the Majorana-like equation, we have enriched the spectrum by one additional quantum number n. Physically, going from one equation to the other amounts to introducing a radial degree of freedom into a system describing originally a rigid rotator. This radial degree of freedom has the effect of mixing an infinite set of Majorana particles of different representations $[0, iv]$. As a result all form factors show the q^2 behavior of the hydrogen charge distribution, which is $(q^2)^{-2}$. This is the reason why the hydrogen-like wave equation has been able to explain the dipole fits to nucleon form factors.

Consider now the structure functions of the ground state. Since the calculation is somewhat tedious in this case, we refer to the original paper for further details. The result is

$$F_1(\xi) = 0 \tag{60}$$

$$F_2(\xi) = \frac{8}{3\pi} C \xi^2 (1-\xi)^3 D^{-3}(\xi) \tag{61}$$

where

$$C = \frac{\sinh \Theta_1 - N_1^2}{N_1^2}; \qquad N_1^2 = \sinh \Theta_1 - \frac{m_+ - m_-}{2m} \cosh \Theta_1 \tag{62}$$

$$D(\xi) \equiv \cosh^2 \Theta_1 (\xi - \xi_0)^2 + \left(\frac{m_+ - m_-}{2m} \right)^2 \tag{63}$$

$$\xi_0 \equiv \frac{1}{2} \left(1 + \frac{m_+ m_-}{m^2} \right) \tag{64}$$

The angle Θ_1 is related to the q^2-dependence of the nucleon form factors.

They behave in this model as[30]

$$\left(1 - \frac{q^2}{4m^2} \cosh^2 \Theta_1\right)^{-2}$$

so that we have to take

$$\frac{4m^2}{\cosh^2 \Theta_1} \approx 0.71 \ \mathrm{BeV}^2$$

The resulting curve is plotted in Figure 1 for several values of the parameters m_1, m_2. The solution has the following properties.

1. The structure functions are still completely longitudinal.
2. The threshold behavior of $\xi = 1$ is now correctly given by $(1-\xi)^3$.
3. The overall size of all curves is again much too high compared with the proton structure.
4. There is an unwanted zero at $\xi = 0$.
5. The peak moves from the right to the left if one decreases m_1/m_+.
6. In the limiting case that m_1, m_2 take the true values of electron and proton mass, we find a sharp peak at small $\xi = m_e/m_+ \ll 1$

of height: $F_2\left(\dfrac{m_e}{m_+}\right) = \dfrac{8}{3\pi} \dfrac{1}{\alpha} \dfrac{m_+}{m_p}$

and width: $\Delta\xi = \alpha \dfrac{m_e m_p}{m_+^{\,2}}$

All these properties can easily be understood. The longitudinal charge of the cross section originates, as in the Majorana equation, in the Klein-Gordon type of the current operator.[20, 25] Good property 2 was to be expected on the basis of the correct falloff of hydrogen-like form factors. All the other properties can be traced back to the physical origin of the wave equation: a hydrogen atom is a two-body system with the photon coupling to one constituent of unit charge (the electron).†

As a consequence the mean-square charge per proton is too large; constituents of fractional quark charges would be needed to reach the right order of magnitude. Because of the two-body nature we also understand that $F_2(0)$ vanishes. As we have discussed before, infinitely many constituents are necessary to guarantee that $F_2(0) \neq 0$.

†Remember that in Schrödinger theory the photon in the hydrogen atom is coupled only to the electron.

In connection with point 6 we notice that in the parton model $F_2(\xi)/\xi$ denotes the probability of the incoming photon hitting a parton that carries the fraction ξ of the total momentum. Since in our case the only parton being coupled is the constituent of mass m_1, the fraction of the total momentum carried by it will be roughly m_1/m_+, and there we expect the structure function to have its maximum. Inspection of Eq. 61 shows that this is indeed the case. The peak lies roughly at the minimum of the denominator $D(\xi)$, which is

$$\xi = \xi_0 = \frac{m^2 + m_1^2 - m_2^2}{2m^2} \tag{65}$$

For small binding energies this coincides exactly with m_1/m_+.

The connection with the parton point of view can be made quite precise if we go to the limit of the true hydrogen atom. In this limit we can use the known hydrogen wave function

$$\psi_{100}(\mathbf{p}^*) = \frac{\sqrt{8}}{\pi} \left[\left(\frac{p^*}{\alpha\mu} \right)^2 + 1 \right]^{-2}, \qquad \mu = \frac{m_e m_p}{m_+} \tag{66}$$

to calculate the probability of finding the electron at a longitudinal momentum p_L^*

$$P(p_L^*) = \int \frac{d^2 p_T^*}{(\alpha\mu)^2} |\psi_{100}(\mathbf{p}^*)|^2$$

$$= \frac{8}{3\pi} \left[\left(\frac{p_L^*}{\alpha\mu} \right)^2 + 1 \right]^{-3} \tag{67}$$

Now consider the atom at very high momentum. Then the momentum of the electron will be

$$p_e \to \frac{m_e}{m_+} \left(1 + \frac{p_L^*}{m_e} \right) p \equiv \xi p \tag{68}$$

such that p_L^* is related to ξ by

$$p_L^* = m_+ \left(\xi - \frac{m_e}{m_+} \right) \tag{69}$$

Inserting this into Eq. 67 and multiplying by a factor $m_+^2/\alpha m_e m_p$ in order to obtain a normalized distribution in the variable $\xi \in [0,1]$, we obtain

$$\frac{F_2(\xi)}{\xi} = \frac{8}{3\pi} \frac{1}{\alpha} \frac{m_+^2}{m_e m_p} \left(\frac{m_p}{m_+}\right)^6 \left[\left(\frac{m_+}{\alpha m_e}\right)^2 \left(\xi - \frac{m_e}{m_+}\right)^2 + \left(\frac{m_p}{m_+}\right)^2\right]^{-3} \quad (70)$$

There is a sharp peak at $\xi = m_e/m_+$, as expected, with a width of $\Delta\xi = \alpha(m_e m_p/m_+^2)$ corresponding to the Rydberg spread of electron momentum.

The exact result of Eq. 61, on the other hand, becomes in this limit

$$\frac{F_2(\xi)}{\xi} = \frac{8}{3\pi} \frac{1}{\alpha} \left(\frac{m_p}{m_e}\right)^2 \xi(1-\xi)^3 \left[\left(\frac{m_+}{\alpha m_e}\right)^2 \left(\xi - \frac{m_e}{m_+}\right)^2 + \left(\frac{m_p}{m_+}\right)^2\right]^{-3} \quad (71)$$

Obviously, the parton approximation coincides exactly with this result except where both functions are extremely small.

What can be done to improve the results? Obviously it is possible to arrive at a small area by taking solutions with very small "parton" masses.[†] Compared with the experimental curve, however, these solutions are peaked too strongly on the left-hand side of the ξ interval. As a next step, therefore, we will have to introduce mixing of the parton masses with a stress on low-mass partons. Just as in the case of radial mixing of Majorana particles, this procedure can be carried out most concisely by constructing new wave equations on a space containing one more quantum number (we call it "massal").

Even if we may expect to reproduce the gross features of the experimental function, it is doubtful whether the new wave function will be able to avoid the zero at $\xi = 0$. Phenomenologically speaking, the nonzero experimental value is due to diffraction scattering, or Pomeron exchange. All recent work on duality has taught us that we should not count on obtaining such diffraction effects in resonance models (even if their spectrum increases exponentially, as in the Veneziano model).

5. LIGHT-CONE STRUCTURE OF MAJORANA-TYPE EQUATION

Let us now investigate the scale properties of the first model, with an infinitely rising mass spectrum, in coordinate space. Consider the con-

[†]Since $F_2(\xi)/\xi$ is the quantity which remains normalized: $\int_0^1 F_2(\xi)/\xi \, d\xi = 1$.

nected commutator of two currents:[20]

$$[j_\mu(x),j_\nu(y)]_c = \frac{1}{i} : \psi^\dagger(x)\left(i\overset{\leftrightarrow}{\partial}_\mu - 2\mu\Gamma_\mu\right)G(x-y)\left(i\overset{\leftrightarrow}{\partial}_\nu - 2\mu\Gamma_\nu\right)\psi(y):$$

$$- \frac{1}{i} : \psi^\dagger(y)\left(i\overset{\leftrightarrow}{\partial}_\nu - 2\mu\Gamma_\nu\right)G(y-x)\left(i\overset{\leftrightarrow}{\partial}_\mu - \mu\Gamma_\mu\right)\psi(x): \quad (72)$$

where $G(x)$ is the commutator function

$$[\psi(x),\psi^\dagger(y)] = \frac{1}{i}G(x-y) \quad (73)$$

It can be shown that the leading term of this commutator at the light-cone singularity is quite simple:

$$G(x) = \frac{1}{2\pi}\epsilon(x_0)[\delta(x^2)e^{-i\mu\Gamma x} + \cdots] \quad (74)$$

where the terms omitted are at most singular like $\Theta(x^2)$. Notice that the most singular term differs from the commutator function of the Klein-Gordon field only by the simple factor $e^{-i\mu\Gamma x}$. In standard analyses of the relation between scaling and light-cone structure[25] it has been shown that for a current commutator of type 72 and a light-cone singularity given by Eq. 74, the structure function $F_2(\xi)$ can simply be calculated as the Fourier transformation of the matrix element of the bilocal operator

$$O(x,0) = \psi^\dagger(x)e^{-i\mu\Gamma x}\psi(0) \quad (75)$$

One finds[20]

$$\int_{-\infty}^{\infty} d\xi \, e^{i\xi xp} \frac{F_2(\xi)}{\xi^2} = \langle p|O(x,0)|p\rangle + \text{H.c.} \quad (76)$$

to be taken at lightlike x. If one chooses the laboratory frame $p=(m,0,0,0)$, and $x=(t,0,0,-t)$, the right-hand side becomes for the Majorana equation

$$\langle p|O(x,0)|p\rangle + \text{H.c.} = n_{1/2}{}^2 u^+ \left(\tfrac{1}{2}\tfrac{1}{2}\right) e^{i(p-\mu\Gamma)x} u\left(\tfrac{1}{2}\tfrac{1}{2}\right)$$

$$= \frac{m}{m-\mu} e^{imt}\left(1 + i\frac{\mu t}{2}\right)^{-2} \quad (77)$$

Inverting relation 76, we obtain the result:[20]

$$F_2(\xi) = \frac{4m^3}{\mu^2(m-\mu)}\xi^2[\Theta(1-\xi)(1-\xi)e^{-2(m/\mu)(1-\xi)} + (\xi \to -\xi)] \quad (78)$$

In comparing the previous result of Eq. 34 we identify the first term with the resonance contributions. Since in this calculation we have made full use of locality of the theory, all unphysical solutions are automatically included. The second term represents the Z graphs involving the spacelike solutions. Notice that as a consequence of the diseased mass spectrum $F_2(\xi)$ does not vanish outside the interval $[-1,1]$ as it should. It is gratifying to see, though, that outside this interval $F_2(\xi)$ is very small.

Let us now come to the important question raised in Section 1: Can this model with an indefinitely rising resonance spectrum in the s-channel conserve naive canonical scale transformations at the light cone?[16]

Let us introduce the canonical scale transformations of a field according to Wilson.[10] For this we inspect the strongest short-distance singularity of operator products. The result is that we can assign the canonical dimension 1 to the field $\xi(x)$ such that the leading part of any short-distance expansion commutes with all the corresponding scale transformations:

$$\psi(x) \to e^{\alpha}\psi(e^{\alpha}x) \quad (79)$$

Take, for example, the commutator of two scalar currents $j(x) =$ $: \psi(x)\psi(x):$. It has the form

$$[j(x),j(0)]_c = \frac{1}{2\pi i}\epsilon(x^0)\delta(x^2)[O(x,0) + \text{H.c.}] + \cdots \quad (80)$$

The bilocal operator, $O(x,0)$, can be expanded in terms of local tensors:

$$O(x,0) = \sum_{n=0}^{\infty} \frac{1}{n!}O_{\mu_1\cdots\mu_n}^n(0)x^{\mu_1}\cdots x^{\mu_n} \quad (81)$$

with

$$O_{\mu_1\cdots\mu_n}^n(x) = \psi^\dagger(x)\overleftarrow{D}_{\mu_1}^+\cdots\overleftarrow{D}_{\mu_n}^+\psi(x) \quad (82)$$

Here $\overleftarrow{D}_\mu^+$ is a kind of covariant derivative:

$$\overleftarrow{D}_\mu^+ \equiv \overleftarrow{\partial}_\mu - i\mu D_\mu \quad (83)$$

We now see that the leading small x singularity of expansion 80 and 81 is indeed invariant under scale transformations 79.

Consider now, on the contrary, the set of all tensor operators $O^n_{\mu_1 \cdots \mu_n}(x)$ appearing along the leading light-cone singularity. By applying scale transformations 79 we see that any $O^n_{\mu_1 \cdots \mu_n}(x), n \geqslant 1$, is of mixed dimensions, the dimensional content starting with 2 in each of them and going up to $n+2$. Thus the canonical scale transformation according to Wilson is not conserved along the whole leading light-cone singularity.

This is not really a surprising result. There is a term

$$-i\mu\psi^\dagger(x)\Gamma^\mu \overset{\leftrightarrow}{\partial}{}^\mu \psi(x) \tag{84}$$

in the Lagrangian that is responsible for the infinite rise of the mass spectrum. It is exactly this term which now causes the dimensions of $O^n_{\mu_1 \cdots \mu_n}(x)$ to be mixed. If we set $\mu = 0$ we find

$$d_n \equiv \dim[O^n_{\mu_1 \cdots \mu_n}(x)] = n+2 \tag{85}$$

as in the simple field theoretic models with soft scale breaking (considered by Brandt and Preparata).

One may now wonder whether in spite of the strong breaking there is some other symmetry in the system responsible for the scaling properties of the structure functions. The answer is yes.

For simplicity, let us first assume the Γ_μ matrices to commute. In this case the argument can be formulated unblurred by technical difficulties.

Consider the x-dependent transformations

$$\psi(x) \to e^{\alpha} e^{i\mu\Gamma x\alpha} \psi(e^{\alpha}x) \tag{86}$$

Since they transform the local fields $\psi(x)$ to nonlocal fields† at the dilated place $e^{\alpha}x$, one would not, at first, identify them with dilations. However, the additional x-dependent part drops out completely when we are dealing with observables. Indeed, under Eq. 86

$$O^n_{\mu_1 \cdots \mu_n}(x) \to e^{(n+2)\alpha} O^n_{\mu_1 \cdots \mu_n}(e^{\alpha}x) \tag{87}$$

Therefore our modified transformations act like proper scale transformations as far as the observables are concerned. In addition, the dimensions of the operators $O^n_{\mu_1 \cdots \mu_n}(x)$ are now purely $d_n = n+2$.

---

†The transformed fields no longer satisfy Heisenberg's equation of motion. They still commute at spacelike distances, though.

If one wants to formulate the whole argument in an operatorial language (i.e., in terms of commutators of some scale charge operators with fields), one can do so only by considering equal-light commutators of operator products rather than light-cone expansions. In this case one also may dispose of the assumption of commutativity of the matrices.

An equal-light commutator of two local operators $A(x), B(y)$ is defined by

$$[A(x), B(y)]_{x^+ = y^+} \tag{88}$$

where

$$x^+ \equiv \frac{1}{\sqrt{2}} (x^0 + x^3) \tag{89}$$

A canonical treatment of our model can be carried out completely in terms of equal-light commutators[31] if one considers x^+ as an independent variable, rather than x^0. The canonical momenta become now

$$\pi \equiv \psi^\dagger \left(\overleftarrow{\partial}_- - i\mu\Gamma_- \right), \qquad \pi^\dagger = (\partial_- + i\mu\Gamma_-)\psi \tag{90}$$

They commute with the fields at equal light as:

$$i[\pi^\dagger(x)\psi^\dagger(0)]_{x^+ = 0} = \tfrac{1}{2}\delta(x^-)\delta^2(x^\perp) \tag{91}$$

This can be obtained from commutator 73 at equal light†

$$[\psi(x), \psi^\dagger(0)]_{x^+ = 0} = \frac{1}{4i}\epsilon(x^-)\delta^2(x^\perp)e^{-i\mu\Gamma_- x^-} \tag{92}$$

by applying the operator $(\partial_- + i\mu\Gamma_-)$.

Notice that, contrary to the equal-time case, $\psi(x)$ and $\psi^\dagger(x)$ fail to commute at equal light. The same statement holds for the commutator of the canonical momenta among each other:

$$i[\pi^\dagger(x), \pi(0)]_{x^+ = 0} = \tfrac{1}{2}(\partial_- + i\mu\Gamma_-)\delta(x^-)\delta^2(x^\perp) \tag{93}$$

Consider now the Noether current of naive scale transformations:[32]

$$\mathsf{D}^\mu(x) = \frac{\delta \mathcal{C}}{\delta \partial_\mu \psi}(1 + x\partial)\psi(x) + \text{H.c.} - x^\mu \mathcal{C} \tag{94}$$

†Here we have used

$$\frac{1}{2\pi i}\epsilon(x^0)\delta(x^2)|_{x^+ = 0} = \frac{1}{4i}\epsilon(x^-)\delta^2(x^\perp); \qquad \Theta(x^2)|_{x^+ = 0} = 0$$

We introduce the charge defined on a lightlike plane $x^+ = $ const. by integrating

$$D(x^+) \equiv \int dx^- \, d^2x^\perp \, \mathsf{D}^+(x) \tag{95}$$

This charge has the property of generating transformations 79 by commutation of $D(x^+)$ with the field at equal light:

$$i[D(x^+), \psi(x)] = (1 + x\partial)\psi(x) \tag{96}$$

It is an interesting technical point that the mechanism by which this transformation is generated is quite different from the equal-time case because of the noncommutativity of ψ with $\psi^\dagger$ and π with $\pi^\dagger$ mentioned above.† In order to see this, we consider first the part

$$\int dx^- \, d^2x^\perp \left[\pi(x)(1 + x\partial)\psi(x) + \psi^\dagger(x)\left(1 + \overleftarrow{\partial} x\right)\pi^\dagger(x) \right] \tag{97}$$

of $D(x)$. It contributes to the commutator, $i[D(x^+), \psi(x)]$:

$$\psi^\dagger\left(1 + \overleftarrow{\partial} x\right) + x^+ \int dx'^- \, d^2x'^\perp \, \pi(x')[\partial_+\psi(x'), \psi^\dagger(x)]_{x'^+ = x^+}$$

$$- \tfrac{1}{2}\psi^\dagger(x) \overleftarrow{\partial}_+ x^+$$

The second and third terms in this expression are canceled by the contribution of the other part, $-x^+ \int dx^- \, d^2x^\perp \, \mathsf{C}(x)$, of $D(x^+)$. By rewriting $\mathsf{C}(x)$ in terms of canonical fields,

$$\mathsf{C}(x) = \partial_+\psi^\dagger(x)\partial_-\psi(x) + \partial_-\psi^\dagger(x)\partial_+\psi(x) - g_\perp \psi^\dagger(x)\partial_\perp\psi(x)$$

$$- i\mu\left[\psi^\dagger(x)\Gamma^+ \overleftrightarrow{\partial}_+ \psi(x) + \psi^+(x)\Gamma^- \overleftrightarrow{\partial}_- \psi(x) + \psi^\dagger(x)\Gamma^\perp \overleftrightarrow{\partial}_\perp \psi(x) \right]$$

$$- \chi^2\psi^\dagger(x)\psi(x)$$

$$= \partial_+\psi^\dagger(x)\pi^\dagger(x) + \pi(x)\partial_+\psi(x) - \partial_\perp\psi^\dagger(x)\partial_\perp\psi(x)$$

$$- i\mu\left[\psi^\dagger(x)\Gamma^-\pi(x) - \pi^\dagger(x)\Gamma^-\psi(x) + \psi^\dagger(x)\Gamma^\perp \overleftrightarrow{\partial}_\perp \psi(x) \right]$$

$$- 2\mu^2\psi^\dagger(x)\Gamma_+\Gamma_-\psi(x) - \chi^2\psi^\dagger(x)\psi(x) \tag{98}$$

---

†The noncommutativity of ψ and $\psi^\dagger$ turns out to be required to make up for the (at first sight) somewhat puzzling factor $\tfrac{1}{2}$ on the right-hand side of Eq. 91 in getting the transformation law (Eq. 96).

and using commutators 91 and 92, we find indeed:

$$i\left[\int dx^{-\prime} d^2x^{\perp\prime} \mathcal{C}(x'), \psi^\dagger(x)\right]_{x^{+\prime}=x^+}$$

$$= -\tfrac{1}{2}\partial_+\psi^\dagger(x) + \int dx^{-\prime} d^2x^{\perp\prime}[\partial_+\psi(x'), \psi^+(x')]_{x^{+\prime}=x^+} \quad (99)$$

proving Eq. 96.

Similarly we can introduce the Noether current of the modified scale transformations

$$\tilde{D}^\mu(x) = \frac{\delta \mathcal{C}}{\delta\partial_\mu\psi(x)}(1 + x\partial + i\Gamma_- x^-)\psi(x) + \text{H.c.} - x^\mu \mathcal{C}(x) \quad (100)$$

whose charge generates

$$i\left[\tilde{D}(x^+), \psi(x)\right] = (1 + x\partial + i\Gamma_- x^-)\psi(x) \quad (101)$$

Let us now consider the equal-light commutator of two scalar currents $j(x)$, rather than the small x^2 commutator. We find

$$[j(y), j(x)]_{y^+=x^+} = \frac{1}{4i}\epsilon(z^-)\delta^2(z^\perp)\psi^\dagger(y)e^{-i\mu\Gamma_- z^-}\psi(x) + \text{H.c.},$$

$$z \equiv y - x$$

$$(102)$$

The bilocal operator appearing on the right-hand side can now be expanded as

$$\sum \frac{1}{n!}\psi^\dagger(x)\left(\overleftarrow{\partial}_- - i\mu\Gamma_-\right)^n\psi(x)(z^-)^n + \text{H.c.} \quad (103)$$

The operator of nth order,

$$O^n(x) = \psi^\dagger(x)\left(\overleftarrow{\partial}_- - i\mu\Gamma_-\right)^n\psi(x) \quad (104)$$

obviously satisfies

$$i\left[\tilde{D}(x^+), O^n(x)\right] = [(n+2) + x\partial]O^n(x) \quad (105)$$

so that $O^n(x)$ transform according to Eq. 87 with the pure dimension

$$d_n = n + 2 \quad (106)$$

necessary for invariance of the equal-light commutator (Eq. 102).

There are two reasons why we had to go to the equal-light formulation.

1. On the one hand, while a scale charge $D(x^+)$ at fixed light derived from the Noether current manages to generate transformation 79 on the fields $\psi(x)$, higher derivatives show mixed dimensions if scale breaking is present. This is so since ∂_+ derivatives bring in the commutators

$$i[\partial_+ D(x^+), \psi(x)] \neq 0$$

when calculating

$$i[D(x^+), \partial_{\mu_1} \cdots \partial_{\mu_n} \psi(x)] \neq (n + 1 + x\partial)\psi(x)$$

Thus there is no operator transforming

$$\psi(x) \to e^\alpha \psi(e^\alpha x)$$

and, at the same time, also all

$$\partial_{\mu_1} \cdots \partial_{\mu_n} \psi(x) \to e^{\alpha(n+1)} \partial_{\mu_1} \cdots \partial_{\mu_n} \psi(e^\alpha x)$$

This argument is not bound to our specific model. It holds as well for the simplest Lagrangian containing scale breaking, the free massive scalar field. This is why people doing conformal analyses on the light cone have to classify their operators always in the limit of exact conformal symmetry (in some assumed "skeleton theory"). In an equal-light commutator no derivatives ∂_+ are present, and one can find invariance under commutation with scale charges even in the presence of breaking.

2. The second reason is more specific to our model. If the Γ^μ matrices do not commute, the scale behavior even of the spatial components of the operators $O^n_{\mu_1 \cdots \mu_n}(x)$ will be complicated. At equal light, however, the locality of the commutator forces a $\delta^2(x^\perp - y^\perp)$ to appear, killing the contribution of components Γ_1, Γ_2 (Γ_+ is absent anyhow since $x^+ = y^+$).

It probably goes without saying that the same discussion can be extended to the conformal generators $K_\mu(x^+)$. Also here the naive canonical conformal current is not conserved at the leading light-cone singularity, but there exists again a modified conformal charge which has the correct conservation properties. Also the modified conformal transformations become conventional on the Hermitian observables. As a consequence, the set of fifteen operators $P_\mu, L_{\mu\nu}, \tilde{D}(x^+), \tilde{K}_\mu(x^+)$ can be used to classify equal-light commutators according to representations of the conformal group, just as was done before in the exact conformally invariant limiting theories.[33] Now this classification holds also in the presence of symmetry breaking. Notice, however, that the breaking terms cause the commutation rules of the charges among each other to be different from those of the conformal group (even though the fields transform correctly).

Furthermore, we would like to remark that in the case of commuting Γ_μ matrices the fields $\psi(x)$ become a nonlocal† transform of another field, say, $\tilde{\psi}(x)$:

$$\psi(x) = e^{i\mu\Gamma x}\tilde{\psi}(x)$$

which satisfies a Klein-Gordon-like equation:

$$(\Box + \mu^2\Gamma^2 + \chi^2)\tilde{\psi}(x) = 0$$

that has no infinitely rising mass spectrum when $j\to\infty$ (it is, in fact, degenerate) and scales trivially at the light cone. Perhaps this property is the basic origin of the nice scaling properties of the model. It is a curious fact also that the Thirring model is an x-dependent transform of a free field.[34] Moreover, the proof[35] that "nature reads books on free fields,"[36] when dealing with the leading singularity in light-cone expansion, depends on a similar transformation. At present we do not know of any reasons for the similarity among these different models.

Finally, we want to point out that our model allows for a one-parameter manifold of scale-invariant limiting theories ("skeleton theories"). In fact, letting $\mu\to 0, m\to 0$ with $\rho = m/\mu$ fixed,‖ we obviously arrive at a nontrivial structure function (see Eq. 78). We mention this point since the question has been raised whether there exists any skeleton theory which is different from a free-field theory. The argument was stimulated by the observation that a conformally invariant theory contains an infinite set of different conserved local currents.§

We do not know of any uncontroversial definition of a free-field theory. Hence we cannot tell whether or not the limiting theory presented here should be called free. The nontrivial shape of the structure functions should probably be considered a result of an internal interaction (causing the infinite rise of the mass spectrum). Notice that only in the limit $\rho\to\infty$,

---

†In the sense that the field $\psi(x)$ does not satisfy Heisenberg's equation of motion any more. It still commutes at spacelike distances.

‖ Note the formal similarity with the Callan-Symanzik conformally invariant limit in standard field theory. If we let first $\mu\to 0$ and then $m\to 0$, we arrive at the analog of the Gell-Mann/ Low limit. For a discussion of these limits in the Thirring model see ref. 37.

§See Chapter 4 in this volume.

corresponding to setting first $\mu = 0$ and then $m \to 0$, does the structure function reduce to a $\delta(1 - \xi)$ function, since in this case the spectrum is degenerate at $m = 0$.

6. SUMMARY

Standard infinite-component wave equations which have been studied extensively in the past provide us with structure functions with finite scaling limits. We have shown that they can serve as useful models for the study of the interrelation of infinitely rising resonance structures, light-cone properties, and the parton picture of deep inelastic scaling phenomena.

The mass spectra of these models are somewhat unphysical. Quantitatively, however, the structure functions turn out to be determined almost completely by the properties of the healthy particles of the spectrum.

One important feature of the structure function, the threshold behavior $\alpha(1 - \xi)^3$ at $\xi = 1$, is easily accommodated by choosing a hydrogen-like wave equation. The region of smaller ξ, on the other hand, presents some problems since the wave equations investigated show a typical two-body character, with the photon coupling to one constituent of charge 1. For this reason the resulting structure function is too high and shows a zero at $\xi = 0$. The size error can in principle be corrected by mixing many wave equations of low constituent ("parton") mass. For this one would have to increase the Hilbert space by an additional, "massal" quantum number. The nonzero value of $F_2(0)$, however, seems hard to obtain in such wave equations, since it is a typical diffraction effect for which resonance models cannot account.

In a particular model we have found the result that infinitely rising resonances prevent the naive canonical scale transformations, which are conserved in a short-distance expansion, from being conserved also along the whole leading light-cone singularity. However, a suitable symmetry transformation can still be found which is responsible for the scaling properties of the model.

Finally we have found that conformal analyses of operators appearing at the leading light-cone singularity of commutators can be carried out also in the presence of symmetry breaking if attention is restricted to the equal-light parts of such commutators.

ACKNOWLEDGMENTS

I am grateful to Professor H. Leutwyler for stressing the importance of equal-light commutators for an understanding of the scale properties of infinite-component models. I also thank Professors R. Gatto and B. Schroer for discussions.

REFERENCES

1. Y. Nambu, *Progr. Theoret. Physics, Suppl.*, **37+38**, 368 (1966); A. O. Barut and H. Kleinert, *Phys. Rev.*, **156**, 1546 (1967); *Proceedings of the IV Coral Gables Conference*, Freeman, 1967, pp. 76–105.
2. H. Kleinert, *Fortschr. Physik*, **16**, 1 (1968).
3. A. O. Barut and H. Kleinert, *Phys. Rev. Letters*, **18**, 754 (1967); H. Kleinert, *ibid.*, **1**,, 1027 (1967); B. Hamprecht and H. Kleinert, *Fortschr. Physik*, **16**, 635 (1968).
4. A. O. Barut, D. Corrigan, and H. Kleinert, *Phys. Rev. Letters*, **20**, 167 (1968).
5. H. Kleinert, *Springer Tracts in Modern Physics*, Vol. 49, p. 89 *Springer-Verlag, Berlin*, 1969.
6. H. Bebie and H. Leutwyler, *Phys. Rev. Letters*, **19**, 618 (1967); H. Kleinert, Montana State University Preprint (1967); M. Gell-Mann, D. Horn, and J. Weyers, *Proceedings of the Heidelberg Conference on High Energy Physics and Elementary Particles*, 1967; B. Hamprecht and H. Kleinert, *Phys. Rev.*, **180** 1410 (1969).
7. D. Corrigan, B. Hamprecht, and H. Kleinert, *Nucl. Phys.*, **B11**, 1 (1969).
8. I. T. Grodsky and R. F. Streater, *Phys. Rev. Letters*, **20**, 695 (1968).
9. M. Breidenbach et al., *Phys. Rev. Letters*, **23**, 935 (1969); E. D. Bloom et al., *ibid.*, **23**, 930 (1969), and SLAC Publ. 796, Report presented at the XV International Conference on High Energy Physics, Kiev, USSR (1970); M. Kendall et al., report presented at the Cornell Conference on Electromagnetic Interactions (1971).
10. K. Wilson, *Phys. Rev.*, **179**, 1499 (1969).
11. J. D. Bjorken and E. A. Paschos, *Phys. Rev.*, **185**, 1975 (1969).
12. R. Brandt and G. Preparata, *Nucl. Phys.*, **B27**, 541 (1971).
13. For a review see S. Coleman, "Ettore Majorana," lecture given at the 1971 International School of Physics.
14. K. Wilson, *Phys. Rev.* **D2**, 1473. 1478 (1970).
15. E. D. Bloom and F. J. Gilman, *Phys. Rev. Letters*, **25**, 1140 (1970); G. Domokos and S. Kovesi- Domokos, *Phys. Rev. D*, **3**, 1184, 1191 (1971).
16. A. F. Grillo and H. Kleinert, Berlin preprint, December 1971.
17. V. Rittenberg and H. R. Rubinstein, *Phys. Letters*, **35B**, 50 (1971); E. D. Bloom and F. J. Gilman, *Phys. Rev. D*, **4**, 2993 (1971).
18. S. D. Drell and T. M. Yan, *Phys. Rev. Letters*, **24**, 181 (1970).
19. M. I. Pavkovic, *Ann. Phys.*, **62**, 1, and **64**, 474 (1971).
20. H. Bebie, V. Gorge, and H. Leutwyler, Bern preprint (1971).
21. E. Majorana, *Nuovo Cimento*, **9**, 335 (1932).
22. D. Stoyanov and I. T. Todorov, *J. Math. Phys.*, **9**, 2146 (1968).
23. H. Bebie, F. Ghielwetti, V. Gorge, and H. Leutwyler, *Phys. Rev.*, **177** 2140 (1969).
24. A. O. Barut and H. Kleinert, *Phys. Rev.*, **156**, 1546 (1967).
25. H. Leutwyler and J. Stern, *Nucl. Phys.*, **B2**, 77 (1970); R. Jackiw, R. van Royen, and G. West, *Phys. Rev. D*, **2**, 2473 (1970).

26. A. O. Barut and H. Kleinert, *Phys. Rev.*, **156**, 1541 (1967).

27. H. Kleinert, *Lectures in Theoretical Physics*, Gordon and Breach, New York, 1968,

28. H. Kleinert, *Phys. Rev.*, **168**, 1827 (1968).

29. H. Kleinert, *Nucl. Phys.*, **B37** to be published.

30. H. Kleinert, *Phys. Rev.*, **163**, 1807 (1967).

31. K. Bardakci and G. Segré, *Phys. Rev.*, **159**, 1263 (1967); H. Leutwyler, *Acta Phys. Austriaca*, Suppl. V (1968) and *Springer Tracts in Modern Physics*, Vol. 50, p. 29, Springer-Verlag, Berlin, 1969; J. Jersak and J. Stern, *Nuovo Cimento*, **59**, 315 (1969); H. Leutwyler, J. R. Klauder, and L. Streit, *ibid.*, **66A**, 536 (1970); J. B. Kogut and D. E. Soper, *Phys. Rev. D*, **1**, 299 (1970); J. D. Bjorken, J. B. Kogut, and D. E. Soper, *ibid.*, **3**, 1382 (1971); J. M. Cornwall and R. Jackiw, *ibid.*, **4**, 367 (1971); A. Miklavc and C. H. Woo, University of Maryland preprint (August 1971); F. Jegerlehner, Bern preprint (February 1972).

32. H. Kleinert, *Proceedings of the XI Internationale Universitätswochen für Kernphysik, Schladming, Austria, 1972*, Chapter II.

33. S. Ferrara, R. Gatto, and A. F. Grillo, *Nucl. Phys.*, **B32**, 349 (1971).

34. B. Klaiber, *Lectures in Theoretical Physics*, Vol. XA, Gordon and Breach, New York, 1968; J. H. Lowenstein and B. Schroer, *Phys. Rev. D*, **3**, 1981 (1971).

35. K. Dietz and K. Meetz, Bonn preprint (1972).

36. H. Fritsch and M. Gell-Mann, talk presented at the International Conference on Duality and Symmetry, Tel-Aviv, Israel, 1971; see Chapter 7 of this volume.

37. M. Gomes and J. H. Lowenstein, University of Pittsburgh Preprint NYO-3829-90 (1972).

CHAPTER 11

Some Astrophysical Speculations at Very High Energies

H. A. KASTRUP

1. INTRODUCTION

Allow me a few unphysical remarks to begin with. When I became involved in the "conformal group" about 10 years ago (against the earnest advice of several people with tenure), I soon realized that it was looked at, among a large part of the physics community, almost like an "obscenity" a decent physicist just would not mention in public (how the situation was in private I don't know!). Time and other factors, however, have changed this too.

Gratifying as these social changes are, the physical results are not yet overwhelming. Despite several interesting and encouraging results in the realm of broken dilatation and conformal symmetries, many problems remain. As my contribution is intended to add some new problems, let us look first at some of the problems already known.

1. Experimentally we see "scaling" to an amazing degree in electron-nucleon scattering ("Bjorken scaling") and in hadron-nucleon collisions ("Feynman scaling"). However, the underlying dynamical frameworks and their relation to a scheme of asymptotic dilatation (or scale) and conformal invariance (operationally defined in coordinate space) are not very clear, despite interesting insights obtained in the last 1 or 2 years. After Wilson made his very important proposal[1] as to how to put a notion of asymptotic dilatation invariance into an operational form by making operator expansions in the neighborhood of vanishing Euclidean distances of two field quantities, Gatto and his collaborators discussed[2] the relation of these expansions to current algebra and Bjorken scaling. In an interesting paper[3] Mack analyzed this connection without using equal-time commutators and discussed Bjorken scaling for the inelastic electromagnetic nucleon structure functions from Wilson's expansion, positivity, and some smoothness assumptions (unsubtracted dispersion relation). Both positivity and smoothness assumptions play a central role, and for this reason there seems to be no one-to-one relation between dilatation invariance, as incorporated into Wilson's expansions, and Bjorken scaling.

If one requires asymptotic operator expansions not only for vanishing Euclidean but also for Minkowski distances, one gets the light-cone expansions as proposed by several people.[4] If one *assumes* the light-cone singularities of the relevant current-current matrix element to be dominant and to be canonical, then scaling á la Bjorken follows. However, I do not know[5] any convincing argument that the Bjorken limit in momentum space should be determined by the singularities on the light cone and nothing else! It seems that the postulates of canonical light-cone dominance, on the one side, and Wilson's expansions plus smoothness conditions as discussed by Mack, on the other side, are somehow equivalent, but no exact mathematical statements about this exist.

All this shows that the relation between Bjorken scaling in inelastic electron-nucleon scattering and dilatation invariance at short distances or on the light cone is not simple, at least at the present state of our insights. The situation becomes even more intricate (or strange!) if one applies[6] conformal invariance to the light-cone expansions by requiring the operators on the right-hand and left-hand sides of the expansions to be irreducible tensor operators with respect to the special conformal generators. The implication[6] that all the operators on the right-hand side with their higher and higher spins have to be conserved currents is surprising indeed, and the meaning of this is not yet clear.

Not yet understood at all is the relation (if any!) between Feynman scaling in purely hadronic interactions and approximate dilatation (conformal) invariance formulated in coordinate space, for instance, in the sense that the degree of homogeneity of certain space-time singularities of the quantity[7]

$$\langle p_1 p_2 | j(x) j(0) | p_1 p_2 \rangle$$

is determined by an appropriate operational definition of asymptotic dilatation invariance in a way perhaps similar to that in the case of inelastic electron-nucleon scattering. I shall come back to this point at the end of the chapter.

Despite their importance, the operator expansions do not contain very much dynamical information. I shall mention two recent proposals to bring more dynamical properties into a scheme of asymptotic dilatation and (or) conformal invariance.

2. Fritsch and Gell-Mann proposed[8] an extension of the light-cone expansions by abstracting algebraic closure relations from the free quark-gluon model, with canonical dimensions on the light cone even for interacting fields. This field is presently under intense investigation; and as soon as the high-energy neutrino beams in Batavia are operating, we shall know more about the validity of some of the sum rules derived in the framework of that scheme.

3. A very interesting proposal[9,10] for combining dilatation and conformal invariance in the dynamical framework of Green's functions is due to Polyakov and Migdal, followed by an extensive analysis[11-14] by Mack and Todorov, Mack and Symanzik, Schroer, and others. The crucial observation of Polyakov (for nonrelativistic correlation functions) was that conformal invariance, in addition to dilatation invariance, determines not only the two-point function but also the three-point function up to very few parameters. When the higher n-point functions are built up by skeleton expansions, the free parameters are in principle determined by integral (Dyson-Schwinger) equations. The big problem is to find nontrivial solutions of these equations. The present status of this very interesting field has been summarized by Mack.[15]

Again, the relation of this dynamical approach to physical processes still has to be unambiguously established and analyzed; for instance, how the operator expansions fit in, and whether one can derive Bjorken scaling, must be determined.

4. From all that I have said above it is clear that we need more comparisons with experiments in order to see in what way (if at all) nature makes use of some kind of asymptotic dilatation and conformal invariance

at very high energies, by starting from a suitable operational definition of these symmetries in coordinate space. This is one reason why I want to discuss an additional attempt to make contact between the real world and some more or less reasonable hypothesis about the way in which dilatation and conformal invariance may show up as an approximate symmetry at very high energies. The main idea is as follows.[16]

Suppose that some reactions not only show scaling at very high energies but also conserve, at least approximately, dilatation and conformal momenta, perhaps in the weak sense that in some quasi-elastic scattering reactions the expectation values of these momenta are approximately the same before and after those collisions. Such an assumption is similar to that of Nambu and Lurie[17] about the weak conservation of chirality in certain reactions.

Suppose further that we have a highly relativistic gas of particles reacting with each other in the sense just described, that is, conserving dilatation and conformal momenta, at least in a reasonable approximation. If such a very hot gas is in equilibrium, we expect equilibrium distribution functions to exist [18, 19] which are solutions of the relativistic Boltzmann equation and the logarithms of which are linearly related to the quantities conserved in those binary or "quasi"-binary collisions.

The most important example of such a gas might have been the universe right after the big bang. For this reason the following discussion may be of some physical, as well as mathematical, interest.

In order to separate the purely mathematical part from the much more difficult physical one, I shall discuss first the most important properties of a highly relativistic gas in equilibrium such that its binary collisions conserve dilatation or conformal momenta.

Afterwards I shall try to make contact with some known properties of the universe. The most difficult task is the analysis of several known high-energy processes which show scaling and which might have led, at least approximately, to distribution functions of the type mentioned above. If such distributions were present right after the big bang, then they might have had a very important effect on the evolution of the universe, as we shall see.

2. PROPERTIES OF DISTRIBUTION FUNCTION
FOR SYSTEMS WITH DILATATION
OR CONFORMALLY INVARIANT BINARY COLLISIONS

In this part we can use the results of Ehlers, Geren, and Sachs,[20] who extended previous work by Tauber and Weinberg.[20] We merely have to apply these results to the flat Minkowski space.[21] Accordingly, a locally isotropic distribution function $f(x,p)$ for particles with momentum p and vanishing or negligible rest masses has the general form

$$f(x,p) = g[\xi^{\mu}(x)p_{\mu}]$$

where g is a differentiable function, and $\xi^{\mu}(x)$ a conformal Killing vector, that is, it has the property

$$\partial_{\nu}\xi_{\mu} + \partial_{\mu}\xi_{\nu} = g_{\mu\nu}\lambda(x)$$

$\lambda(x)$ being a scalar function. The Killing vector defines the basic velocity field $u^{\mu}(x)$ by

$$\xi^{\mu}(x) = \alpha(x)u^{\mu}(x), \qquad \xi^{\mu}\xi_{\mu} = \alpha^2$$

In order to simplify our discussion technically, we shall deal only with Boltzmann distributions here; the generalizations to Bose-Einstein and Fermi-Dirac statistics can be obtained by using, for example, the results of ref. 18.

a. Dilatations

The transformations

$$D(\alpha): x^{\mu} \rightarrow \hat{x}^{\mu} = e^{\alpha}x^{\mu}, \qquad \alpha \text{ a real constant}$$

give the conformal Killing vector

$$\xi_D{}^{\mu}(x) = \left(\frac{\partial \hat{x}^{\mu}}{\partial \alpha}\right)_{\alpha=0} = x^{\mu}$$

and the corresponding equilibrium distribution function is

$$f(x,p) = F_D \exp\left[-\frac{p^{\mu}u_{\mu}(x)}{kT(x)} \right] \tag{1}$$

where

$$u^{\mu}(x) = \frac{x^{\mu}}{(x^2)^{1/2}}, \quad x^2 > 0, \ kT(x) = \frac{1}{\beta_D(x^2)^{1/2}}, \quad \text{and} \ F_D, \beta_D = \text{const}$$

The invariant particle density $n(x)$ is defined by the current

$$n^\mu(x) = \int \frac{d^3p}{p^0} p^\mu f(x,p) = n(x)u^\mu(x)$$

and has the value

$$n_D(x) = 8\pi F_D [kT(x)]^3$$

The energy-momentum tensor $T_{\mu\nu}(x)$ is defined by

$$T_{\mu\nu}(x) = \int \frac{d^3p}{p^0} p_\mu p_\nu f(x,p) = (\hat\mu + \hat p)u_\mu u_\nu - g_{\mu\nu}\hat p$$

where $\hat\mu(x)$ is the proper energy density, and $\hat p(x)$ is the proper pressure. Because of the negligible rest masses the trace $T_\mu^{\ \mu}$ vanishes, and we have $3p = \hat\mu$,

$$\hat p_D(x) = 8\pi F_D [kT(x)]^4$$

Because $u_\mu = \partial_\mu(x^2)^{1/2}$, the flow associated with the velocity field is hypersurface orthogonal. In addition we have

$$u_{\mu;\nu} \equiv \partial_\nu u_\mu(x) = \left(\frac{1}{x^2}\right)^{1/2}(g_{\mu\nu} - u_\mu u_\nu) \tag{2}$$

that is, the expansion velocity θ has the value $3/(x^2)^{1/2}$. The acceleration $\dot u_\mu = u_{\mu;\nu}u^\nu$ vanishes.

Transformation to co-moving coordinates is obtained by the substitution

$$x^0 = \tau \cosh w, \qquad r = \tau \sinh w, \qquad \theta \to \theta, \qquad \varphi \to \varphi$$

$$\tau = (x^2)^{1/2}, \qquad ds^2 = d\tau^2 - \tau^2[dw^2 + \sinh^2 w(d\theta^2 + \sin^2\theta\, d\varphi^2)] \tag{3}$$

In the co-moving system the velocity field is given by $\bar u^\mu = g_0^{\ \mu}$.

We see that the system so obtained is just Milne's universe,[22] which has been discussed extensively in the literature,[23] so that we do not need to repeat those discussions here. What is remarkable is that we obtain the system by the *dynamical* requirement that the binary collisions be invariant under dilatations.

Let us illustrate this dynamical background of the expansion by the following example. The scattering of an ultrarelativist particle off a potential $1/r$ conserves[24] the dilatation momentum $D = x^\mu p_\mu$. If we rewrite this as

$\mathbf{x} \cdot \mathbf{p} = p_0 x^0 - D$, we see that for constant D the virial $\mathbf{x} \cdot \mathbf{p}$ increases linearly with time, that is, the motions of the particles in the system cannot be bounded!

Up to now we have taken into account dilatation invariance only. In reality we always have energy-momentum conservation. If we incorporate energy conservation, we obtain the same formulas as above, but temperature and velocity field now take the forms

$$kT(x) = \left(\beta_t^2 + 2\beta_t \beta_D x^0 + \beta_D^2 x^2 \right)^{-1/2}$$

$$(u^0(x), \mathbf{u}(x)) = kT(x) \left(\beta_t + \beta_D x^0, \beta_D \mathbf{x} \right)$$

This means that we have two parameters instead of one determining the temperature and other properties, where the new one, β_t (the index t refers to time translation) is just the inverse temperature at $x = 0$! It vanishes only if $T(x=0) = \infty$.

b. Special Conformal Transformations

The special conformal (SC) transformations

$$\mathrm{SC}(c) : x^\mu \to \hat{x}^\mu = \frac{x^\mu - c^\mu x^2}{\sigma(x;c)}, \qquad \sigma(x;c) = 1 - 2c \cdot x + c^2 x^2$$

give the four conformal Killing vectors:

$$\xi_\alpha = (\xi_\alpha^\mu), \qquad \xi_\alpha^\mu = 2x^\mu x_\alpha - g_\alpha^\mu x^2, \qquad \alpha, \mu = 0, 1, 2, 3$$

We choose a constant timelike unit vector $b, b^2 = 1$, and define the timelike vector $\xi_c^\mu = \xi_\alpha^\mu b^\alpha$, $\xi_c^2 = (x^2)^2$. In this case the equilibrium distribution function, velocity, and temperature fields are given by

$$f(x,p) = F_c \exp\left(\frac{-u^\mu p_\mu}{kT(x)} \right)$$

$$u^\mu(x) = -x^2 \partial^\mu \left(\frac{b \cdot x}{x^2} \right), \qquad kT(x) = \frac{1}{\beta_c x^2}, \qquad F_c, \beta_c = \text{const.}$$

(4)

From this we get for the invariant density and the invariant pressure:

$$n_c(x) = 8\pi F_c (kT)^3, \qquad \hat{p}_c(x) = 8\pi F_c (kT)^4$$

Differentiation of the velocity field gives

$$u_{\mu;\nu}(x) = \dot{u}_\mu u_\nu + \left(\frac{2x \cdot b}{x^2}\right)\left(g_{\mu\nu} - u_\mu u_\nu\right)$$

$$\dot{u}_\mu = u_{\mu;\nu} u^\nu = \left(\frac{2}{x^2}\right)\left(x \cdot b u_\mu - x_\mu\right)$$

(5)

that is, now the acceleration does not vanish! With $b = (1,0,0,0)$ we get $u_\mu = -x^2 \partial_\mu (x^0/x^2)$, which shows the flow to be hypersurface orthogonal. Transformation to co-moving coordinates is obtained by the mapping

$$\tau = \frac{x^0}{x^2}, \quad \rho = \frac{r}{x^2}, \quad \theta \to \theta, \quad \varphi \to \varphi, \quad u_\mu \to \bar{u}_\mu = (\tau^2 - \rho^2)g_{\mu 0}$$

$$ds^2 = (\tau^2 - \rho^2)^{-2}[d\tau^2 - d\rho^2 - \rho^2(d\theta^2 + \sin^2\theta\, d\varphi^2)]$$

From the expression for the line element we see that the system is isotropic, but not homogeneous. This means that we do not have a Robertson-Walker metric and no Friedman universe!

For our astrophysical discussions below it is important to have red-shift-distance relations. Suppose that light having wavelength λ and emitted at $(t, \mathbf{x}) \leftrightarrow (\tau, \rho)$ arrives at $\mathbf{x} = 0$ at the time $t_0 = t + r/c$ with wavelength λ_0. Then one obtains in the usual manner for the red shift $z = (\lambda_0 - \lambda)/\lambda$ and those distances the following relations:

$$\rho = \left(\frac{\tau_0}{2}\right)z, \quad \tau = \left(\frac{\tau_0}{2}\right)(z+2)$$

(6)

$$r = \frac{1}{2}\frac{z}{1+z}t_0, \quad t = \frac{1}{2}\frac{2+z}{1+z}t_0, \quad \frac{1}{x^2} = \left(\frac{1}{t_0}\right)^2(1+z)$$

(7)

For $z \ll 1$ the first of Eqs. 7 reduces to Hubble's law:

$$r = \left(\frac{1}{H_0}\right)z, \quad H_0 = \frac{2}{t_0}$$

(8)

For larger red shifts, however, Hubble's law is not a good approximation and would give distances larger than the actual ones.

At this point two comments are in order.

1. For $r^2 \ll t^2$, that is, "locally," the system is isotropic *and* homogeneous, and Hubble's law (Eq. 8) is valid. The corresponding local

Robertson-Walker metric has an expansion function $R = R_1 t^2$, $R_1 = \text{const.}$; this is not a solution of Friedman's equation,[23] but one can show that it is a solution of the corresponding Brans-Dicke equation[25] with $\omega = -\frac{3}{2}$ (see ref. 26), vanishing spatial curvature, and the Brans-Dicke scalar:

$$\frac{1}{\varphi(t)} = \left(\frac{1}{\varphi_1}\right)t^6, \qquad \varphi_1 = \frac{2^8 \pi^2 F_c}{g\beta_c^4}$$

2. Incorporating energy conservation of the binary collisions gives, in the same manner as in the case of the dilatations above, the following modifications:

$$kT(x) = \left[\beta_t^2 + 2\beta_t\beta_c(t^2 + r^2) + \beta_c^2(x^2)^2\right]^{-1/2}$$

$$(u_0(x), \mathbf{u}(x)) = kT(x)\left(\beta_t + \beta_c(t^2 + r^2), 2t\beta_c\mathbf{x}\right)$$

The parameter β_t again is the inverse temperature for $x = 0$. For very large times it becomes negligible.

3. SOME VERY PRELIMINARY ASTROPHYSICAL REMARKS

It is obviously tempting to compare the systems that we have been discussing with our expanding universe. Because the first one is the well-known model of Milne, I shall confine myself to the second system, the "conformal" one.

Locally, that is, for $r^2 \ll t^2$, the factor 2 in Hubble's constant $H_0 = 2/t_0$ is remarkable. If taken seriously, the factor 2 in $t_0 = 2/H_0$ would eliminate an "age" problem,[27] if there is one, and if there is any relation at all of our system to the realities surrounding us! Even if our system had something to do with the properties of the universe right after the big bang, the question remains whether there would be still traces around.

Furthermore, we have a strong decrease of the density $n_c(t)$ with time t because $n_c(t)t^6 = \text{const}$. This has to be compared with the much weaker gravitational decrease in, for instance, the Einstein-De Sitter model,[23] where $n(t)t^2 = \text{const}$.

In our neighborhood traces of our distribution in the form of neutrinos, photons, or fast cosmic rays may still be around. Something amusing is the following. The motion of very fast particles in the gravitational potentials $1/r$ conserves not only energy, angular momentum, and dilatation momentum, but also the time component of the conformal momenta. Thus the motion (scattering) of very fast cosmic rays in the gravitational centers of relatively slow masses does not destroy the "conformal" properties of a gas of fast particles. Somehow the potentials $1/r$ act similarly to the energy-conserving walls of a box filled with a gas.

If the "conformal" distribution was of some importance right after the big bang, the more traces would probably be found the farther one goes back in time, or the larger the red shifts z are. Now we have seen that, for red shifts which are not small compared to 1, we have a considerable modification of Hubble's law, as well as strong deviations from homogeneity. I am not able to propose a detailed mechanism, but it is, of course, tempting to associate some of the remarkable properties of quasars with our system, in the sense that the remnants of the "primeval" conformal distribution are somehow coupled to quasars. More work is certainly needed to clarify this point and to go beyond uncertain speculations!

4. HIGH-ENERGY PROCESSES WHICH MIGHT HAVE LED TO CONFORMAL DISTRIBUTION FUNCTIONS

A very important problem in the context of our considerations is the following: Which high-energy processes that we know about might give rise, at least in a reasonable approximation, to the "dilatational" and conformal distribution functions discussed above? Although I shall not be able to give a convincing answer to this question, there are a number of theoretical and experimental indications that those systems should be taken seriously.

In general, in this section I shall discuss several reactions with cross sections of a form which can be related to an effective dilatation and conformally invariant "potential," such as the Coulomb potential, or a Born approximation in kinematical regions where all rest masses are negligible and where there could be approximate conservation of dilatation and conformal momenta.

a. Purely Electromagnetic Interactions in Lowest Order

(1) Compton scattering off electrons for s, $|t| \gg m_e^2$:

$$\frac{d\sigma}{d|t|} = \frac{2\pi\alpha^2}{s^2}\left(\frac{s}{|t|} + \frac{|t|}{s}\right)$$

$$s = (p_e + p_\gamma)^2, \qquad t = (p_e - p'_e)^2, \qquad p'_e = \text{momentum after scattering}$$

(2)   Electron-electron scattering for s, $|t| \gg m_e{}^2$:

$$\frac{d\sigma}{d|t|} = \frac{2\pi\alpha^2}{t^2 s^2}(t^2 + 2st + 2s^2)$$

The above two cross sections can be obtained from the dilatation and conformally invariant Lagrangian in quantum electrodynamics without the electron rest mass term. Higher orders, which will have to include that mass term, give nonscaling corrections, but we have at least approximate scaling.[24]

b.   Inclusive Semihadronic Processes

Not only does the reaction $e + N \rightarrow e' +$ anything show scaling of the structure functions, but also the differential total cross section is Coulomb-like:[28, 29]

$$\frac{d\sigma_{\text{tot}}}{d|t|} \approx \frac{4\pi\alpha^2}{t^2}.$$

This process may be looked at, at very high energies, as an effective binary electron scattering off a Coulomb potential. However, in such a case we have conservation of the dilatation momentum[24] and of the time component of the conformal momenta, where that component has the form

$$K^0 = 2x^0(x \cdot p) - p^0 x^2 - 2gr, \qquad g = \text{coupling const.}$$

We see that in this case we have some kind of quasi-binary collision, which we need in order to obtain the distribution functions of interest to us.

In weak interactions we can apply the same reasoning only[30] if there is an intermediate boson W and if the momentum transfer of the leptons is larger than its mass m_W.

c.   Purely Hadronic Interactions

In inclusive hadronic collisions $a + b \rightarrow c +$ anything, "Feynman" scaling is observed[31] at very large energies. In other words, the cross section for the particle c with longitudinal center of mass momentum $p_{\|}$ and transverse momentum $p_{\perp}$ is to a good approximation of the form

$$\frac{d^2\sigma}{p_{\perp} dp_{\perp} dy} = f(p_{\perp}, y), \qquad y = \frac{2p_{\|}}{\sqrt{s}}$$

Either if the function $f(p_\perp, y)$ factorizes, $f(p_\perp, y) = f_1(p_\perp) f_2(y)$, or if we integrate over $p_\perp$, we get

$$\frac{d\sigma}{dy} = g(y)$$

This form of the production cross section may be interpreted as follows. A cross section in *one* space dimension, defined by the decrease $\Delta j = - \sigma j n(x^3) \Delta x^3$ of the current density $j(x^3)$ along Δx^3, is dimensionless. This implies that, if the dynamics do not contain any fixed length like rest masses or coupling constants with nonvanishing dimension of length and so forth, the production cross section for one particle in the final state, after summing over all other secondaries, can only be a function of the ratio y. In this sense purely hadronic interactions exhibit one-dimensional (longitudinal) dilatation invariance.[24] A formal field theoretical example for such a situation provides the Thirring model. The example is formal because there seems to be no nontrivial S-matrix.

We have seen that there are a number of important high-energy reactions which might have led, right after the big bang, to approximate distributions for the primeval matter which may have been at least partially of the type I have discussed above. This is, of course, a rather weak statement, its weakness having various obvious sources, for some of which I am fully responsible, for others not so much! But I hope I have indicated that this field is worth investigating in the context of approximate and broken conformal symmetries.

REFERENCES AND NOTES

1. K. G. Wilson, *Phys. Rev.*, **179**, 1499 (1969).

2. S. Ciccariello, R. Gatto, G. Sartori, and M. Tonin, *Ann. Phys. (N.Y.)*, **65**, 265 (1971).

3. G. Mack, *Nucl. Phys.*, **B35**, 592 (1971).

4. Y. Frishman, *Ann. Phys. (N.Y.)*, **66**, 373 (1971); R. Brandt and G. Preparata, *Nucl. Phys.*, **B27**, 541 (1971).

5. H. Leutwyler and P. Otterson, Chapter 1 in this volume.

6. S. Ferrara, R. Gatto, A. F. Grillo, and G. Parisi, *Phys. Letters*, **38B**, 333 (1972).

7. A. H. Mueller, *Phys. Rev. D*, **2**, 2963 (1970).

8. H. Fritsch and M. Gell-Mann, "Proceedings of the Coral Gables Conference on Fundamental Interactions at High Energy," University of Miami, 1971; Chapter 7 of this volume.

9. A. M. Polyakov, *Zh. Eksperim. i Teor. Fiz. Pis. Red.*, **12**, 7538 (1970); transl. *JETP Letters*, **12**, 7381 (1970).

10. A. A. Migdal, *Phys. Letters*, **37B**, 98, 386 (1971).

11. G. Mack and I. T. Todorov, Triest Preprint IC/71/139; Chapter 5 in this volume.

12. G. Mack and K. Symanzik, Desy Preprint 72/20; Chapter 5 in this volume.

13. B. Schroer, Chapter 3 in this volume.

14. G. Parisi and L. Peliti, *Lettere Nuovo Cimento*, **2**, 627 (1971).

15. G. Mack, Chapter 5 in this volume.

16. H. A. Kastrup, *Phys. Letters*, **37B**, 521 (1971).

17. Y. Nambu and D. Lurie, *Phys. Rev.*, **125**, 1429 (1962).

18. J. Ehlers, "General Relativity and Cosmology," in *Proceedings of the International School of Physics*, "Enrico Fermi," Academic Press, New York, 1971.

19. J. M. Stuart, *Lecture Notes in Physics*, Vol. 10, Springer-Verlag, Berlin, 1971.

20. J. Ehlers, P. Geren, and R. K. Sachs, *J. Math. Phys.*, **9** 1344 (1968); G. E. Tauber and J. W. Weinberg, *Phys. Rev.*, **122**, 1342 (1961).

21. We use the metric $g_{00} = -g_{11} = -g_{22} = -g_{33} = 1$, all others vanish; we further have $\hbar = 1 = c$ and write ∂_μ for $\partial/\partial x^\mu$.

22. E. A. Milne, *Kinematic Relativity*, Oxford University Press, 1948.

23. H. P. Robertson and T. W. Noonen, *Relativity and Cosmology*, Saunders, Philadelphia, 1968; W. Rindler, *Essential Relativity*, Van Nostrand-Reinhold, New York, 1969.

24. H. A. Kastrup, "Habilitation," thesis, Munich, 1964; the larger part of this thesis is contained in *Nucl. Phys.*, **58**, 561 (1964).

25. C. Brans and R. H. Dicke, *Phys. Rev.*, **124**, 925 (1961).

26. J. L. Anderson, *Phys. Rev. D*, **3**, 1689 (1971).

27. A. R. Sandage, *Phys. Today*, February 1970, p. 34.

28. H. A. Kastrup, *Phys. Rev.*, **147**, 1130 (1966); *Schladming Lectures in Particles, Currents, Symmetries*, by P. Urban, Springer-Verlag, Vienna, 1968, p. 407.

29. J. D. Bjorken, *Proceedings of the International School of Physics*, "Enrico Fermi," Academic Press, New York, 1968.

30. H. A. Kastrup, *Nuovo Cimento*, **48A**, 271 (1967).

31. Oxford Conference on High Energy Collisions, April 1972; proceedings to be published.

Index